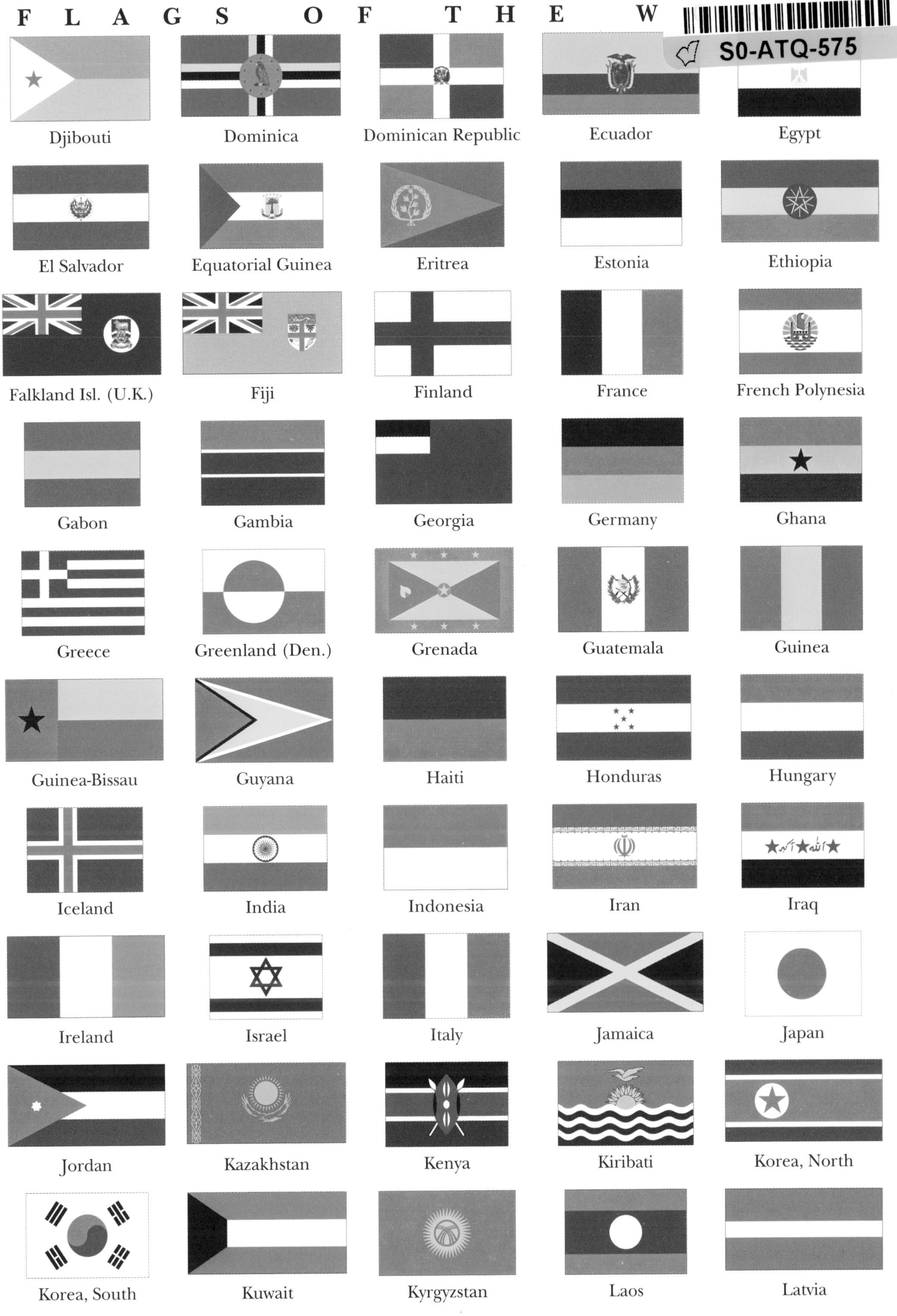
FLAGS OF THE W
Djibouti
Dominica
Dominican Republic
Ecuador
Egypt
El Salvador
Equatorial Guinea
Eritrea
Estonia
Ethiopia
Falkland Isl. (U.K.)
Fiji
Finland
France
French Polynesia
Gabon
Gambia
Georgia
Germany
Ghana
Greece
Greenland (Den.)
Grenada
Guatemala
Guinea
Guinea-Bissau
Guyana
Haiti
Honduras
Hungary
Iceland
India
Indonesia
Iran
Iraq
Ireland
Israel
Italy
Jamaica
Japan
Jordan
Kazakhstan
Kenya
Kiribati
Korea, North
Korea, South
Kuwait
Kyrgyzstan
Laos
Latvia

WORLD GEOGRAPHY

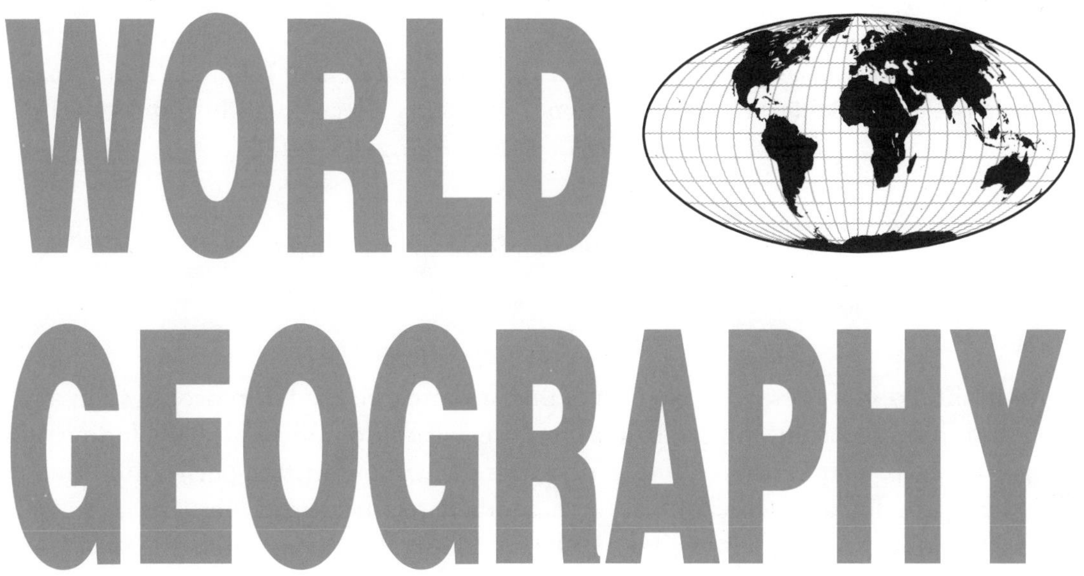

WORLD GEOGRAPHY

Volume 2

North America and the Caribbean

Editor
Ray Sumner
Long Beach City College

Managing Editor
R. Kent Rasmussen

SALEM PRESS, INC.
Pasadena, California   Hackensack, New Jersey

Editor in Chief: Dawn P. Dawson

Managing Editor: R. Kent Rasmussen
Manuscript Editor: Irene Struthers Rush
Production Editor: Cynthia Beres
Photograph Editor: Philip Bader
Assistant Editors: Andrea Miller, Heather Stratton
Research Supervisor: Jeffry Jensen
Acquisitions Editor: Mark Rehn
Page Design and Layout: James Hutson
Additional Layout: William Zimmerman
Graphics: Electronic Illustrators Group
Cover Design: Moritz Design, Los Angeles, Calif.

Frontispiece: North America from space. *(PhotoDisc)*

∞ The paper used in these volumes conforms to the American National Standard for Permanence of Paper for Printed Library Materials, Z39.48-1992 (R1997).

Library of Congress Cataloging-in-Publication Data

World geography / editor, Ray Sumner ; managing editor, R. Kent Rasmussen.
p. cm.
Contents: v. 1. The World. — v. 2. North America and the Caribbean. — v. 3. Central and South America. — v. 4. Africa. — v. 5. Asia. — v. 6. Europe. — v. 7. Antarctica, Australia, and the Pacific. — v. 8. Glossary and Appendices.
Includes bibliographical references (p.).
ISBN 0-89356-024-3 (set : alk. paper) — ISBN 0-89356-276-9 (v. 1 : alk. paper) — ISBN 0-89356-277-7 (v. 2 : alk. paper) — ISBN 0-89356-335-8 (v. 3 : alk. paper) — ISBN 0-89356-336-6 (v. 4 : alk. paper) — ISBN 0-89356-399-4 (v. 5 : alk. paper) — ISBN 0-89356-650-0 (v. 6 : alk. paper) — ISBN 0-89356-699-3 (v. 7 : alk. paper) — ISBN 0-89356-723-X (v. 8 : alk. paper)
1. Geography—Encyclopedias. I. Sumner, Ray.

G133.W88 2001
910′.3—dc21

2001020281

First Printing

PRINTED IN THE UNITED STATES OF AMERICA

Contents

North America and the Caribbean

Regions

United States 339

Canada 343

Mexico 348

Greenland and the Arctic 352

The Caribbean 355

Physical Geography

Physiography and Hydrology 361

Physiography of North America 361
Hydrology of North America 367
Physiography of the Caribbean 373

Climatology 393

North America 393
The Caribbean 399

Biogeography and Natural Resources

Natural Resources 405

North America 405
The Caribbean 412

Flora and Fauna 414

North American Flora 414
North American Fauna 419
Caribbean Flora and Fauna 424

Human Geography

People 431

North America 431
The Caribbean 436

Population Distribution 438

North America 438
The Caribbean 459

Culture Regions 461

North America 461
The Caribbean 470

Exploration 473

North America 473
The Caribbean 478

Political Geography 482

North America 482
The Caribbean 487

Urbanization 491

North America 491
The Caribbean 498

Economic Geography

Agriculture 503

North America 503
The Caribbean 525

Industries 528

North America 528
The Caribbean 533

Engineering Projects 537

North America 537

Transportation 544

North America 544
The Caribbean 550

Trade 553

North America 553
The Caribbean 558

Communications 561

North America 561
The Caribbean 566

Gazetteer 587

Index to Volume 2 **XV**

WORLD GEOGRAPHY

REGIONS

United States

The United States of America is the world's fourth largest country in area, with 2.78 million square miles (2.35 million sq. km.). It is the third largest country in population, with approximately 275 million people at the end of the twentieth century. Its forty-eight contiguous states are located in North America between Canada and Mexico, with Alaska in northwestern North America and Hawaii in the Pacific Ocean. In addition, the United States has possessions in the Caribbean Sea and the Pacific Ocean.

Topography. From the Atlantic Coastal Plain the Appalachian Mountains rise, running from southern Canada to northern Alabama. To the east, between the Appalachians and the coastal plain, is the Piedmont, a region of rolling hills and plateaus. West of the Appalachians are more plateaus and rolling hills and the valleys of rivers such as the Ohio, Tennessee, and Mississippi. Further to the west are the Great Plains, a vast grassland extending from Canada to Texas. The plains give way to the Rocky Mountains, one of North America's great mountain chains, which stretches from Canada down to central New Mexico. Mount Elbert at 14,433 feet (4,399 meters) is the tallest peak in the Rockies and in Colorado. To the west of the Rockies is the Great Basin, a desert area with inland drainage. The western edge of the Great Basin abuts the Cascade Range and the Sierra Nevada. West of the Cascades and Sierra Nevada are valleys, then coastal ranges.

Alaska is home to Mount McKinley, the tallest mountain in North America at 20,320 feet (6,194 meters). The Hawaiian Islands are volcanics, rising from the sea floor—what geologists refer to as a hot spot. In fact, the west coast of the United States, including Alaska, is part of what is known as the Pacific Ring of Fire. This refers to the fact that there the earth's tectonic plates converge, or slip past each other, resulting in earthquakes and volcanic activity.

U.S. map Page 377

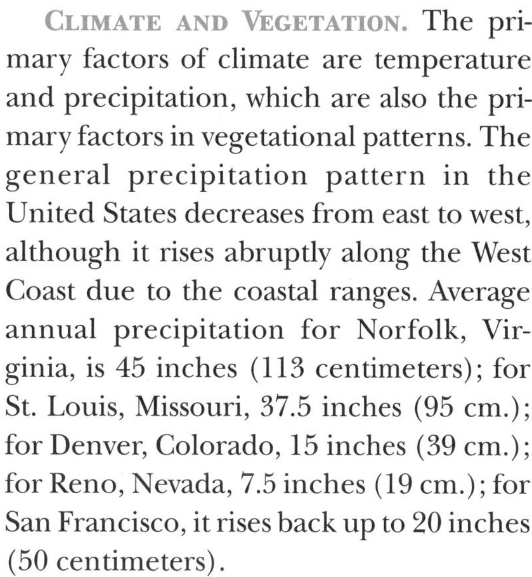

Climate and Vegetation. The primary factors of climate are temperature and precipitation, which are also the primary factors in vegetational patterns. The general precipitation pattern in the United States decreases from east to west, although it rises abruptly along the West Coast due to the coastal ranges. Average annual precipitation for Norfolk, Virginia, is 45 inches (113 centimeters); for St. Louis, Missouri, 37.5 inches (95 cm.); for Denver, Colorado, 15 inches (39 cm.); for Reno, Nevada, 7.5 inches (19 cm.); for San Francisco, it rises back up to 20 inches (50 centimeters).

Mississippi River Page 573

Temperatures decrease to the north, although coastal locations are generally warmer than more inland locations at the same latitude as a result of the moderating effects of the oceans. For example, the normal January maximum temperature in Houston, Texas, is 61 degrees Fahrenheit (16.1 degrees Celsius); in Omaha, Nebraska, 31 degrees Fahrenheit (–0.6 degrees Celsius); in Bismarck, North Dakota, 20 degrees Fahrenheit (–6.7 degrees Celsius). San Francisco, California, has a normal January maximum almost 27 degrees Fahrenheit (14 degrees Celsius) warmer than that of Omaha, although both are at approximately the same latitude. The same situation exists for Seattle, Washington, and Bismarck. San Francisco and Se-

Rocky Mountains Page 384

Cascade Range Page 516

attle are warmer in the winter and cooler in the summer than Omaha and Bismark because of their coastal locations.

Because of the relationship between vegetation and climate, the vegetational pattern is similar to the climate pattern. The lush forests of the east give way to the Great Plains where too little precipitation falls to support trees. Beyond the Great Plains are the high deserts of the Great Basin and the deserts of the Southwest. The Great Plains are grassland, while the deserts are more sparse. The one exception is the Sonoran Desert of southern Arizona which, because of its rainfall pattern, supports the greenest desert in the world. To the west of the deserts, more forests are located. They are fed by precipitation deriving from the moist winds coming in from the Pacific Ocean and rising up over the mountains, leading to plentiful rain and snow.

EXPLORATION AND EARLY SETTLEMENT. It is believed the first inhabitants of the Americas migrated from Asia across the Bering Strait approximately 30,000 years ago. These people scattered throughout North, Central, and South America. In the United States, they now are referred to as Native Americans. Many scholars believe the Vikings reached the coast of present-day Canada, and possibly the present-day United States, as early as 1000 C.E. In 1492 Christopher Columbus, an Italian explorer sailing for Spain, was the first European of his time to visit the Americas, when he landed in the Bahamas, Cuba, and Hispaniola. John Cabot, an Italian-English explorer, first visited the North American mainland in 1497.

Bering Strait map Page 445

St. Augustine, in present-day Florida, was established by the Spanish in 1565 and Jamestown, in present-day Virginia, by the English in 1607. In 1620 the Pilgrims arrived from England via the Netherlands seeking religious freedom and established Plymouth Colony in present-day Massachusetts. Later in the seventeenth century, France and England began a series of wars over their colonial holdings. The result in North America was the French and Indian War (1754-1763), in which the British were victorious. Colonists soon grew weary of being taxed by the British with no representation in governmental affairs, which led to the American Revolution (1775-1783) and the establishment of the United States of America. The Constitution became law in 1788; in 1789, George Washington became the first president.

Jamestown Page 583

WESTWARD EXPANSION. The first major U.S. westward expansion was the Louisiana Purchase in 1803, which increased the size of the United States dramatically. In 1823 President James Monroe issued the Monroe Doctrine, which stated that European powers should not interfere with the newly established countries in the Americas. The United States used this policy in annexing Texas in 1845. This led to the Mexican-American War (1846-1848), won by the United States, and the establishment of the Rio Grande as the border between Texas and Mexico.

In 1846 the United States and Great Britain established the forty-ninth north parallel west to the Pacific Ocean as the border between the United States and Canada. In 1853 the United States purchased the area south of the Gila River in Arizona and New Mexico from Mexico to establish a southern rail link with the Pacific coast, in what is termed the Gadsden Purchase.

WAVES OF IMMIGRATION. There have been three primary waves of immigrants to the United States since European colonization. The first wave comprised two distinct groups and lasted until about 1870. One group of the first wave included the English, Germans, Scotch-Irish, and others from northern and western Europe. The other group in the first wave was made up of the black Africans forced to migrate as slaves. The second wave, which lasted approximately fifty years, consisted mostly of eastern and southern Europeans. In 1921 the United States adopted a quota system restricting immigration. In the 1960's, those restrictions were relaxed and the third wave began, dominated by Asians and Latin Americans.

Cultural Regions. The three primary waves of immigration were separated not only by time but also by space. Combined with early settlement patterns, the waves of immigration were instrumental in forging the regional cultures now present in the United States. The first wave, dominated by northern and western Europeans and Africans, went into the eastern United States. The English settled in New England and throughout the southern part of the country; the Scotch-Irish settled primarily in the Appalachian Mountains; many Germans settled in the mid-Atlantic region and the Midwest; Scandinavians settled primarily in Wisconsin, Minnesota, and the Dakotas. African slaves were sent to the South along the coastal plain and in the Mississippi River Valley—the primary areas of plantations.

In the second wave, Southern and Eastern Europeans moved into the mid-Atlantic states and then throughout the Midwest and Great Plains. In the third wave, Asians entered from the west rather than the east, settling primarily in the western United States; Latin Americans are found mostly in the Southwest.

The result is the cultural mosaic that includes such diverse regions as New England, the South, the Midwest, and the

Perceptual and Vernacular Regions of the United States

Terms such as "the South," "the Southwest," and "the Midwest" are used and understood in daily life in the United States. Some geographers study the usage of these terms to try to understand how and why people apply them to certain places. For example, research shows that almost all Americans identify Alabama and Mississippi as in the South, Arizona and New Mexico as in the Southwest, and Nebraska and Iowa as in the Midwest. Where is Oklahoma, besides being central to these six states?

In a study, thirteen states were identified as being southern, with Oklahoma included next to last, eight states were identified as being in the Southwest, with Oklahoma the last to be included, and fourteen states were included in the Midwest, with Oklahoma included ninth. Therefore, Oklahoma is considered to be in all three regions, but on the margins of each. This is reflected in Oklahoma's settlement and culture. Oklahoma north of Interstate 40 was settled primarily from the Midwest and is similar to the Midwest in topography and vegetation. South of Interstate 40 and east of Interstate 35, settlement was primarily from the South (including the forced relocation of Native Americans along the Trail of Tears) and the land is similar to that of the South in topography and vegetation; to the west of Interstate 35 and in the Panhandle, Oklahoma is similar to the Southwest in topography and vegetation. In many respects, Oklahoma is the place where the South, the Southwest, and the Midwest merge. Texas, to the south, is seen more as southern and southwestern and is not seen as midwestern. Texas has stronger southern and southwestern influences and blends those two regions without the midwestern influence.

Southwest. New England was originally settled by the English and today reflects that strong influence. The South mixes English, Scotch-Irish, and African influences, and the Southwest mixes Latin American, Native American, and European influences.

ECONOMY. The United States has one of the world's most advanced economies, with more than 70 percent of its workers employed in service industries. This type of economy is termed "postindustrial." When the United States was founded, most workers were farmers. As the Industrial Revolution came to its shores, many people left farms for factories and the United States grew to be the industrial giant of the world. In the postindustrial economy, the United States has remained the world's industrial leader but with far fewer manufacturing employees. Capital-intensive manufacturing, relying on computers and mechanization, has replaced many manual-labor-intensive activities. The United States had the largest single economy in the world in the year 2000 and one of the world's highest incomes per capita.

URBANIZATION. The United States has continually become more urban. Every year, a greater percentage of its residents move to cities. In mid-1998, approximately 80 percent of U.S. residents lived in metropolitan areas. The largest U.S. metropolitan area was New York City, with a 1998 metropolitan population greater than 20 million; New York City's population was 7.4 million. The two other dominant U.S. metropolitan areas were Los Angeles, with 15.8 million residents, and Chicago, with 8.8 million. The ten largest cities in the U.S. in 1999 were New York, Los Angeles, Chicago, Houston, Philadelphia, San Diego, Phoenix, San Antonio, Dallas, and Detroit.

New York City Page 575

James D. Lowry, Jr.

FOR FURTHER STUDY

Birdsall, Stephen S., John W. Florin, and Margo L. Price. *Regional Landscapes of the United States and Canada.* 5th ed. New York: John Wiley & Sons, 1999.

Carney, George O. *Baseball, Barns, and Bluegrass: A Geography of American Folklife.* Lanham, Md.: Rowman & Littlefield, 1998.

Garreau, Joel. *The Nine Nations of North America.* New York: Avon, 1981.

Guinness, Paul, and Michael Bradshaw. *North America: A Human Geography.* Totowa, N.J.: Barnes and Noble, 1985.

Jordan, Terry G., and Matti Kaups. *The American Backwoods Frontier.* Baltimore: Johns Hopkins University Press, 1989.

McKnight, Tom. *Regional Geography of the United States and Canada.* 2d ed. Upper Saddle River, N.J.: Prentice Hall, 1992.

Meinig, Donald W. *Southwest: Three Peoples in Geographical Change, 1600-1970.* New York: Oxford University Press, 1971.

Paterson, J. H. *North America.* 9th ed. New York: Oxford University Press, 1994.

Shortridge, James R. *The Middle West.* Lawrence: University Press of Kansas, 1989.

Zelinsky, Wilbur. *The Cultural Geography of the United States: A Revised Edition.* Englewood Cliffs, N.J.: Prentice Hall, 1992.

Canada

Canada is the second-largest country in the world; only Russia has a larger area. Its 3.85 million square miles (9.97 million sq. km.) make it about the same size as Europe, and it covers six time zones. However, despite the country's great physical size, its population is comparatively small: only 31 million people in 1999.

Canada is bounded by the Atlantic Ocean on the east, the Arctic Ocean on the north, the Pacific Ocean and Alaska on the west, and the Great Lakes and the United States on the south. The United States is its only contiguous neighbor. The country is made up of ten partly self-governing provinces and three territories. Ottawa is the capital city.

Canada's provinces and territories can be grouped into five major regions—the north, the Atlantic Provinces, Quebec, Ontario, and the west. Residents of each region have a strong sense of regionalism, identifying themselves as different from people in the other regions of Canada.

The North. Canada has many zones in which distinct physical geographical features are found. The vast, cold, dry Arctic in the north—the region that includes most of Canada's territory above 60 degrees north latitude—has permanently frozen soil (permafrost), which makes life difficult. Vegetation in the Arctic is sparse. Lichens and mosses dominate and cling to the rocky surface in the barren landscape. Somewhat farther south, in the tundra zone, discontinuous permafrost enables the ground to thaw for a few brief weeks in the summer. The treeline is the region spanning the tundra, south of which trees can survive.

On the western edge of this northern Arctic region are the Rocky Mountains. The Yukon Territory has the highest mountain peak in the country—Mount Logan. The MacKenzie River, Great Bear Lake, Great Slave Lake, and Hudson Bay are some of the exceptional physical features of the north. Settlements are sporadic, but can be found as far north as Baffin Island and Ellesmere Island.

Canada map Page 378

Hudson Bay Page 569

The total population of Canada's Arctic region in the late 1990's was estimated at 100,000 persons, residing in the Yukon, Northwest, and Nunavut Territories, whose capital cities are Whitehorse, Yellowknife, and Iqaluit, respectively. The original population of this region were the Inuit people (also called Eskimos), who dominate in the eastern half of the Arctic region. The north is rich in natural resources and has mining operations, oil drilling in the Arctic Ocean, and other developments that extract natural resources from the ground.

Atlantic Canada. The Atlantic provinces officially include Newfoundland and the three Maritime Provinces—Nova Scotia, New Brunswick, and Prince Edward Island. The first Europeans who came to North America were the Vikings who landed on the island of Newfoundland. In the year 1000, they established a settlement on the site of L'Anse aux Meadows on Newfoundland. Originally settled by the Beothuk people, who were later exterminated by the Europeans, Newfoundland was part of Great Britain until 1949, when it became Canada's tenth province.

The province of Nova Scotia was settled originally by the Micmac peoples. Nova Scotia and Newfoundland were sighted in 1497 by John Cabot, who claimed the re-

Italian navigators John and Sebastian Cabot, who led voyages of exploration for England in the late fifteenth century, were the first Europeans who extensively explored North America. (Library of Congress)

gion for England. In 1605 a fort was founded in the Annapolis Valley of Nova Scotia, named Port Royal by French explorer Samuel de Champlain. This was the first European settlement north of Florida and the first French colony in North America, and is Canada's oldest settlement. Nova Scotia is known for fishing, coal mining, and tourism, which brings many people to visit sights such as the Fortress of Louisbourg, Lunenberg, Halifax, and the Cape Breton island and highlands.

New Brunswick Page 574

New Brunswick was originally part of Nova Scotia. After the American Revolution, thousands of British Loyalists were expelled from the United States, and many settled in New Brunswick. The city of St. John, founded in 1785, is the oldest incorporated city in Canada. The capital of New Brunswick is Fredericton, located upriver from St. John. Noted natural attractions in the province are the Reversing Falls and the Bay of Fundy.

Charlottetown, the capital of Prince Edward Island, is where the Dominion of Canada was formed in 1867. The island is small, low in elevation, with predominantly red soil that is excellent for farming. Potatoes from the region are well recognized across Canada, their status as favored as Idaho potatoes in the United States. The stories of Anne of Green Gables originated in this island. The ethnic makeup of Prince Edward Island is similar to that of the other Maritime Provinces, with many residents having English roots.

QUEBEC. The largest province in Canada is the most European in culture. This is a result of the overwhelming presence of the French language and culture, which has existed in the region since the St. Lawrence River was explored in 1535 by Jacques Cartier, followed by Samuel de Champlain and others. Located almost completely within the Canadian Shield, the province is rich in natural resources, including minerals, forests, and rivers with hydroelectric potential. Only the St. Lawrence River Valley in the southern part of the province has land suitable for agriculture, and it is there that the majority of the population resides.

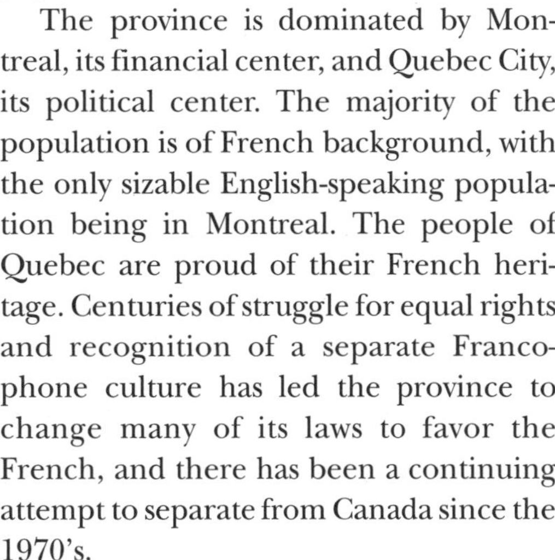

Montreal Page 573

The province is dominated by Montreal, its financial center, and Quebec City, its political center. The majority of the population is of French background, with the only sizable English-speaking population being in Montreal. The people of Quebec are proud of their French heritage. Centuries of struggle for equal rights and recognition of a separate Francophone culture has led the province to change many of its laws to favor the French, and there has been a continuing attempt to separate from Canada since the 1970's.

Quebec City Page 449

ONTARIO. Ontario is the wealthiest and most populated province in Canada. Most of its people live in the southern part of the province, where Canada's largest city—Toronto—is found. Among the manufacturing industries in this region are the steel mills of Hamilton, the automobile manufacturing plants in Windsor and Oshawa, and the high-tech industries of Ottawa. Ottawa is also the nation's capital, and its large parliament buildings and other attractions bring many visitors to the area. Ottawa was chosen by Queen Victo-

Toronto Page 507

THE HEARTLAND-HINTERLAND CONCEPT

Geographers have promoted the "heartland-hinterland" concept to illustrate Canada's regional geography. Canada's heartland is southern Ontario and Quebec, where most of the manufacturing industries are located. The hinterland includes all provinces and regions that are farther away from the core of the country, from where raw materials are shipped to be manufactured.

Iron ore from mines in the Canadian Shield are shipped to the steel mills of Hamilton, where finished sheet-metal products are taken to nearby Oshawa for automobile manufacturing plants. Culturally, the heartland attracts artists and intellectuals to cities and universities. Financial headquarters are found in the downtown sections of Toronto and Montreal. In the heartland-hinterland model, the heartland has more power and influence, while the peripheral provinces and regions in the hinterland have less power and influence in a wide area of matters.

ria for the site of the capital over Montreal and Toronto.

The most southern point in Canada is found at Point Pelee and Pelee Island on Lake Erie. The climate and vegetation in this southern region of the province can be quite mild in the winters, with humid and often hot summers. Broadleaf forests dominate. Further north, where the summers are warm to cool and winters are sometimes cold, vegetation changes to the boreal trees of the Canadian Shield. The Hudson Bay region in the far northern section of Ontario has arctic conditions. Cities in the northern section of Ontario include Sudbury, which is well known for mining, Thunder Bay, and Sault Sainte Marie. Scenic attractions include Niagara Falls and Sibley Peninsula.

Niagara Falls Page 576

Western Canada. The remaining provinces of Canada constitute Western Canada—the four provinces west of Ontario to the Pacific Ocean. The majority of the south central part of this region is rich prairie farmland, but the far eastern, northeastern, and northern parts are dominated by the Canadian Shield. The coastal province of British Columbia, on the western edge of the region, is dominated by the Rocky Mountains, which range throughout the province. Climatic conditions vary in this area.

Calgary Page 514

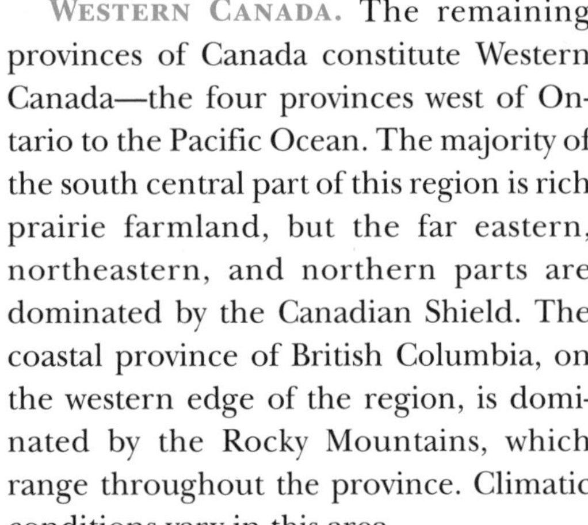

Edmonton Page 446

In the central Prairie Provinces, conditions usually involve warm to hot summers, with cold Arctic winds common in the winter. The region mostly experiences a dry continental climate. On the west coast, however, the maritime influence brings a great deal of moisture, and winters are generally cloudy with much precipitation. Winters are wet and mild, but summers can be quite warm and pleasant. Higher elevations experience cooler temperatures, and snow dominates in the interior of the province during the winter.

Vancouver Page 581

Victoria Page 582

The Prairie Provinces of Manitoba, Saskatchewan, and Alberta were settled following the building of the Canadian Pacific and Canadian National Railroads at the end of the nineteenth century. At the beginning of the twentieth century, the region experienced a major boom in wheat farming and became a major wheat-growing area. The crop could be planted in the spring and ripened in the short growing season, which can be as little as three months in the northern margin of the plowed land areas. Toward the west, the climate is drier and cattle ranching is dominant. Since the advent of mechanization, many farmers from the Prairie Provinces have moved away from the land, resulting in an outmigration of people from rural areas.

The major cities of the region include Winnipeg, Regina, Saskatoon, Calgary, and Edmonton. All those cities were influenced by the coming of the railroad and developed into major grain and meat markets. Three of the cities became provincial capitals. After the 1950's, the discovery of coal, oil, and natural gas in Alberta brought new industries and more people to the province. It has prospered because of these discoveries and is one of the wealthiest Canadian provinces.

In the mountainous region of British Columbia are some localized lowland areas in which mining, farming, fruit-growing, and tourism are common. Fishing, especially for salmon, is also a major industry along the coast. The majority of the population is found in the Fraser River Valley in southern British Columbia and on Vancouver Island. The cities of Vancouver and Victoria dominate. Immigration to the Vancouver region has been great in the latter part of the twentieth century, particularly from Asia.

Culture. Canada is officially a multicultural country, which recognizes the many ethnic groups that have emigrated there. Atlantic Canada is dominated by descendants of earlier English, Irish, and Scottish settlers, and Quebec has the French. Ontario has a variety of ethnic groups, especially in cities such as Toronto. Italians, Poles, Greeks, Chinese, Scandinavians, and others are found throughout the province. Farther west, large population clusters of Germans, Ukrainians, and Scandinavians are found, while in British Columbia there is a growing concentration of East Indians and Chinese.

Popular culture in Canada is similar to that in the United States. The favorite sport in the country is ice hockey, followed by Canadian football and baseball. Regional affiliation and loyalty of fans to sports teams is evident across the country as well, although the Montreal Canadiens and Toronto Maple Leafs maintain the strongest followings across the country as a result of their tradition in hockey history.

Mika Roinila

FOR FURTHER STUDY

Birdsall, Stephen S., John W. Florin, and Margo L. Price. *Regional Landscapes of the United States and Canada.* 5th ed. New York: John Wiley & Sons, 1999.

Bone, Robert. *The Regional Geography of Canada.* New York: Oxford University Press, Don Mills, 2000.

Coulter, Tony, and William Goetzmann, eds. *Jacques Cartier, Samuel de Champlain and the Explorers of Canada.* New York: Chelsea House, 1993.

Guinness, Paul, and Michael Bradshaw. *North America: A Human Geography.* Totowa, N.J.: Barnes and Noble, 1985.

Kalman, Bobbie. *Canada: The Land (The Lands, Peoples and Cultures).* Toronto: Crabtree, 1993.

Konrad, Victor. *Geography of Canada.* East Lansing: Michigan State University Press, 1996.

Kruger, Ralph. *This Land of Ours: A New Geography of Canada.* Toronto: Harcourt Press, 1991.

McCann, Larry, and Angus Gunn, eds. *Heartland and Hinterland: A Regional Geography of Canada.* 3d ed. Scarborough, Ontario: Prentice Hall, 1999.

McKnight, Tom. *Regional Geography of the United States and Canada.* 2d ed. Upper Saddle River, N.J.: Prentice Hall, 1992.

Paterson, J. H. *North America.* 9th ed. New York: Oxford University Press, 1994.

Robinson, J. Lewis. *Concepts and Themes in the Regional Geography of Canada.* Vancouver, British Columbia: Talonbooks, 1993.

Sorensen, Lynda. *Canada: The Land.* Vero Beach, Fla.: Rourke, 1995.

INFORMATION ON THE WORLD WIDE WEB

Canadiana: The Canadian Resource Page is a good starting point for Internet information about Canada and its geography. (www.cs.cmu.edu/Unofficial/Canadiana/)

The Statistics Canada site collects statistics on economy, geography, population, and government. (www.statcan.ca/english/Pgdb/)

Mexico

Mexico
Page 379

Shaped like a funnel that links North America with Central America, Mexico covers an area of almost 780,000 square miles (1.97 million sq. km.) making it the world's eighth largest nation and the third largest in Latin America, after Brazil and Argentina.

Volcano
Page 578

Physiography. The landmass of Mexico curves southeastward from 32 degrees north latiude at Tijuana, Baja California, to 15 degrees north latitude at Tapachula, Chiapas; and from longitude 117 degrees west at Tijuana to roughly 87 degrees west at Cancún. Mexico's northern border with the United States extends more than 1800 miles (3,000 km.) from the Gulf of Mexico in the east to the Pacific Ocean in the west. In the east, more than half the U.S.-Mexico border is formed by the Rio Bravo (Rio Grande in the United States). To the southeast, the Mexican states of Campeche and Chiapas border Guatemala, and the state of Quintana Roo borders Belize.

Landforms. Mexico is located at the intersection of four tectonic plates—the North American, the Caribbean, the Pacific, and the Cocos. As the plates move, they push up mountain ranges such as the Neovolcanic Belt on the southern edge of the Mexican, or Central, Plateau. Some are active volcanoes that erupt periodically. Earthquakes often occur; the one

Mexico's position at the intersection of four tectonic plates makes it susceptible to earthquakes, such as the devastating 1985 Mexico City quake that killed thousands of people and caused $4.1 billion in damage. (National Oceanic and Atmospheric Administration)

that struck Mexico City in 1985 killed thousands of people and caused $4.1 billion in damage.

Millions of years ago, the peninsula of Baja California in the northwest was attached to Mexico's mainland. As Baja California detached and moved northwest, the Gulf of California (called the Sea of Cortés in Mexico) opened. Many species of fish and animals live in these nutrient-rich waters. The Pacific gray whale migrates about 12,000 miles (20,000 km.) every year to calve in the Pacific lagoons of southern Baja California. Mexico has tried to curb commercial fishing in these waters to protect the marine life found here, but lack of funding has made enforcement of laws difficult.

Mountains dominate Mexico's landscape. The Sierra Madre Occidental, Mexico's largest range, extends along the western coast. It was here that the Spanish discovered some of the world's richest silver deposits, in the mid-sixteenth century. Mexico's second great mountain range, the Sierra Madre Oriental, runs parallel to the eastern coast, along the Gulf of Mexico.

The Mexican Plateau, a rugged central plateau that makes up most of Mexico, lies cradled between the Sierra Madres, or "mother ranges." The wide plains of the plateau average more than 6,000 feet (1,829 meters) above sea level. At the south end of the plateau lies the Valley of Mexico, where Mexico City, the capital, is located. The Valley of Mexico's year-round cool temperatures and rich, volcanic soils have attracted some of the densest populations in all of Latin America.

The the Neovolcanic Range south of Mexico City includes towering snow-capped volcanoes. The highest, Mount Orizaba, rises to 18,700 feet (5,747 meters) and is Mexico's highest peak and the third highest in North America. The Sierra Madre del Sur are low mountains along the southern Pacific coast.

Mexico narrows in the south to form the Isthmus of Tehuantepec, where the Pacific Ocean and the Gulf of Mexico are separated by only about 137 miles (220 km.). The Yucatán Peninsula of southeastern Mexico is the country's flattest region.

Regions of Mexico. The Central Plateau is Mexico's core region, with four-fifths of the population and several large cities, including the capital, Mexico City. It has vast plains and broad valleys at altitudes of around 6,550 feet (2,000 meters). Because of the higher elevations, the region's climate is pleasant, making it a desirable place to live. Mexico City, at about 7,350 feet (2,240 meters) above sea level, enjoys moderate temperatures.

Sierra Madre Page 384

Mexico City is a huge, busy, overpopulated, polluted metropolis and the center of government and commerce for Mexico. The oldest capital of the New World is rich in both indigenous and colonial history and is the home of one-quarter of the Mexican population. Built on the site of the ancient Aztec capital city, Tenochtitlán, Mexico City's foundation is the soft, unstable lake bed of Lake Texcoco. Mexico City has been sinking at an annual rate of approximately 6 inches (15 centimeters). The largest church in Latin America, Mexico City's cathedral, is situated there, in the world's largest Roman Catholic diocese.

Mexico City Pages 448, 571

An estimated twelve hundred rural migrants arrive in Mexico City daily seeking a better life. The city is encircled by *ciudades perdidas*, or "lost cities." Mexico City wrestles with severe water shortages, terrible pollution, uncontrollable traffic congestion, and the inability to provide even the most basic services, such as garbage pickup and disposal, to many of its inhabitants.

Mexico's Gulf Coast region—centered on the states of Veracruz and Tabasco—is

Noted for its basalt sculptures of colossal human heads, Olmec civilization flourished in central Mexico between 1200 and 400 B.C.E. (PhotoDisc)

one of the most rapidly developing regions of Mexico. Rich volcanic and alluvial soils make it one of the most productive agricultural zones in tropical Latin America. It has lush, tropical coastal plains and cooler inland mountains. The city of Veracruz is Mexico's leading port. This region was once home to three major pre-Columbian cultures—the Olmec "mother culture" of Mexico; the Totonacs of Central Veracruz; and the Huastecs. Centuries later, the Spanish conquistadores, accompanied by Catholic priests, set out from here to conquer Mexico for "God, Gold, and Glory."

Toltec ruins Page 449

Chichén Itzá Pages 379, 510

Further south along the Gulf Coast lies the Yucatán Peninsula, Mexico's third region. This is a flat, low-lying area of approximately 43,630 square miles (113,000 sq. km.), with a 994-mile (1,600-kilometer) shoreline that borders both the Gulf of Mexico and the Caribbean Sea. It is composed of limestone and coral and acts like a stone sponge, absorbing rain into the ground. The rain forms underground rivers that dissolve the soft limestone, causing the formation of sinkholes (cenotes), which the Maya used as water wells. There are no surface streams or rivers on this peninsula. Beautiful beaches and warm water have made tourist resorts in Cancún and Cozumel some of the best in the world. Some of the finest archaeological sites in the Americas are found on the Yucatán Peninsula. They include Chichén Itzá, a well-preserved Maya site, and Uxmul, a late-Classic Maya temple site.

The South is Mexico's fourth region.

This is the heartland of Mexico's indigenous population and is dominated by the cultures, traditions, way of life, and spiritual beliefs of the Olmecs, Zapotecs, Mixtecs, and Maya. With the exception of oil-rich Tabasco state, the South is Mexico's poorest region. It is decades behind central and northern Mexico in development and has fewer and smaller cities. In Oaxaca, the state with the largest concentration of indigenous people, half the population lacks electricity, modern sewage disposal, and adequate food, and the illiteracy rate is very high.

Northern Mexico is the fifth major region of Mexico. It stretches from the beaches of Baja California to the marshes and islands of the Gulf of Mexico. Two great deserts, the Chihuahuan Desert—the largest in North America—and the Sonoran Desert, are located here. The United States-Mexico border delimits this region to the north and is a broad transition zone defined by a unique blend of Mexican and U.S. languages, food, and music.

The border economy is dominated by maquiladora businesses—in which local workers assemble goods for U.S. firms—and tourism. In the northeast, industrial towns like Monterrey, Reynosa, and Matamoros bring jobs and foreign investment to the region. The sparsely populated arid plains of northern Mexico are devoted to cattle ranching and produce some of the finest beef in the Americas. In the arid northwest, irrigated agriculture and dams on the Colorado, the Sonora, and the Yaqui Rivers make it possible for farmers to raise wheat, cotton, and vegetables on some of Mexico's most fertile land.

Human Geography. Mexico is the most populous Spanish-speaking nation in the world. *Mestizos* (people of mixed Spanish and native blood) form the majority of its population (60 percent), vastly outnumbering indigenous people, who are estimated at just over 13 million. The blending of Spanish and indigenous cultures makes Mexico's culture unique in Latin America.

Baja California Page 515

Mexico's population in the year 2000 was estimated at 100 million, placing it eleventh worldwide, behind China, India, and the United States, but ahead of Japan and Germany. About 75 percent of all Mexicans live in urban areas, with one-quarter of the population living in Mexico City and the surrounding State of Mexico. About 90 percent of the population identify themselves as Roman Catholics; Mexico is the second-largest Roman Catholic nation in the world, after Brazil. Several preexisting indigenous spiritual traditions were absorbed by the Catholic faith, making it easier for the native people to em-

Chichén Itzá

The Maya, whose civilization is considered to have been one of the most advanced indigenous American cultures, flourished in Mexico between 250 and 900 c.e. Chichén Itzá is the best preserved of Mexico's Maya ruins, with temples, an observatory, and the largest ballcourt in Mexico. Kukulcan, or El Castillo, is the tallest, most imposing pyramid on the site. The Maya developed an advanced knowledge of astronomy, mathematics, and architecture. Although the Maya were long considered a peaceful race, it is now known that they used torture, mutilation, and human sacrifice for religious rituals and sporting events.

brace Catholicism. Mexico is reforming its economy and has experienced successful industrial growth. Expanded trade with the United States and Canada under the North American Free Trade Agreement (NAFTA) has aided economic growth.

Carol Ann Gillespie

For Further Study

Blouet, Brian W., and Olwyn M. Blouet. *Latin America and the Caribbean: A Systematic and Regional Survey.* 3d ed. New York: John Wiley, 1997.

Clawson, David L. *Latin America and the Caribbean: Lands and Peoples.* New York: McGraw Hill, 1999.

Philip, G. D. E. "Mexico." Rev. ed. *World Bibliographical Series,* vol. 48. Oxford, England: Clio Press, 1993.

Pick, J. B. *Atlas of Mexico.* Boulder, Colo.: Westview Press, 1989.

Simpson, Leslie Byrd. *Many Mexicos.* 4th ed. Berkeley: University of California Press, 1967.

"A Survey of Mexico." *Economist* (October 28, 1995): 1-18.

Greenland and the Arctic

Arctic map Page 381

The region of Greenland and the Arctic, one of the most sparsely populated areas on Earth, extends from northern Alaska eastward through northern Canada to Greenland. Its southern edge is defined by the tree line that marks the boundary between the southern forests and the northern tundra. The entire region shares an Arctic environment characterized by long, cold winters and short, cool summers. Average daily temperatures for January range between –22 and –31 degrees Fahrenheit (–30 to –35 degrees Celsius). Average July daily temperatures range from 41 to 50 degrees Fahrenheit (5 to 10 degrees Celsius).

Year-round low temperatures, combined with annual total precipitation amounts of approximately 8 inches (200 millimeters), produce a cold, desert-like environment where only highly adapted species can survive. Because there is total darkness during the winter months and constant daylight during the summer, the area north of the Arctic Circle is often referred to as the Land of the Midnight Sun.

Arctic Page 382

The only soils in this treeless region are poorly developed and underlain by permafrost—ground that remains permanently frozen. During the summer months at lower latitudes, the surface layers of soil thaw and plant roots penetrate only to the depth of the thawed ground (about 3.3 feet/1 meter). The vegetation consists of low, ground-level plant species, including sedges, mosses, lichens, and woody dwarf willow in lower latitudes.

This region is sparsely populated by Inuit (Eskimos) who trace their ancestry back to a common Thule culture dating back more than a millenium. They have developed a unique way of life that is specially adapted to the harsh Arctic environment.

The Arctic. The Arctic is best described by its terrestrial and marine ecological areas, or ecozones. There are three terrestrial ecozones in the Arctic; the

The year-round presence of ice floes in the Arctic impedes shipping, thereby limiting the region's development. (PhotoDisc)

Northern Arctic ecozone epitomizes the conditions that most people associate with the Arctic. This ecozone extends over most of the Arctic Islands. The vegetation here is sparse. There are fewer than twenty species of mammals, including caribou, musk ox, arctic fox, polar bear, arctic hare, and lemming.

The Southern Arctic terrestrial ecozone consists of rolling plains containing many lakes, with the occasional outcrop of bedrock of Precambrian Shield. Being slightly milder than the zone to the north, it has many wetland areas, which are home to a variety of sedges, mosses, and migrating waterfowl.

The Arctic Cordillera terrestrial ecozone is a mountainous region covering Eastern Baffin and Devon Islands and parts of Ellesmere and Bylot Islands. These ice cap-covered mountains reach up to 6,500 feet (2,000 meters) in height. At lower elevations, there are some hardy plants; other than polar bears along the coasts, terrestrial mammals are largely absent.

The three Arctic marine ecozones differ in terms of ice conditions and marine life. The Arctic Basin marine ecozone is almost entirely covered by a massive, permanent ice cap, roughly centered on the North Pole, that covers the area from the Beaufort Sea, north and east to the northern tip of Greenland. The few animal species present include whales, seals, polar bears, and walruses that live along the edge of the ice pack.

Seals
Page 381

The Arctic Archipelago marine eco-

Alligators in the Arctic?

The Arctic was not always the cold and desolate place that it currently is. On Ellesmere Island in the far Arctic North, the fossilized remains of alligators, rhinoceros, tapirs, and tortoises—species found only in tropical forests—have been discovered. The remains of ancient redwood trees and the skull of an ancient flying lemur (today found only in Madagascar and southeast Asia) also indicate that the environment was once lush, warm, and moist. This evidence suggests that millions of years ago, landmasses in the Arctic region were physically connected to other landmasses. As a result of tectonic forces and continental drift, the area that is now the Arctic separated and drifted further north and, through time, a different set of environmental conditions was established.

zone, extending from Greenland to Alaska, consists of a maze of channels, straits, and fjords that run among the Arctic islands, where open water exists in some areas for 2-3 months every year. This region is best known from the adventures of early European explorers who came in search of the elusive Northwest Passage. This ecozone contains polynyas, areas of permanently open water, which contain significant concentrations of marine life, including whales, seals, polar bears, and arctic cod. Humans are also attracted to these areas; the edges of polynyas have long served as locations for Inuit settlements. The Inuit, the traditional indigenous people of the Arctic, persist in their traditional hunting and fishing way of life in this region.

Polar bear Page 378

The Northwest Atlantic marine ecozone extends from the edge of Lancaster Sound and Greenland. The warmer and shallower water is home to a variety of marine life, including twenty-two whale species and six species of seals.

Greenland. The largest island in the world, Greenland extends from Cape Morris Jesup in the north to Cape Farewell in the south. While politically part of Europe, geographically it is part of North America. It experiences the same cold, dry climatic characteristics as the Arctic, although there is greater variation in temperature and precipitation. Approximately 84 percent of the island is covered with the Greenland Ice Cap, a thick sheet of ice more than 10,000 feet (3,000 meters) deep. The ice flows through the coastal mountain valleys to the sea, forming dramatic glaciers, most notably the Ilulissat Icefjord. A small amount of open land exists along the southern and central western coasts, which have human settlement and sparse arctic vegetation.

Both the Greenland and Arctic Inuit peoples (also known as Eskimos) trace their ancestry back to the Thule culture, found throughout the eastern Arctic and Greenland more than 1,000 years ago. Led by Erik the Red, the Vikings came into contact with the Thule on their arrival in Greenland. The Vikings, the first Europeans to settle in Greenland, arrived in 982 and established two main settlements, the Eastern Settlement (near present-day Qaqortoq) and the Western Settlement (centered on Godthåbsfjord), which were abandoned before the fifteenth century. Starting in the eighteenth century, the Danish established outposts at Nuuk, Qasigiannguit, Narsaq, and Maniitsoq.

A self-governing administrative division of the Kingdom of Denmark, Greenland has about fifty-nine thousand residents living in small villages and towns along its west coast. In addition, the United States constructed the massive Thule Air Base on the northwest coast for strategic purposes. Its construction forced the resettlement of an entire Greenlandic village to a location 60 miles (100 km.) north at Qaanaaq.

Catherine A. Hooey

For Further Study

"Across a Frozen Sea." *National Geographic* (January, 1996).

Burch, Ernest S., Jr., and Werner Forman. *The Eskimos.* Norman: University of Oklahoma Press, 1988

"Ellesmere Island—Life in the High Arctic." *National Geographic* (June, 1988).

Hiscock, Bruce. *Tundra: The Arctic Land.* New York: Atheneum, 1986.

"Hunters of the Lost Spirit: Greenlanders." *National Geographic* (February, 1983).

Jones, Gwyn. *The Norse Atlantic Saga.* London: Oxford University Press, 1964.

Information on the World Wide Web

The National Tourist Board of Greenland Web site provides links to information on the geography, geology, history, people, and communities of Greenland. (www.greenland-guide.dk)

The Arctic Studies Center at the Smithsonian Institution, dedicated to the study of Arctic peoples, cultures, and environments, maintains a helpful Web site with information on Arctic history and geography. (www.mnh.si.edu/arctic)

The University of Regina's Web site "Ecozones of Canada" features information about Canadian Arctic environments. (www.cprc.uregina.ca/ccea/ecozones)

The Caribbean

The Caribbean Sea is an extension of the western Atlantic Ocean that is bounded by Central and South America to the west and south, and the islands of the Antilles chain on the north and east. It is separated from another large body of water, the Gulf of Mexico, on the west by the Yucatán Channel, which runs from the north tip of Mexico's Yucatán Peninsula to the southern tip of Florida. The sea covers more than 1 million square miles (2.7 mill. sq. km.).

The Caribbean islands, from the Bahamas to Trinidad, form the core of the Caribbean region. They are usually divided into two major groupings—the Greater Antilles of Cuba, Hispaniola (the island shared by Haiti and the Dominican Republic), Puerto Rico, and Jamaica; and the Lesser Antilles, which contains two parallel chains of smaller islands. Islands in the inner arc, such as Montserrat and Martinique, have formed around volcanic peaks. Coral limestone islands, such as

Caribbean Page 382

Martinique Page 570

The Caribbean's seemingly idyllic tropical beaches have made the region popular among North American tourists. (L. Paul Mann/mercurypress.com)

Barbados, form the outer arc. All the Caribbean islands lie in the Atlantic hurricane track from June through November.

In the Caribbean island realm, African and European influences have been historically strong, and plantation agriculture, tied to international markets, has dominated. Central America's Belize (formerly British Honduras) is sometimes grouped within the Caribbean because of its historical and cultural ties to the former British island colonies. However, Hispanic migration from neighboring Central American countries has affected the demographic and cultural landscape of Belize.

The Caribbean region is rich in ethnic and cultural diversity. Peoples of African, European, and Asian heritage mingle in a tropical Caribbean environment. Many languages, cuisines, and religions are encountered. Nevertheless, the region as a whole has a distinctive regional character based on historical and cultural features and present economic circumstances.

Caribbean Commonalities. All the islands were once European colonies, whose indigenous Amerindian cultures were virtually eradicated. Spain took control of the Greater Antilles in the sixteenth century, followed by Great Britain, France, and the Netherlands, who carved up the Lesser Antilles among them. Britain took Jamaica from Spain in 1655, and France acquired what later became Haiti in 1697. In the twentieth century, as many Caribbean countries gained political independence, the United States played the major economic and geopolitical role in this strategic region, making Puerto Rico and the U.S.Virgin Islands dependencies.

Sugarcane, slavery, and the plantation fashioned the economic and cultural landscape of the Caribbean. Sugarcane plantations, on a large capitalist scale, drove the physical transformation of the islands and led to a demographic revolution involving the forced migration of millions of Africans as an enslaved labor force, followed by a smaller flow of indentured laborers, chiefly from the Indian subcontinent and China. Today, the entire Caribbean displays pronounced Afro-Caribbean cultural traits.

Finally, the Caribbean is fragmented, consisting of many small states with restricted economic resources and large, underemployed labor pools. Poverty is a feature of the Caribbean, whose people themselves are important exports. Caribbean economies rely on capital, markets, and goods from outside the region, including foreign tourists.

Olwyn M. Blouet

For Further Study

Anthony, Michael. *Historical Dictionary of Trinidad and Tobago.* Lanham, Md.: Scarecrow Press, 1997.

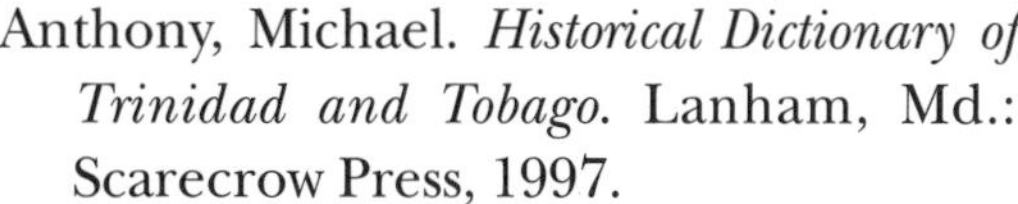

Blouet, Brian W., and Olwyn M. Blouet, eds. *Latin America and the Caribbean: A Systematic and Regional Survey.* 3d ed. New York: John Wiley & Sons, 1997.

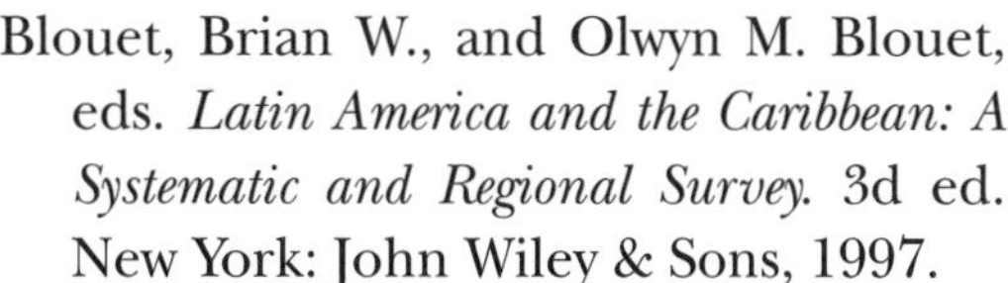

Boswell, Thomas P., and Dennis Conway. *The Caribbean Islands: Endless Geographic Diversity.* Piscataway, N.J.: Rutgers University Press, 1992.

Clawson, David L. *Latin America and the Caribbean: Lands and Peoples.* New York: McGraw Hill, 1999.

Macpherson, John. *Caribbean Lands.* Essex, England: Longman, 1984.

Sealey, Neil. *Caribbean World: A Complete Geography.* New York: Cambridge University Press, 1992.

Suchlicki, Jaime. *Historical Dictionary of Cuba.* Lanham, Md.: Scarecrow Press, 2000.

Virgin Islands Page 582

Sugarcane Page 506

Physical Geography

Physiography and Hydrology

Physiography of North America

The North American region covers much of the Western Hemisphere, ranging about 5,000 miles (8,000 km.) north and south—from southern Mexico and the Caribbean to the near-polar lands of Canada and Greenland—and about 9,300 miles (15,000 km.) east and west—from the Aleutian Islands of Alaska to the eastern coast of Greenland. The majority of this landmass is situated within an area that is politically divided into Canada, the United States, and Mexico. It is naturally bounded by the Pacific, Arctic, and Atlantic Oceans.

The southernmost country, Mexico, lies only 14 degrees north of the equator, and northernmost Greenland is 84 degrees north latitude. Longitudinally, the region spans about one quarter of the earth, from the easternmost tip of Greenland, at longitude 13 degrees west (close to the longitude of the western coast of Ireland in Europe), to Attu Island, the westernmost island in Alaska's Aleutian chain, at longitude 173 degrees east (across the international date line).

Volcanism and Diastrophism. Physiography concerns the character of land surfaces, from the gently rolling plains and lower hills to mountains and more spectacular scenery. However, discussions of the physiography of a continent or a region often begin with the higher and more rugged features, because they are more noticeable as defining characteristics, and they provide natural boundaries to set one physiographic region apart from another. These dramatic, mountainous landscapes are created through one of two physical processes that deform the earth's surface, volcanism and diastrophism.

Physiography map Page 383

Volcanism is an earth-forming process involving molten rock material that cools to form volcanic landforms. The term is derived from Vulcan, the Roman god of fire. Volcanic landforms are created when magma (molten rock) moves within the earth's crust and comes out onto the surface as lava (surface magma), or buckles and warps overlying rock without exiting the surface. All landforms created in this fashion are composed of igneous rock—rock made from magma or lava that cools and turns solid.

Surface volcanic features—volcanoes, cinder cones, spatter cones, lava flows—are immediately visible as landforms. The Cascade Mountain range, which runs from northern California to southern British Columbia in Canada, contains many volcanic peaks created from surface volcanic activity. Although internal igneous rocks form under the surface of the

Cascade Range Page 516

Death Valley Page 517

crust, they may become visible at the surface when the near-surface igneous masses are exposed, as overlying bedrock is weathered and eroded away. The core rock of several North American mountain ranges is igneous.

The Black Hills of South Dakota is a localized area of mountains produced from such internal volcanism; the Sierra Nevada in California and several of the ranges in the Rocky Mountain chain were pushed up and given surface relief by this type of intrusive volcanic activity. Many volcanic landforms are geologically recent features. Active volcanoes are still changing form and spewing lava today.

DIASTROPHISM. Diastrophism involves folding, faulting, tilting, warping, and uplift of the earth's crust. The resulting deformations produce mountains, hills, ridges, and valleys. Death Valley, the lowest point of elevation in North America, was created when deep faults (cracks in the earth's crust) allowed a large block of the crust to sink downward. Most of Nevada is covered by a series of parallel, fault-block mountains produced when a similar cracking of the surface throughout the region produced widespread subsidence and uplift of large blocks of crust.

The ranges of the Appalachian Mountain chain in eastern North America were produced when adjacent blocks of continental crust were pushed together. This compression folded and buckled the surface into a rugged landscape, which has since been weathered and eroded into a series of ridges and valleys that comform to the different rock beds (resistant or more easily eroded) that make up this mountain province.

VOLCANIC NATIONAL PARKS

Because volcanic landforms are so dramatic, many have been preserved within national parks and national monuments. Mexico's Popocatépetl National Park, located southeast of Mexico City, contains two volcanoes over 17,000 feet (5,300 meters) high. In 1996 the Popocatépetl volcano began belching sulphurous gases and periodically shuddering with minor eruptions; access to the park was restricted until the volcano ceased its activity. Mount Saint Helens, the last volcano to erupt in the continental United States in the twentieth century, is part of the only U.S. National Park Service site designated a volcanic monument. However, many other volcanoes and volcanic features are preserved within U.S. park sites.

NATIONAL PARKS AND MONUMENTS AT EXTINCT VOLCANOES

Park or monument	*State*
Denali National Park	Alaska
Katmai National Park	Alaska
North Cascades National Park	Washington
Mount Rainier National Park	Washington
Crater Lake National Park	Oregon
Lassen Volcanic National Park	California
Capulin Volcano National Monument	New Mexico

NATIONAL PARKS AND MONUMENTS AT AREAS OF CINDER CONES, LAVA FLOWS, VOLCANIC NECKS, OR GEOTHERMAL HOT SPRINGS AND GEYSERS

Park or monument	*State*
Lava Beds National Monument	California
Devils Postpile National Monument	California
Craters of the Moon National Monument	Idaho
Sunset Crater Volcano National Monument	Arizona
El Malpais National Monument	New Mexico
Devil's Tower National Monument	Wyoming
Yellowstone National Park	Wyoming

Many ranges in the Rocky Mountain chain were created or altered through diastrophism. Many individual ridges are the product of upturned and tilted rock beds. The ridges stand high above adjacent valleys because they are made of rock that is more resistant to erosion and has not worn down as quickly as the more easily eroded rock of the valleys.

Landforms and Physiographic Regions. North America is one of the most diverse continents in terms of physiography, resources, climate, and vegetation. Although the total area of North America is similar to that of Africa, its variety of landforms and environments is much greater because of the more diverse geological history and the greater expanse of latitudes covered by this region. North America contains high mountains, low mountains and rolling hills, canyons and plateaus, vast plains, continental and alpine glaciers, great rivers and lakes. This diversity of physiography across a broad swath of latitude has produced temperate-zone rain forests, subtropical forests, conifer and deciduous forest, grasslands, deserts, and Arctic and alpine tundra. The North American realm can be regionally divided into six distinct physiographic regions.

Western Highlands. The Western Highlands contain the highest mountain ranges and most spectacular mountain scenery in North America. It rises from the flatness of the interior plains to a region of steep slopes and rugged terrain, and is the source of water for most of the west's rivers. This physiographic province includes the highest slopes of the Continental Divide; the mountains of the Far West (in California, Oregon, Washington, British Colombia); and the rugged, irregular mountains and plateaus of the intermountain region (the Columbia Plateau, Colorado Plateau, and the Basin and Range country of Nevada).

Highest and Lowest

The highest average elevations in North America run along the western side of the continent, from Alaska to Mexico. The lower elevations are found along the coastal plains and in the center of the continent. The highest mountain in North America is Mount McKinley at 20,320 feet (6,194 meters), located in the Alaska Range. The highest peaks in Canada and the continental United States are also found in the western highlands. Mexico's highest peak is a volcano in the eastern part of the country, Pico de Orizaba (Citlaltéptl), which rises to more than 18,700 feet (5,700 meters). Two other massive volcanoes near Orizaba exceed 17,000 feet (5,300 meters). Although these volcanoes lie only 18 degrees north of the equator, they are capped by glacial ice throughout the year because of cold temperatures at such extreme altitudes.

The lowest point of land in North America is in the western highlands region, surrounded by high mountains: southeastern California's Death Valley, at an altitude of 284 feet (87 meters) below sea level. This is a deep graben valley, produced when parallel faults—or fractures in the earth's crust—allowed this block of crust to settle downward between the mountains of the Panamint Range and Amargosa Range.

The Western Highlands region spans the length of the western margin of the continent, from northern Alaska to central Mexico. The principal mountain ranges of this large highland region include the Sierra Nevada of California; the Great Basin Ranges of Nevada and western Utah; the Cascade Mountains of California, Oregon, Washington, and British Columbia; the Brooks Range of Alaska; and the Rocky Mountains, which run from central Alaska to Mexico.

Rocky Mountains Page 384

The Rocky Mountain chain comprises several individual mountain ranges that intertwine along this western spine of North America. Ranges include the

At 20,320 feet (6,194 meters), Alaska's Mount McKinley is the tallest mountain in North America. (PhotoDisc)

Wrangell Mountains Page 384

Sierra Madre Page 384

Alaska, St. Elias, and Wrangell Mountains of Alaska; Mackenzie and Continental Ranges of Yukon, British Columbia, and Alberta; Bitteroot and Flathead Range and Salmon River Mountains of Idaho and Montana; the Tetons and Wind River Range of Wyoming; the Wasatch and Uinta Mountains of Utah; the Sawatch and San Juan Mountains of Colorado; the Sangre de Cristo Mountains of Colorado and New Mexico; the Sacramento Mountains of New Mexico; the Davis Mountains of western Texas; and the Sierra Madre Oriental and Sierra Madre Occidental of Mexico.

Because of the spectacular, beautiful appearance of the Western Highland landscapes, and because lands here remained unsettled for so long and are owned by the governments of the United States, Canada, and Mexico, many scenic areas have been set aside as national parks and monuments. Some of the largest and most famous national parks in all three of these countries are found within the Western Highlands physiographic province.

Appalachian Highlands. This physiographic province includes the ranges and plateaus of eastern North America, a highland region trending northeast-southwest across much of southeastern Canada and the eastern United States. The Appalachian Highlands region presents a highly folded, ridge-and-valley landscape. These mountains are considerably lower in elevation than the Rocky Mountains, largely because they formed long before the Rocky Mountains and have been greatly worn down during millions of years of weathering and erosion.

Individual mountain ranges that collectively make up the Appalachian chain include the Long Range Mountains of Newfoundland, Laurentian Mountains of

Quebec, White Mountains of New Hampshire, Green Mountains of Vermont, Adirondack and Catskill Mountains of New York, Allegheny Mountains of Pennsylvania and West Virginia, Blue Ridge Mountains of Virginia, Great Smoky Mountains of Tennessee and North Carolina, Ozark Mountains of Missouri and Arkansas, and the Ouachita Mountains of Arkansas and southeastern Oklahoma.

The Ozarks and Ouachitas are separated from the principal Appalachian chain by more than 300 miles of flat terrain across the Mississippi River valley, but these latter two ranges are geologically, physiographically, and even culturally part of the Appalachian realm. The mountain ranges are punctuated here and there by broad, flat-to-undulating upland regions known as plateaus, such as the Allegheny Plateau in western New York and Pennsylvania, the Cumberland Plateau in Tennessee, and the Ozark Plateau in Missouri.

Gulf and Atlantic Coastal Plains. Descending from the Appalachian Mountains toward the Atlantic Ocean, the landscape gradually slopes toward the gently rolling, low platform of the Piedmont region and finally levels off to a flat coastal plain nearer the ocean. This entire region is underlain by relatively unconsolidated marine sediments that extend out to sea to constitute the continental shelf. This low-lying, sandy, forested region of eastern North America (sometimes called the flatwoods) runs from the mid-Atlantic states to coastal Florida. It is crossed in several places by a winding maze of creeks and broadly meandering rivers that end near the ocean in bays, estuaries, and swampy wetlands.

The largest and most famous of these swamps are the Dismal Swamp along the Virginia-North Carolina border, and the Okefenokee Swamp in southern Georgia-northern Florida. Low-lying, sandy islands lie just off shore along most of the coastline. Many of these islands are quite long and form barriers to the sea, especially along the northern Florida and North Carolina coasts. Some barrier islands are wide enough for urban development, but most are narrow and remain lightly inhabited or uninhabited.

West Virginia Page 583

Wetlands Page 387

On Florida's western coast, similar physiography is seen along the Gulf of Mexico coastal plain, stretching from western Florida to eastern Mexico. There are barrier islands, flat, sandy plains, and poorly drained rivers that end in wetlands. The largest swamp along the Gulf coastal plain is in the Mississippi River delta region, the so-called "bayou" region of Louisiana. The southern Atlantic and Gulf coastal plains are subtropical in climate and vegetation

Central Plains. Between the highlands of the Rocky Mountains and the highlands of the Appalachian Mountains lies the continental interior; a broad, mostly even landscape in the United States and Canada that occupies roughly one-fourth of the continental landmass. This physical province is often thought of as flat and featureless, yet most of the surface here is gently rolling, frequently dissected by streams and rivers. Wind and water have etched the plains to create eroded hills, such as the central Texas Hill Country, and "badlands" in parts of the Dakotas, Kansas, and Oklahoma.

The continent's largest area of sand dunes—a maze of dunes and ridges that rise to several hundred feet (more than one hundred meters)—lies in a huge, rolling, grassland-covered region known as the Sand Hills of Nebraska, which covers almost one-third of that state. High hills and low mountains interrupt the sloping plains in southwestern Oklahoma (the Wichita Mountains) and southwestern South Dakota (the Black Hills); the latter are really mountains that rise to more than 7,000 feet (2,130 meters).

The western edge of the Central Plains, where the Front Range of the Rockies abruptly rises, is at an elevation of 4,000-5,000 feet (1,215-1,520 meters). From here, the land surface gradually descends to the east at an average slope of 10 feet per mile (1.9 meters per kilometer). Much of the land surface in this physiographic province is composed of unconsolidated, or recently consolidated, materials transported and spread from the Rocky Mountains by the east-flowing rivers. The northern portion of this physical province has been scraped by numerous glacial advances, and continental glacial sediments—sand and silt—cover much of the northern plains. The North American prairie, the native grassland region of the continental interior, covers most of this physiographic region of the Central Plains, although scattered trees and forests are more common in the eastern portion of this province.

Canadian Shield. The eastern half of Canada, most of Greenland, and a portion of the north central United States is part of this largest physiographic province in North America: an area of ancient crystalline rock covering 1.1 million square miles (3 million sq. km.). A "shield" is a geological term referring to a large, stable block of the earth's crust that has been unaffected by mountain-building for a long time. These ancient masses of crust typically form the core or central nucleus of each of the continents.

Sometimes called the Laurentian Shield, the Canadian Shield is such a mass of stable rock at the core on the North American continent. It is covered with forest and tundra and is composed of Precambrian-age crystalline rock, 1 to 3 billion years old. The shield mass is twice as large as appears at the surface; to the west and south of the exposed shield, the rock is overlain by more recent geologic deposits. Therefore, the shield is found only at some depth beneath the surface in western Canada and in the eastern and central United States. Long ago, wide areas of this rock mass were severely compressed and contorted, and in these disturbed zones a large variety of minerals has been found. This is the most important region of nonengery minerals in Canada, producing significant quantities of gold, nickel, copper, uranium, and iron ore.

The present surface of the shield bears little resemblance to the ancient disturbances of rock compression, because the surface has been repeatedly eroded as glaciers have expanded and retreated with each ice age. The result is a gently rolling surface covered with glacially scoured, rounded hills, a thin or nonexistent soil cover, a chaotic surface-water drainage system, swamps and muskegs, and thousands of lakes, large and small, created when water filled in the numerous depressions that were gouged out by glacial erosion after the continental glacier melted. Some of these lakes have disappeared over time, leaving behind clay-filled beds and offering some fertile ground in the otherwise soil-bare region of the shield. Along the eastern margins of the shield are several mountain ranges and hills that reach elevations exceeding 4,000 feet (1,200 meters), but elsewhere across the region, the topography is more gently undulating.

Dale R. Lightfoot

For Further Study

Birdsall, Stephen S., John W. Florin, and Margo L. Price. *Regional Landscapes of the United States and Canada.* 5th ed. New York: John Wiley & Sons, 1999.

Getis, Arthur, and Judith Getis. *The United States and Canada: The Land and the People.* Chicago: William C. Brown, 1995.

Kiver, Eugene P., and David V. Harris. *Geology of U.S. Parklands.* 5th ed. New York: John Wiley & Sons, 1999.

McKnight, Tom. *Regional Geography of the United States and Canada.* 2d ed. Upper Saddle River, N.J.: Prentice Hall, 1992.

Paterson, J. H. *North America.* 9th ed. New York: Oxford University Press, 1994.

Sayre, April Pulley. *Grassland: Exploring Earth's Biomes.* New York: Twenty-First Century Books, 1995.

Hydrology of North America

Hydrology is the study of water's properties, distribution, and circulation. Any study of North America's hydrology must deal with all the water on the continent, including the rivers, lakes, glaciers, wetlands, and groundwater. Hydrology has had a great impact on human settlement and economics of this continent.

Excluding water locked in the Antarctic and Greenland ice caps, Canada holds about 20 percent of the world's freshwater. Almost 8 percent of Canada's surface (290,000 square miles/750,000 sq. km.) is covered by lakes and rivers. By contrast, lakes and rivers cover slightly more than 2 percent of the United States and an even smaller percentage of Mexico. The differences in coverage are largely due to each nation's geographical location and the resulting differences in precipitation. Another important factor is the degree of development and change that the hydrology of the land has undergone with human settlement.

Water Cycle. Water continually moves through a cycle called the hydrologic cycle. It first reaches the ground surface through precipitation. It then either evaporates or transpires back into the air, sinks into the ground, or flows overland as runoff until it collects and eventually empties into lakes or streams. The streams can be tributaries to larger rivers, which continue flowing downhill until the water empties into the oceans. Water from the oceans then evaporates, and some of this moist air blows over the land and precipitates. In this way, North America's freshwater is continually renewed. However, the amount of precipitation and water flowing in streams varies by season and from year to year. On average, the continental United States receives approximately 4 million cubic miles (16 million cubic km.) of precipitation each year, which eventually makes its way back through the water cycle.

Hydrology map Page 385

Hydrology and Topography. North America can be divided into water drainage basins, also called watersheds. Drainage basins are the total land area that a river and its tributaries drain. The largest drainage basin in North America is the Mississippi River system, which drains a land area of 1,260,000 square miles (3,220,000 sq. km.). This is the third largest drainage basin in the world, after South America's Amazon River and Central Africa's Congo River.

Mississippi River Page 573

Areas of high elevation, such as mountain ranges, separate drainage basins from each other and are called drainage divides. In North America, the Continental Divide formed by the Rocky Mountains helps determine which way water generally flows. Near the East Coast, the Appalachian Range also acts as a drainage divide. Water that falls on the western side of the Rocky Mountains eventually empties into the Pacific Ocean. Water that falls between the Rocky Mountains and Appalachians and south of the Great Lakes eventually reaches the Gulf of Mexico. Water that falls on the eastern side of the Appalachians or in the Great Lakes drainage basin generally flows toward the East Coast and into the Atlantic Ocean. Water from a large part of central Canada flows into the Hudson Bay.

Mississippi River Page 508

Rocky Mountains Pages 384, 386

Water in north central Canada generally empties into the Arctic Ocean. In Mexico, water on the western side of the Continental Divide flows into the Pacific Ocean or Gulf of California. Water on the eastern side eventually flows into the Gulf of Mexico.

Rivers. The Mississippi River, one of the longest in North America, has tributaries from thirty-two states and two Canadian provinces. Its drainage basin covers about 40 percent of the continental United States as well as parts of Canada. The river flows for 2,350 miles (3,760 km.) and eventually empties into the Gulf of Mexico. It has an average flow rate of approximately 4.8 million gallons (18,400 cubic meters) per second, the largest in North America. The Mississippi River is a vital part of the United States' economy, because it provides water for irrigation and industry in ten states as well as an excellent means of transporting goods from the northern and central states to the rest of the world.

River flow rates in North America vary dramatically with season, rainfall, and

Located in the Rocky Mountains, the Continental Divide separates most of the continent into two great drainage basins. (Heather Stratton)

snowmelt. For example, Canada's Saskatchewan River has a maximum flow rate that is almost sixty times larger than its smallest recorded flow rate. The river with the largest average flow rate in Canada is the St. Lawrence River, which flows from the Great Lakes. The longest river in Canada is the Mackenzie River, which empties into the Arctic Ocean after flowing through the Northwest Territories. Its drainage basin is the second largest in North America and the twelfth largest in the world (680,000 square miles/ 1,760,000 sq. km.).

Rivers in Mexico flow generally eastward into the Gulf of Mexico or westward into the Pacific Ocean or Gulf of California. The Rio Grande flows south and southeast for 1,800 miles (3,000 km.) from the San Juan Mountains in southern Colorado, becoming part of the border between Mexico and the United States. The Rio Grijalva and Rio Usumacita have the largest flow rates (105 billion cubic meters per year) of all the rivers in Mexico. Together, they account for almost one-third of the total flow of all Mexico's rivers combined. They are each 440 miles (700 km.) long and flow into the Gulf of Mexico.

Lakes. The five Great Lakes—Erie, Huron, Michigan, Ontario, and Superior—lie in the central region of North America, mostly along the border between Canada and the United States. Lake Michigan is the only one of the Great Lakes entirely within the United States. These lakes were instrumental in enabling early European colonists to penetrate rapidly into the center of the continent. Today, approximately one-quarter of Canadians and one-tenth of U.S. citizens live in the region of the Great Lakes—more than 33 million people in all. The Great Lakes region is important to 25 percent of Canada's agriculture and 7 percent of the United States' agriculture. Industry in Canada and the United States also is heavily dependent on the Great Lakes region.

These five lakes extend more than 750 miles (1,200 km.) from east to west. They hold roughly 5,500 cubic miles (23,000 cubic km.) of water, which is about one-quarter of all the freshwater held in the world's lakes. The only lake system equal to this volume is Lake Baikal in Russia. The Great Lakes together cover 94,000 square miles (244,000 sq. km.) and are the largest inland water body in the world. Individually, three of the six largest inland water bodies by surface area are Lakes Superior, Huron, and Michigan. Lake Superior is the largest of the five Great Lakes, in both area and depth. It could easily hold the water of the other four lakes combined. The drainage basin for the Great Lakes totals about 290,000 square miles (750,000 sq. km.).

Canada contains more lake surface area than any other country in the world, including more than five hundred lakes larger than 40 square miles (100 sq. km.). Other large lake systems in Canada include the Great Bear Lake (12,125 square miles/31,400 sq. km.) and Great Slave Lake (10,965 square miles/28,400 sq. km.), both located in the Northwest Territories. By area, these two lakes are the ninth and tenth largest inland surface water bodies in the world. Lake Winnipeg in Manitoba Province is the twelfth largest inland surface water body in the world by area, but with a maximum depth of only 60 feet (18 meters), its total water volume is relatively smaller.

Lake Michigan Page 388

Mexico has few large lakes because of its dry climate. Its largest lake is Lake Chapala, between the states of Jalisco and Michoacán. It is 50 miles (80 km.) long and has a surface area of 420 square miles (1,080 sq. km.).

Not all lakes in North America contain freshwater. The Great Salt Lake in Utah is even saltier than the oceans. It covers an area of about 21,500 square miles (55,000 sq. km.). Fifteen thousand years ago, this large lake (which geologists call Lake Bonneville) was about fourteen times larger. Over time, evaporation and a drier climate reduced the size of the lake and increased the concentration of salts, resulting in today's Great Salt Lake.

Lake Tahoe Page 386

In contrast to the saline water of the Great Salt Lake, a large lake with some of the world's purest water is Lake Tahoe, on the border between California and Nevada in the Sierra Nevada range. Surrounded by tall mountains, Tahoe is a young lake fed by runoff and snowmelt. Until recently, this water was so clean that it needed no treatment to meet drinking water standards and was so clear that a person could see to depths of more than 100 feet (30 meters) from the surface.

Wetlands Page 387

Groundwater. An enormous amount of freshwater, called groundwater, lies beneath the surface of the earth. There is about twice as much groundwater in North America as the water in all its lakes and rivers. In the United States, approximately 50 percent of the population depends upon groundwater for the majority of its drinking water. In many areas, groundwater is pumped up to the surface through wells for use, but most groundwater flows slowly into lakes and rivers. In this way, groundwater can recharge rivers and keep them flowing even during droughts. Nearly all the people of Florida get their drinking water from groundwater. One of the most important aquifers in that state is the Biscayne, which supplies water to most of southern Florida.

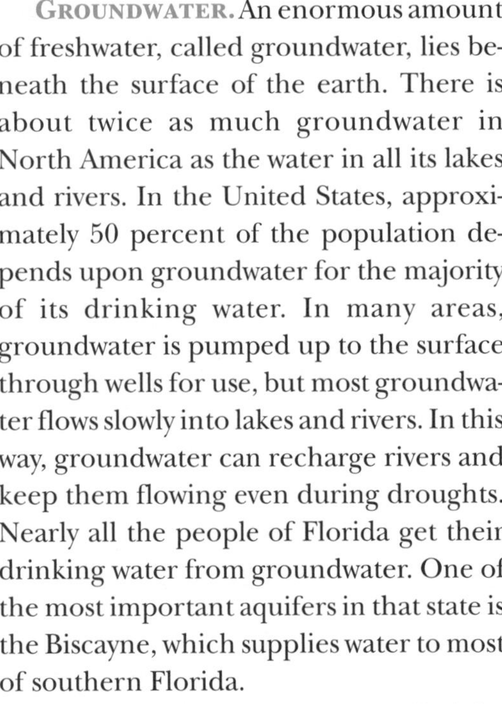

The High Plains Aquifer, also called the Ogallala Aquifer, spans the midwestern and southwestern states of South Dakota, Wyoming, Nebraska, Colorado, Kansas, Oklahoma, New Mexico, and Texas. This aquifer once held more freshwater than all the lakes and rivers of the world combined. It is especially important to agriculture, because it provides almost one-third of the groundwater used for agriculture in the United States. By the 1990's, it was noticed that the rate of water recharging this important aquifer was much less than the rate at which it was being pumped out, so that this aquifer is gradually being depleted.

Overpumping of groundwater has caused problems in other parts of North America. In California's San Joaquin Valley, overpumping to support the rich agriculture in the region has caused the land in some areas to sink by up to 33 feet (10 meters) since the 1920's. In the Houston-Galveston area of Texas, the land has sunk more than 10 feet (3 meters), making the area more susceptible to seasonal flooding. Another dramatic case is Mexico City, which relies almost entirely upon its aquifer for its water supply. The large growth in the city's population has resulted in rapid depletion of this water supply resource at the same time that industrial pollution has lowered the water's quality.

Wetlands. Swamps, marshes, bogs, and fens make up the wetlands, which are an important part of North America's hydrology. They not only are important ecologically but also help purify water, recharge groundwater aquifers, and act as holding areas for flood waters to reduce flood damage. The extent of wetlands in North America has changed dramatically. Before colonization by Europeans, the United States had approximately 350,000 square miles (890,000 sq. km.), but by 2000 it had less than half this amount. Alaska contains most of the United State's wetlands. The Everglades in Florida is another large wetlands area.

Canada has not experienced the same magnitude of wetlands reduction, except in more populated areas such as near the Great Lakes. Canada contains approximately one-fourth of all the world's wetlands, covering about 14 percent of Canada's surface area. The wetlands along the shores of the Great Lakes have been reduced by more than 50 percent since the nineteenth century, as towns and agriculture developed along their shores.

Glaciers and Ice. Worldwide, glaciers and ice sheets cover about 10 percent of the land surface and make up about three-quarters of the world's freshwater. Most of this is in Antarctica and Greenland. In the northern latitudes of North America, much of the water exists as ice. Greenland is covered by 660,000 square miles (1,700,000 sq. km.) of ice. After Antarctica and Greenland, Canada has the largest ice-covered area (96,500 square miles/250,000 sq. km.). The United States has 29,000 square miles (75,000 sq. km.) of area covered by ice, most of which is in Alaska. Ice often has existed in an area for a long time, as opposed to the relatively short time water spends in rivers and lakes. Ice in some of Canada's glaciers is more than 100,000 years old.

Human Impact on North American Hydrology. Only 2.2 percent of the area of the United States is covered by bodies of water; however, the vast majority of the human population lives near these water bodies. Water bodies provide a ready source of accessible water for drinking, industry, and irrigation. People have sought to control water bodies to benefit themselves. When a dam is built, a special kind of lake, called a reservoir, is created behind it. The reservoir can be a reliable source of water during times of drought. Dams, together with levees, also are useful in controlling floods to prevent damage to communities. The downside of this type of control of hydrology is that it can affect the amount of water that flows as well as the water's usefulness.

One example is the Colorado River, which is the longest river west of the Rocky Mountains at about 1,450 miles (2,330 km.) in length. The Colorado has many large dams along it, including Glen Canyon and Hoover Dams. As a result of the enormous reservoirs behind these dams, large amounts of water are lost to evaporation. It is estimated that 9 percent of the water in the Colorado River that comes into Lake Powell, the reservoir behind the Glen Canyon Dam, evaporates. Losses from this and other reservoirs increase the salinity of the water. Water is also taken

Colorado River Page 517

Lake Powell Page 388

The California Water Plan

Because of California's population growth, the U.S. Department of Interior has estimated that by the year 2020, California will have a water deficit of approximately 780 billion gallons (3 billion cubic meters). Southern California, which includes the cities of Los Angeles and San Diego, has a large population. Because this area does not receive a large amount of rain, it must find external water sources. A vast system of dams, aqueducts, tunnels, and canals has become the greatest water transfer system in the world. Water is brought to Southern California from as far away as 160 miles (250 km.) to the east, from the Colorado River, and from as far away as 500 miles (800 km.) to the north, from the Sacramento River. This large-water use relative to the limited supply has prompted water-saving measures such as irrigation practices, low-flow showerheads, and more water-efficient industrial techniques.

Evaporation of water from Lake Mead, an enormous reservoir behind the Hoover Dam, and runoff from agribusiness increase the salinity of the portion of Colorado River below it, often rendering its water unfit for irrigation, industry, or drinking. (Corbis)

from the river for irrigation of crops. By the time the Colorado River empties into the Gulf of California, the flow has been drastically reduced, and the water is so saline, it often cannot be used for irrigation, industry, or drinking water.

All the major rivers in the continental United States have been dammed, or diverted, drained, except the Yellowstone River, which flows freely for its entire 690-mile (1,110-kilometer) length. It rises in Wyoming and flows through Montana before emptying into the Missouri River.

Thomas R. MacDonald

For Further Study

De Souza, Anthony R., ed. *National Geographic Research and Exploration: Water Issue.* Vol. 9, 1993.

Fradkin, Philip L. *A River No More: The Colorado River and the West.* Los Angeles: University of California Press, 1996.

Klee, Gary A. *Conservation of Natural Resources.* Englewood Cliffs, N.J.: Prentice Hall, 1991.

National Geographic Society. *Water: The Power, Promise, and Turmoil of North America's Fresh Water.* Washington, D.C.: National Geographic Society, 1993.

Outwater, Alice. *Water: A Natural History.* New York: Basic Books, 1997.

Pielou, E. C. *Fresh Water.* Chicago: University of Chicago Press, 1998.

Rapp, Valerie. *What the River Reveals.* Seattle: Mountaineer Books, 1997.

Reisner, Mark. *Cadillac Desert: The American West and its Disappearing Water.* New York: Penguin Books, 1993.

Thompson, Stephen A. *Water Use, Management, and Planning in the United States.* San Diego, Calif.: Academic Press, 1999.

Information on the World Wide Web

The U.S. Geological Survey maintains a Web site dedicated to water resources of the United States, with a variety of articles and educational tools and activities. (water.usgs.gov/)

The U.S. Environmental Protection Agency's Web site discusses issues of water supply, water use, and water quality, with educational material and learning activities in both Spanish and English. (www.epa.gov/watrhome)

Environment Canada's Web site is dedicated primarily to Canadian hydrology but also contains general material related to other areas. The site is available in both English and French and has material for all levels. (www.ec.gc.ca/water/)

Physiography of the Caribbean

The Caribbean region comprises the Caribbean Sea and the many islands that surround it. The region's east-west extent is 1,800 miles (2,800 km.) from the Yucatán Peninsula to Barbados. Its north-south extent is 760 miles (1,200 km.) from the Bahamas to South America. Island groups include the Greater Antilles (Cuba, Hispaniola, Jamaica, and Puerto Rico), the Lesser Antilles, and numerous other small islands.

Geologic History. The oldest rocks of the Caribbean are Permian (200 million years old), but the oldest landscapes date only to the Cretaceous period (70 million years old). Two major mountain-building episodes created the landscapes of today. In the first, the North American and South American plates separated and moved westward. A part of the Pacific plate was forced northeastward between the larger plates, becoming the Caribbean plate. This created a subduction zone that led to volcanism and tectonism in the Greater Antilles. This episode was followed by a long period of quiet, during which the lands eroded and thick limestone deposits were laid on the seafloor.

The second tectonic episode began in the Pliocene epoch and continues today. The Caribbean plate is now moving eastward relative to surrounding plates. Thus, the Greater Antilles are along a lateral fault zone, whereas the Lesser Antilles have formed along a new subduction zone. The Atlantic plate is moving westward 1 to 2 inches (3-4 centimeters) per year, being subducted beneath the Caribbean plate. Volcanic eruptions are the result.

Besides volcanism, the region suffers also from earthquakes around its periphery, especially along the lateral fault in the Greater Antilles and the subduction zone to the east. Violent earthquakes have occurred, destroying the Jamaican cities of Port Royal (1692) and Kingston (1902) and Haiti's Port-au-Prince (twice in the eighteenth century) and Cap Haitien (1842).

Physiographic Regions. The landforms of the Caribbean region are the result of two tectonic episodes and periods of erosion and deposition. Three regions are identified: the Greater Antilles; the High Islands of the Lesser Antilles; and the Low Islands of the Lesser Antilles, the Bahamas, and offshore of South America.

The Greater Antilles, formed early in the geologic history of the Caribbean region, were produced by combinations of volcanism, folding, faulting, and uplift. Evidence of these events is found in the varied rocks of the islands, which include lavas, granites, metamorphic rocks, and limestone. Currently, this region has been relatively quiet, dominated by denudation due to wave and stream erosion and solution weathering.

The highest mountains in the Caribbean region are in the Greater Antilles. They include Pico Duarte (10,400 feet/ 3,175 meters) in the Dominican Republic, the Blue Mountains of Jamaica (7,400 feet/2,257 meters), El Yunque in Puerto Rico (3,500 feet/1,065 meters), and Pico Turquino in the Sierra Maestra of Cuba (6,500 feet/1,972 meters). Land elevations extend below sea level on Hispaniola's Enriquillo Depression (at –130 feet/ –40 meters). The mountains owe their existence to uplift of folded and faulted blocks whose rise ended in the late Tertiary period.

As a result of the combination of high relief and high annual rainfall, denudation rates are high and erosion features are prominent. Rivers have carved deep, steep-sided valleys along which landslides frequently occur. Human removal of native forests has accelerated denudation. Streams deposit their loads on coastal lowlands or in the sea where the material is reworked by waves.

Limestone plateaus containing karst landforms are also common. Limestone, rich in soluble calcium carbonate, is readily weathered into karst features, such as cones and sinkholes. Cone karst is dominated by steep-sided hills, also called *mogotes* or towers, which are remnants of limestone rock after millions of years of solution weathering. The Cockpit Country of Jamaica is a good example of cone karst. It is so rugged that few roads exist there. Sinkholes are common, ranging from small ponds to huge, steep-sided collapse sinks such as the vertical holes up to 200 feet (60 meters) deep at the Rio Camuy caves in Puerto Rico. Karst terrain is associated with underground drainage, which forms caves and subsurface stream passages. Surface streams are usually absent here.

The coastlines of the Greater Antilles are mostly rugged, with cliffs cut by wave erosion. In areas of low relief and low wave energy, extensive beaches and coastal mangrove swamps are found. Coral reefs occur offshore, especially on the windward sides of islands. Reefs are sensitive to sediment pollution, so they seldom occur near stream mouths.

Where streams occur, they tend to be short and steep. Perennial streams, common on the rainy windward sides of these islands, have more even flow regimes. Intermittent streams, typical of the drier lee slopes, are subject to flash flooding, often destroying bridges, roads, and other property.

The islands of the Lesser Antilles are made up of two island arcs, the Inner Arc and the Outer Arc. High islands of the Inner Arc include Saba and St. Kitts in the north, through Nevis, Montserrat, western Guadeloupe, Dominica, Martinique, St. Lucia, St. Vincent, and Grenada in the south. All these islands were formed from relatively recent volcanic eruptions and contain considerable local relief. There have been many volcanic eruptions in these islands in recorded history.

Effects of Volcanoes. Because the primary island landforms are volcanoes, slopes are steep and rugged. On older volcanoes, deep ravines have formed and landslides are common during heavy rains. Eroded volcanoes soon lose their conical shapes. Relatively little flat land is available for agriculture, limiting population densities throughout history.

Other landforms related to volcanoes are steep rock towers, such as the pitons of St. Lucia and similar features on Martinique, formed when thick lava plugged volcanic craters. After millions of years of erosion of the weaker surrounding rocks, the plugs have been exposed and stand in relief. Also related to volcanism are the yellow sulfur springs (*soufriéres* in French), found in St. Lucia, Dominica, and Montserrat. Toxic fumes from these springs have killed most of the surrounding vegetation.

Martinique Page 570

Volcanoes of the Lesser Antilles are composite or stratovolcanoes, large mountains built of layers of ash and lava. Eruptions tend to be explosive, raining layers of ash over everything. Hot clouds of ash, called *nuées ardentes*, accompany many eruptions, flowing downhill at great speeds, killing and destroying everything in their paths. The most notable one erupted in 1902 from Mount Pelée, killing thirty thousand people and completely destroying Martinique's capital, St. Pierre.

The high volcanic islands induce substantial rainfall, which runs off in steep,

Volcanic Eruptions on Montserrat

The Caribbean island of Montserrat became newsworthy in 1995 when a volcano in the Soufriére Hills began to erupt. This stratovolcano, which had not erupted in recorded history, began a series of violent eruptions after three years of ominous earthquakes. The eruption destroyed the capital city of Plymouth. Residents of the island were encouraged to move to the north, away from the eruptions, or to leave the island altogether. By 1997 most of the island's eleven thousand inhabitants had left, and the southern two-thirds of the island were declared off limits, as the volcanic activity continued.

short streams. The smaller high islands tend to lack lee rain shadows, and the uplands are cloaked in lush rain forests.

Effects of Low Relief. The many Low Islands of the Caribbean region lack significant relief, not rising more than 660 feet (200 meters) above sea level. Notable are the Bahamas, the Outer Arc of the Lesser Antilles, and Caribbean islands offshore of South America. Although such islands have varying geologic histories, they all have low relief and a dominance of surface limestone. One significant result of low relief is low annual rainfall. These islands receive less rainfall because they lack the extensive surfaces necessary to produce afternoon convection, and they lack the relief necessary to produce mountain rainfall. They depend on stray thundershowers, mostly from easterly waves and occasional hurricanes. For example, Inagua in the Bahamas receives only 27 inches (685 millimeters) of rain per year, and Bonaire, off the coast of South America, receives only 20 inches (510 millimeters).

Bahamas Page 389

Water. This comparative scarcity of rainfall means that fresh water at the surface is rare. If it exists at all, fresh water occurs in thin subsurface lenses floating on top of salt water. Overuse of such groundwater results in loss of the resource, because freshwater recharge is very slow. Because of the lack of rainfall, the low islands rarely have good soils for agriculture, and they lack the tropical forests of larger islands. These difficult environments were largely avoided by colonizers, and they still suffer from low development, except in a few cases, such as the Bahamas and the Cayman Islands, where tourism and banking have enabled people to thrive.

P. Gary White

For Further Study

Boswell, Thomas P., and Dennis Conway. *The Caribbean Islands: Endless Geographic Diversity.* Piscataway, N.J.: Rutgers University Press, 1992.

Clawson, David L. *Latin America and the Caribbean: Lands and Peoples.* New York: McGraw Hill, 1999.

Macpherson, John. *Caribbean Lands.* Essex, England: Longman, 1984.

Sealey, Neil. *Caribbean World: A Complete Geography.* New York: Cambridge University Press, 1992.

West, Robert C., and John P. Augelli. *Middle America: Its Lands and Peoples.* Englewood Cliffs, N.J.: Prentice Hall, 1989.

Williams, Ann R. "Montserrat: Under the Volcano." *National Geographic* (July, 1997): 58-75.

A train moves through the rolling plains of Colorado, whose terrain typifies the vast grassland that extends from central Canada through Texas. (PhotoDisc)

THE UNITED STATES

Canada

Nome
Barrow
Arctic Ocean
ICELAND
Reykjavik
U.S.A.
Beaufort Sea
GREENLAND
Fort Yukon
Fairbanks
Anchorage
Tuktoyaktuk
Baffin Bay
Yukon Territory
Great Bear Lake
Whitehorse
Northwest Territories
Juneau
Yellowknife
Labrador Sea
Great Slave Lake
Bear Lake
C A N A D A
Newfoundland
Alberta
Hudson Bay
Inukjuak
British Columbia
Churchill
Edmonton
Manitoba
St. John's
Saskatchewan
Labrador City
Calgary
Vancouver
Victoria
Saskatoon
Province of Quebec
Ontario
Regina
Gulf of St. Lawrence
Winnipeg
Prince Edward Island
Quebec
North Bay
Halifax
Montreal
Lake Superior
Ottawa
Lake Huron
Nova Scotia
UNITED STATES
New Brunswick
Lake Ontario
Lake Michigan
Lake Erie
Atlantic Ocean

The only large terrestrial mammal inhabiting the Arctic region, the polar bear is forced by the rigors of the environment to be an aggressive and efficient hunter. (PhotoDisc)

One of the best preserved early Maya sites, Chichén Itzá flourished in Mexico's northern Yucatán Peninsula around 900 to 1100 C.E. The most famous ruin at the complex is the Castillo pyramid, dedicated to the god Kulkulcan (also known as Quetzalcoatl), who is represented by the Chac Mool figure in the foreground. (Corbis)

Mexico

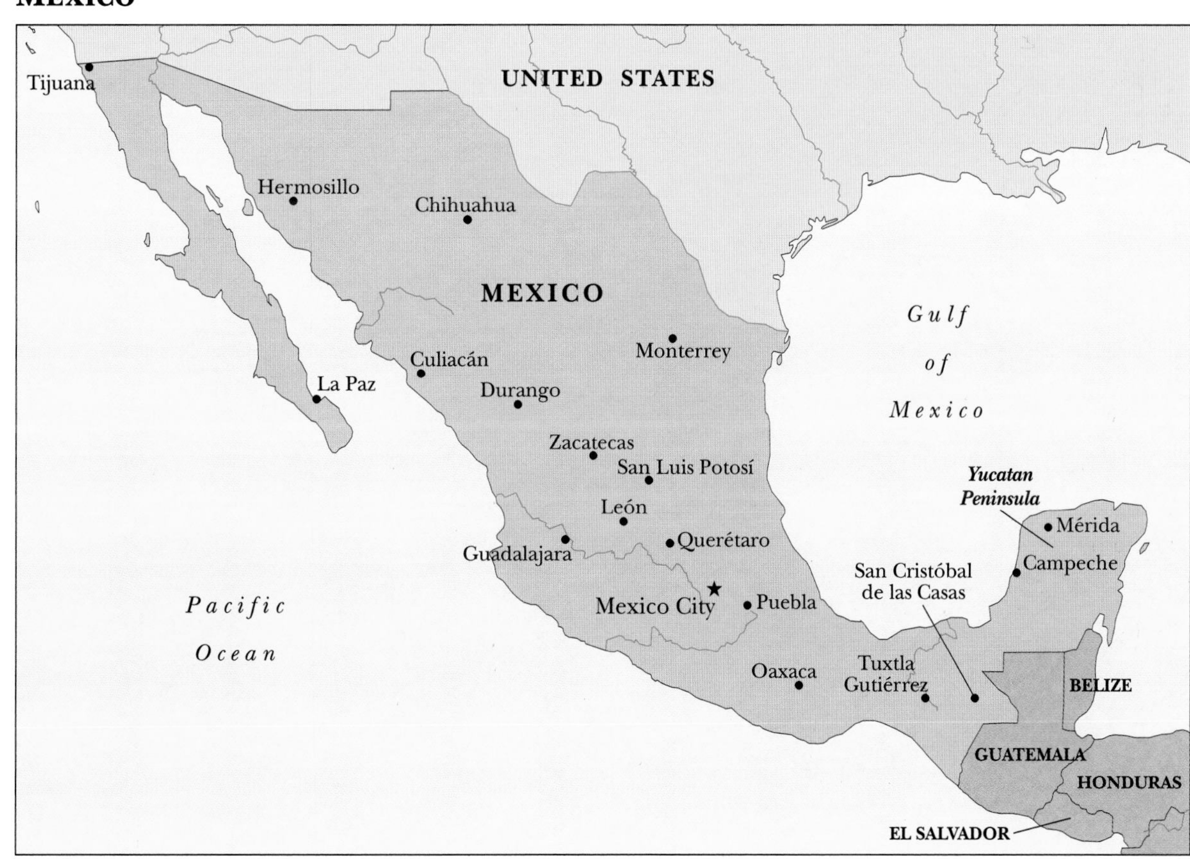

The beach resorts of Acapulco have made that Pacific Coast port one of Mexico's top tourist attractions. (Corbis)

Greenland and the Arctic Region

The profusion of seals in Arctic waters was one of the driving forces behind the region's exploration and commercial development. (PhotoDisc)

Typical arctic landscape. (PhotoDisc)

CARIBBEAN

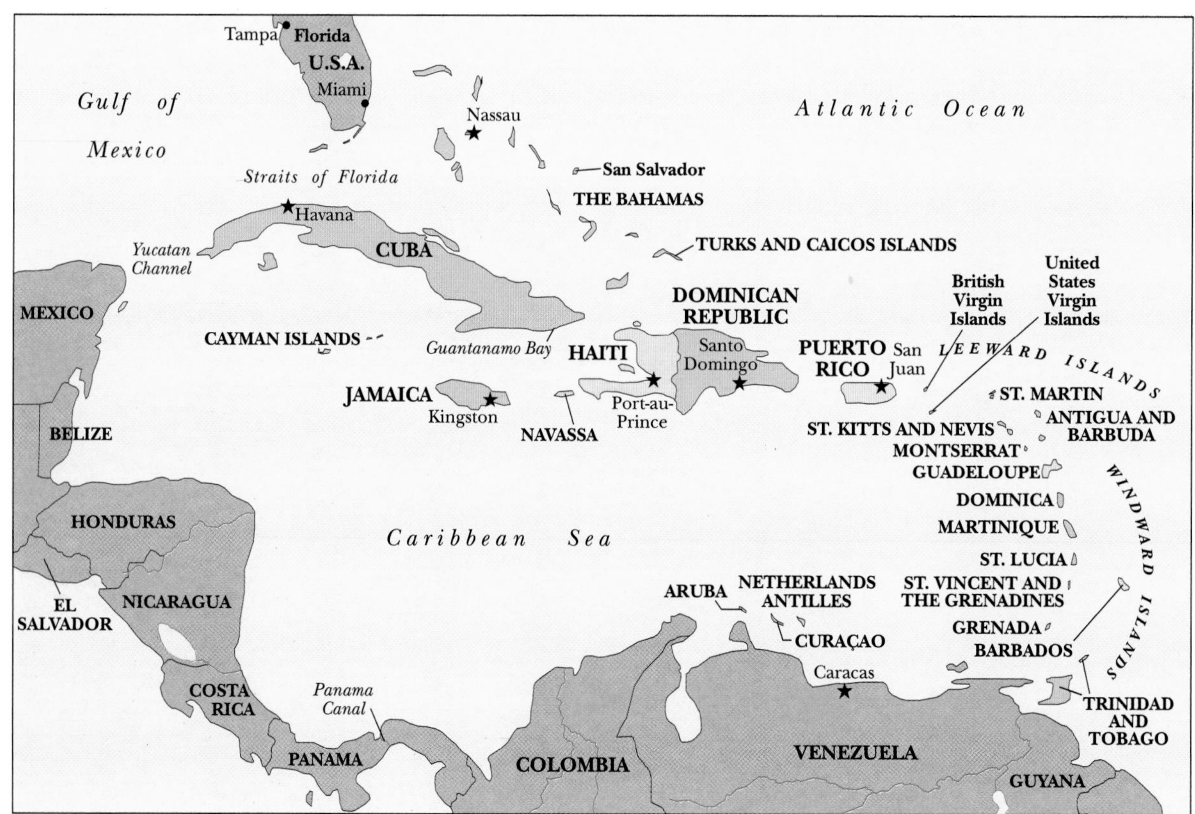

PHYSICAL GEOGRAPHY OF NORTH AMERICA

The Snake River and the Grand Tetons. Formed by glaciation, Wyoming's Grand Teton range offers some of the most spectacular mountain scenery in the Rocky Mountains. (Corbis)

Kennicott Glacier on Mount Blackburn in Alaska's Wrangell Mountains. (PhotoDisc)

Mexico is a largely mountainous country. The Sierra Madre Occidental, its largest range, extends along its western coast. (Clyde L. Rasmussen)

Major Watersheds of North America

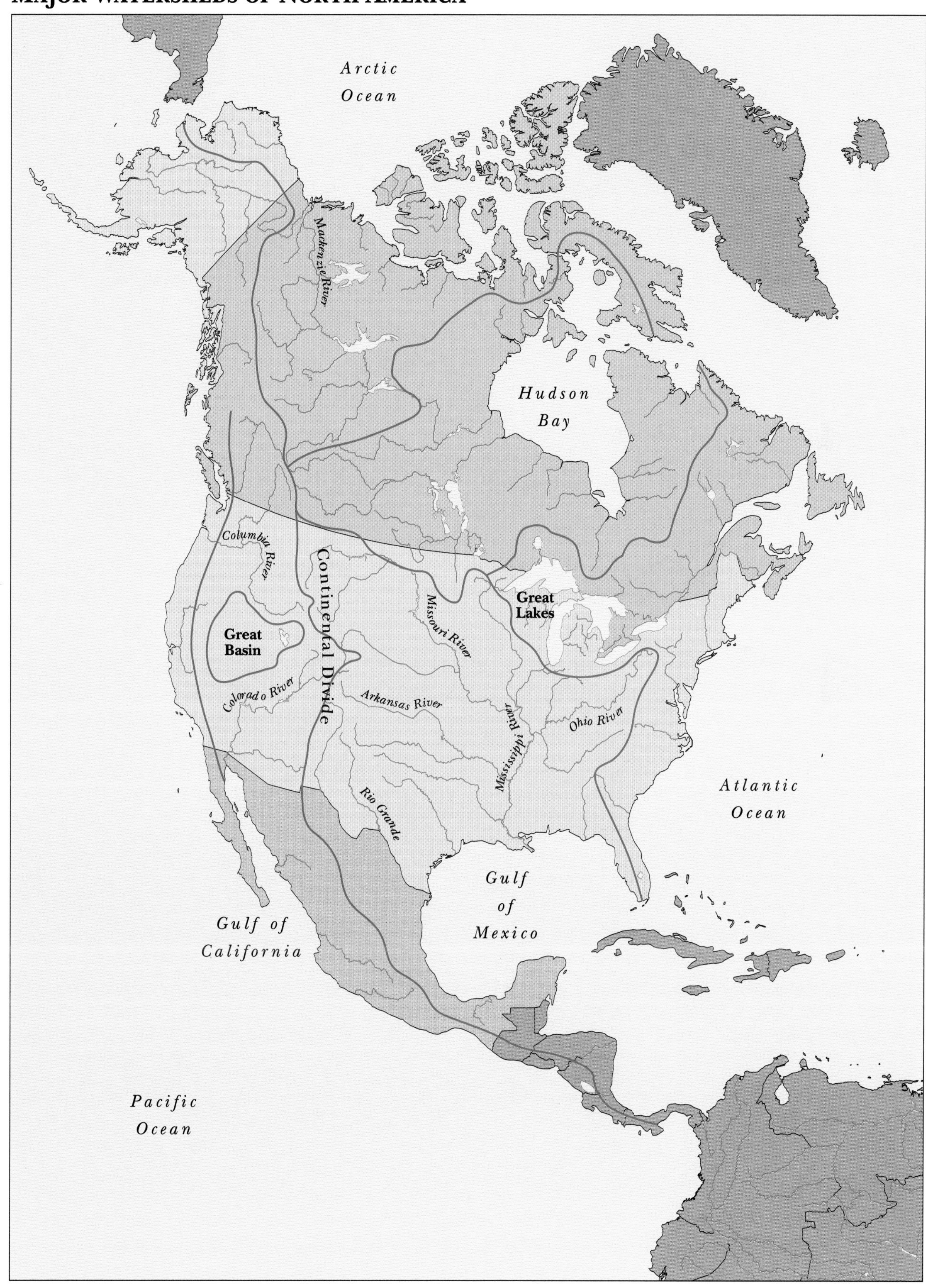

Shoshone Falls, Idaho, perhaps the most beautiful of many waterfalls on the Pacific Northwest's Snake River. Draining an area of 109,000 square miles (282,000 sq. km.), the Snake is the ninth biggest river system in North America and the largest tributary of the Columbia River. (Corbis)

Emerald Bay, on the California side of Lake Tahoe. Covering 187 square miles (484 sq. km.) along the Nevada-California border, Tahoe stands at an altitude of about 6,230 feet (1,900 meters). Before modern development began affecting the lake, it contained some of the clearest and purest water of any large lake in the world. (Corbis)

Swamps, marshes, bogs, and fens make up typical North American wetlands. (PhotoDisc)

Florida wetlands. Wetlands, which help purify water, recharge groundwater aquifers, and act as holding areas for flood waters to reduce flood damage. (PhotoDisc)

Utah's Lake Powell is an artificial lake created by a dam on the Colorado River. Its environment impact has made its creation controversial. Nearly a tenth of the water passing thorough the lake evaporates, thereby helping to raise the remaining water's salinity so much that it becomes unusable. (PhotoDisc)

Southern tip of Lake Michigan, the only Great Lake entirely within the United States. Chicago can be seen on its southwest shore. Snow is covering most of the ground in this winter, 1990, photograph taken from the space shuttle Atlantis. (Corbis)

Grand Bahama and Little Bahama Bank, seen from the space shuttle Columbia *in October, 1992. The white spots in the bank are deposits of calcium carbonate that precipitated from seawater.* (Corbis)

This enhanced satellite view of North America shows driest zones as brown and the wettest zones as green. There was comparatively little cloud cover over the continent at the moment the image was made in 1992; however, Hurricane Andrew can be seen moving through the Gulf of Mexico. (PhotoDisc)

CLIMATIC REGIONS OF NORTH AMERICA

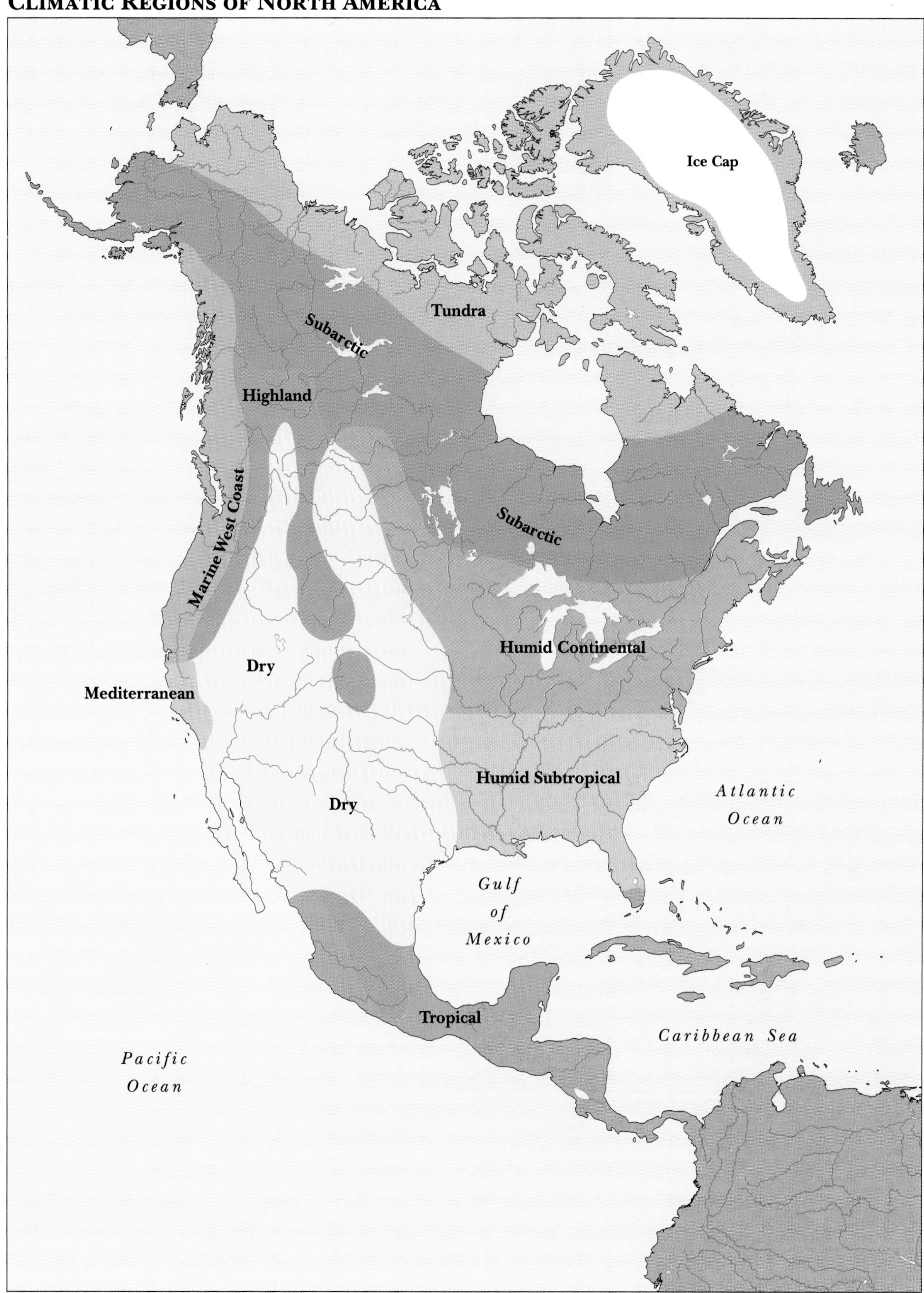

Selected Resources of North America

The timber industry of the Pacific Northwest and western Canada was built, in part, on the ready availability of rivers to move logs to coastal ports. (PhotoDisc)

Rain forest in southern Mexico's Chiapas State. (PhotoDisc)

Climatology

North America

Climates of North America are diverse, ranging from extremely dry to extremely wet, from bitterly cold to oppressively hot. Most of North America's habitable regions are located within the Northern Hemisphere midlatitudes, between 23.5 degrees north (the tropic of Cancer) and approximately 60 degrees north. Midlatitude climates are zones of transition between the warm Tropics and the cold polar regions. Pronounced seasonality exists with regard to weather variables as a wide array of individual weather events occur.

North American Weather. North America has some of the most violent weather in the world. On no other continent is there a regular mix of such vastly different air. This is the result of the unique arrangement of mountains, which are aligned roughly north to south, allowing cold and warm air to mix freely. Warm, moist air from the Gulf of Mexico moves northward into the central portion of the continent, where it mixes with cold, dry air emanating from northern Canada, causing volatile weather.

Most significant weather is associated with migratory midlatitude, or frontal, cyclones. These storms are the largest on Earth, with diameters between 1,000 and 2,000 miles (1,600 and 3,200 km.). Their storm systems have a low-pressure core in which surface air converges and rises, creating clouds and precipitation. A cold front, with heavy precipitation producing cumulonimbus clouds, and a warm front with stratus clouds, also exist. Warm-front precipitation is normally light and widespread.

Climate map Page 390

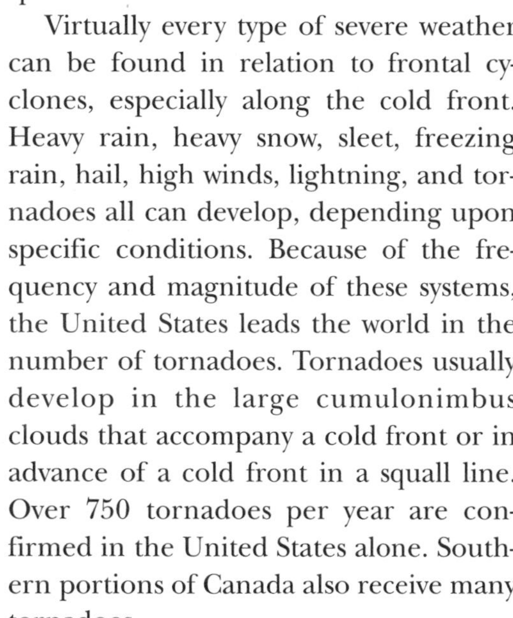

Virtually every type of severe weather can be found in relation to frontal cyclones, especially along the cold front. Heavy rain, heavy snow, sleet, freezing rain, hail, high winds, lightning, and tornadoes all can develop, depending upon specific conditions. Because of the frequency and magnitude of these systems, the United States leads the world in the number of tornadoes. Tornadoes usually develop in the large cumulonimbus clouds that accompany a cold front or in advance of a cold front in a squall line. Over 750 tornadoes per year are confirmed in the United States alone. Southern portions of Canada also receive many tornadoes.

Satellite image Page 389

Dry Climates. Dry climates are a feature of the southwestern regions of the continent. Dry climates, which may be classified as subtropical desert, hot desert, subtropical steppe, and hot steppe, occur when net evaporation rates exceed net precipitation totals. In North America, hot desert climates occur only in the southwestern United States and northern Mexico. Wetter steppe climates surround the true desert core, which is largely centered on the state of Arizona.

North America's dry region is induced by a variety of climatic factors acting in concert. First, the region is located at approximately 30 degrees north latitude in an area of subsiding air, as dictated by the general circulation of the atmosphere. Subsiding air causes clear skies because it discourages clouds and precipitation. Second, the desert region is located along the western portion of the continent near cold ocean currents. The cold California current chills overlying air so it resists rising.

A third factor is the phenomenon known as rain shadow. A rain shadow occurs when warm, moist air traverses a mountain range. As the air ascends the windward side of the mountains, clouds and precipitation occur. Air flow descends over the opposite, or lee, side, where subsidence limits clouds and precipitation. All three factors combine to ensure the predominance of sinking air in the southwestern United States.

The true desert of North America is classified as a subtropical desert, although northern portions may be classified as midlatitude deserts. Although precipitation totals—about 0-10 inches (0-25 centimeters)—are fairly uniform across the months, the most intense precipitation typically occurs during the warm months and is associated with hot, rising air stimulated by high surface temperatures. Precipitation totals increase slightly in association with this summer "monsoon" of the desert southwest.

During other times of the year, rain and snow are generated by migratory frontal cyclones. However, precipitation totals are frequently low, especially during cooler times. Precipitation varies greatly from year to year, since many years may pass with very little precipitation, only to be followed by a year with precipitation far above normal. Monthly or yearly precipitation averages may, therefore, be somewhat misleading and unrepresentative.

The highest natural air temperature ever recorded in the Western Hemisphere—134 degrees Fahrenheit (56.7 degrees Celsius)— was measured at Greenland Ranch, California, on July 10, 1913. However, temperatures in subtropical deserts fluctuate considerably, both daily and seasonally. Daytime summer temperatures can be exceedingly high, while nighttime temperatures can be quite cool because of low humidity levels. Average monthly temperatures can be near 100 degrees Fahrenheit (38 degrees Celsius) for some locations, as daily maximum temperatures frequently climb to 109 degrees Fahrenheit (43 degrees Celsius). Temperatures during the winter months are cool, with average monthly temperatures in January and February near 50 degrees Fahrenheit (10 degrees Celsius). The vast differences between summer and winter result in high annual temperature ranges.

More northerly regions are classified as midlatitude deserts, which are similar to subtropical deserts with regard to precipitation but typically have greater annual temperature ranges than subtropical deserts. While summer temperatures are similar in both regions, winter temperatures are colder in midlatitude deserts than in subtropical deserts.

The true desert of North America is bounded on all sides by the wetter steppe climate transition zone. As in the true desert, annual precipitation varies greatly. However, the annual totals of 10 to 30 inches (25 to 76 centimeters) exceed those of a true desert. Because of higher precipitation totals, steppe grasses proliferate, becoming more widespread, thicker, and taller away from the true desert core. The grasslands ultimately culminate at the boundary of an adjacent climate zone.

Precipitation totals typically reach a maximum during winter for steppe locations on the poleward side of the true desert. Precipitation in these locations is triggered by the passage of migratory midlatitude storm systems. On the equator side of the true desert, precipitation totals maximize during the summer season when thunderstorm activity is greater.

Temperatures in steppe deserts are similar to those in true deserts, except that they vary less by season. Therefore, temperature ranges are smaller than in true deserts. The steppe regions are also reflective of latitude in that poleward locations experience cooler overall temperatures than locations farther equatorward.

Mediterranean Climates. In North America, the Mediterranean climate is found only in a coastal area in the state of California. This climate type is characterized by a distinct summer dry period and a wet winter. The summer dry is induced by the presence of a semipermanent high-pressure cell that dominates over the Pacific Ocean. During the warm season, this Hawaiian High becomes particularly well established and exerts a subsiding force on the atmosphere, which prohibits cloud and precipitation processes. During winter, the high weakens, allowing migratory storms to pass through the region.

The frequency and magnitude of these storm systems is highly variable. Some winters are predominantly dry, while during others, copious precipitation falls. Precipitation generally increases with latitude for this climate type. This is because even during fairly dry winters, northern areas are affected by frontal cyclones passing on the poleward side of the region. Total annual precipitation is approximately 15 inches (38 centimeters).

Temperatures for the region are mild through the cool months and mild to hot during warm months. In general, temperatures are milder near the coast and become more extreme farther inland. Summertime coastal temperatures are typically 68 to 86 degrees Fahrenheit (20 to 30 degrees Celsius), while inland locations can have daily highs near 100 degrees Fahrenheit (38 degrees Celsius). During cool months, inland temperatures can dip below freezing, while coastal locations, moderated by the ocean, remain cool with temperatures in the range of 50 to 61 degrees Fahrenheit (10 to 16 degrees Celsius).

Marine West Coast. North of the Mediterranean climate along the Pacific Coast lies the marine west coast climate region. This region extends along the coastal margins of the continent, from northern California through Alaska. It is typified by mild temperatures through the seasons and a fairly even distribution of precipitation through the months. Temperatures are mild for the relatively high latitude of the region. The moderation of the nearby ocean and the prevalence of frequent low-level cloud cover associated with migratory frontal cyclones ensures mild temperatures.

Although the number of days of precipitation may be high, annual precipitation totals are low, especially near the coast. Much precipitation is generated by vertically limited stratus clouds, which produce only light drizzle. Inland, in higher elevations, the precipitation is much greater: In some locations, it exceeds 100 inches (254 centimeters) per year, similar to tropical rain forest totals. A slight autumn precipitation maximum occurs, and a slight minimum occurs during the summer months. In general, there is a fairly even distribution of precipitation year round.

Even with the relatively high latitudes of this climate region, extreme cold is rare, as is snowfall in lower elevations. Average temperatures are above freezing throughout the year. Snow typically occurs only in higher elevations, where average temperatures are much lower. Temperature ranges are fairly small, mainly because of the moderating influence of the ocean. Temperature ranges increase farther inland, where the moderating effect of the ocean diminishes. Maximum monthly temperatures rarely exceed 75 degrees Fahrenheit (24 degrees Celsius) as maximum monthly averages are usually between 50 and 55 degrees Fahrenheit (10 to 13 degrees Celsius). Monthly temperature averages during winter are usually about 32 degrees Fahrenheit (0 degrees Celsius), as daily winter minimums rarely dip below –20 degrees Fahrenheit (7 degrees Celsius).

Humid Subtropical. Humid subtropical climates have relatively mild winters and long, hot summers. Much of this is related to the maritime influence exerted on the area by the warm waters of the Gulf of Mexico and the southwest North Atlantic Ocean. The southeastern portion of the United States falls into this climate classification.

Average cold-month temperatures are typically between 39 and 60 degrees Fahrenheit (4 and 16 degrees Celsius), but freezing temperatures, although unexpected, are not uncommon. The lowest recorded temperature for southeastern Louisiana was approximately 10 degrees Fahrenheit (–12 degrees Celsius), recorded in 1989. The coldest month in this climate usually is January (approximately 50 degrees Fahrenheit/ 10 degrees C, on average), the time of most frequent freezes. Extremely cold temperatures are relatively uncommon there.

Summer months are normally hot, with average temperatures around 79 to 82 degrees Fahrenheit (26 to 28 degrees Celsius) with rather high relative humidity levels. The average relative humidity on a July morning is typically between 85 and 95 percent. High humidity in conjunction with high temperature produces sultry, oppressive weather with low cooling power. Temperature maximums during the summer months typically approach 95 degrees Fahrenheit (35 degrees Celsius), with temperatures reaching as high as 102 degrees Fahrenheit (39 degrees Celsius).

Precipitation is relatively evenly distributed throughout the year in this area, averaging 40 to 60 inches (102 to 152 centimeters). Heavy precipitation is relatively common, generally associated with summer convective thunderstorms. Such thunderstorms occur almost daily throughout the summer and early autumn months in the southeastern United States as a result of diurnal heating of the land surface.

Tropical cyclones also add to the summer precipitation. North Atlantic tropical cyclones are most common during the late summer. The tropical cyclone is an important component of the precipitation regime of the humid subtropical climate region during the summer and autumn months and may be looked upon as a benefit to the precipitation regime, especially during early autumn.

The driest months of the year are typically October and November, when a tran-

Hurricane Camille

In 1969 Hurricane Camille, the strongest storm to strike the North American continent in the twentieth century, pummeled the coast of Mississippi with maximum sustained winds of more than 212 miles (322 km.) per hour and an associated storm surge of more than 24 feet (7.32 meters). The storm surge, a dome of water that develops beneath the eye of a storm, is responsible for most of the coastal damage during a storm. The hurricane drives this dome of water inland, where it inundates low-lying areas.

sition occurs between precipitation-forcing mechanisms. Frontal cyclones are a common feature in this region during the winter and spring, as the polar jet stream reaches its closest position to the equator (near 30 degrees north). The frequency of frontal cyclones also increases during these times, ensuring a relatively even distribution of precipitation through the region from month to month.

Humid Continental. Humid continental climates are confined to the central to northeastern portion of the continent. Most of the inhabited portions of the United States and Canada lie within this climate region. It is similar to the humid subtropical climates, except that precipitation totals are less and temperatures are lower.

Precipitation is fairly well distributed throughout the year, but a slight maximum is perceptible during the summer months. Precipitation is largely controlled by migratory frontal cyclone passage during all seasons except summer. Summer precipitation is predominantly convective, because it is initiated by surface heating, but some summer precipitation stems from frontal passage. These precipitation events are usually associated with cooler air migrating from northern Canada. Such occurrences spell relief from fairly high summer temperatures. Annual precipitation totals are usually between 20 and 40 inches (51 to 102 centimeters).

Summer temperatures range from fairly warm to hot in the continental interior. The continental landmass itself causes extreme seasonal fluctuations, because the regions are far removed from the moderating effects of large water bodies, which tie up available energy through evaporation processes and heat storage. In summer months, when high solar angles are prevalent, the land heats quickly.

During winter, the opposite occurs: Low solar angles predominate, so there is little surface heating. The absence of a large body of water augments warming or chilling of the surface and the overlying air, depending on the season, so seasonal extremes are typical. Many locations in the humid continental climate region have monthly summertime averages of 81 to 84 degrees Fahrenheit (27 to 29 degrees Celsius), while monthly winter averages range from 30 to 41 degrees Fahrenheit (−1 to +5 degrees Celsius).

Subarctic. In North America, subarctic climates exist north of humid continental climate regions, covering more than half of Alaska and Canada. The region is typically referred to as the boreal forest, because it is dominated by extensive coniferous forest. Summer temperatures are similar to, but cooler than, those of the humid continental climate region. Winter temperatures, however, are much colder than those of the adjacent climate region. Below-freezing average monthly temperatures are quite common. In some locations, average temperatures can be below freezing for up to seven months.

Extreme seasonality of temperatures is the norm, as monthly average temperature ranges may be as high as 70 to 100 degrees Fahrenheit (21 to 38 degrees Celsius). The transition seasons, autumn and spring, are relatively short in comparison with the length of summer and winter, with the latter season extremely long. Precipitation is usually very low, because the cold air temperatures prohibit the storage of large amounts of moisture. Total precipitation is typically between 5 and 20 inches (12 to 50 centimeters), with the majority falling during the warm months.

Tundra. Tundra regions exist poleward of the subarctic climate region. The tundra climate type is named for tundra vegetation, which consists of low-growing flowering plants, shrubs, small trees, lichens, and mosses. Typically, the mean monthly temperature of the warmest month does not exceed 50 degrees Fahrenheit (10 degrees Celsius). The region lies around or poleward of 60 degrees latitude. Because of the high latitude, winter temperatures are extremely cold as the Sun shines for only a few hours each day. Summer temperatures are only slightly above freezing on average, even though there is virtually constant daylight. The constant cold causes permafrost, constantly frozen subsoil. In winter, all soil is frozen, but during the summer months, the top layers of soil thaw. This creates a highly saturated condition, as liquid water cannot penetrate the frozen ground below.

Precipitation amounts are relatively low, typically around 5 inches (13 centimeters) per year. Precipitation is distributed somewhat evenly through the year, but a summertime maximum is prevalent. This is a result of the extreme cold of winter, when air has little moisture-carrying capacity, thus essentially creating a cold desert.

ICE CAP. Greenland is the only location in North America, or the Northern Hemisphere, that is classified as an ice cap region. Ice covers the ground throughout the year there, as mean monthly temperatures remain below freezing. Cold, dense air forms above the chilled Greenland ice cap surface and spills toward lower elevations, ensuring frigid temperatures even along the coast. The region receives little precipitation, as a result of the extremely cold temperatures. The precipitation that does occur is mainly limited to late summer and autumn, when temperatures are highest. Precipitation is typically less than 5 inches (12 centimeters) per year.

HIGHLAND. High elevations are typically included within other climate regions. The climates of mountainous regions are driven by elevation and may not adequately represent any particular climate zone. Highland climates are driven by vertical zonation, which refers to the progression of climatic zones with increasing elevation. The progression of climate zones with height largely mimics the progression of climate zones with increasing latitude. Rapid changes in slope, orientation, and elevation make specific categorization of these regions problematic. Temperature and precipitation regimes change according to these factors. Individual locations may be greatly different from one another even though they may be in close proximity to each other. Highland climates largely exist along the Rocky Mountain spine that runs from Alaska through Canada and the western United States to Mexico.

Anthony J. Vega

FOR FURTHER STUDY

Battan, Louis, J. *Weather in Your Life.* New York: W. H. Freeman, 1983.

Critchfield, Howard J. *General Climatology.*

INFORMATION ON THE WORLD WIDE WEB

North American climate information can be obtained at the National Climatic Data Center's Web site (www.ncdc.noaa.gov/). Climate information specific to Canada can be accessed at the Natural Resources Canada Web site. (climatechange.nrcan.gc.ca/)

UM Weather, a Web site maintained by the University of Michigan, features forecasts, maps, models, and radar and satellite images. (cirrus.sprl.umich.edu/wxnet)

4th ed. Englewood Cliffs, N.J.: Prentice Hall, 1983.

Lutgens, Frederick K., and Edward J. Tarbuck. *The Atmosphere.* 7th ed. Englewood Cliffs, N.J.: Prentice Hall, 1998.

Lyons, Walter A. *The Handy Weather Answer Book.* Detroit: Visible Ink, 1997.

Suplee, Curt. "Untangling the Science of Climate." *National Geographic* (May, 1998): 44-70.

Tufty, Barbara. *1001 Questions Answered About Hurricanes, Tornadoes, and Other Natural Air Disasters.* New York: Dover, 1987.

The Caribbean

The Caribbean extends from Trinidad in the south (10 degrees north latitude) to the northern Bahamas (27 degrees north latitude). With the exception of the northern Bahamas, it lies entirely within the Tropics. Its tropical location means that temperatures on its islands are generally warm year-round, with no major seasonal differences. A typical average annual temperature near sea level is 80 degrees Fahrenheit (27 degrees Celsius), and the coolest month averages above 64 degrees Fahrenheit (18 degrees Celsius).

Climate Controls. Caribbean climates are governed by several factors, including latitude, trade winds, maritime influences, mountains, and nearness to North America. The low latitude of the region causes temperatures to be high all year because of the high sun angles. However, the latitudinal extent of the Caribbean, about 17 degrees, means that there are temperature-related differences from north to south. Temperature varies more by season in the Bahamas than it does southward.

Prevailing winds throughout the Caribbean region are the northeasterly trade winds. These are tropical winds off the ocean, carrying considerable heat and moisture. Typical trade winds have relative humidities of 70 percent or more. Although this alone is not sufficient for precipitation, all that is needed is some triggering mechanism to cause clouds and rainfall. Common triggers are forced rise of the trade winds over mountains (orographic effect), convectional rise of air above heated land surfaces, and the passage of low pressure, often in the form of easterly waves.

The fact that most of the islands of the Caribbean are mountainous has two important consequences. First, because air tends to be cooler at higher altitudes, at a rate of 6 degrees Celsius per 1,000 meters (3.5 degrees Fahrenheit per 1,000 feet), the uplands have cooler climates than at sea level. Although most people of the region live near sea level, in coastal plains and port cities, the wealthy often live in upland suburbs where temperatures are less oppressive.

A second consequence of mountains involves their effects on the trade winds. Mountains force the trade winds to rise, and in the process, the moist air cools and clouds and rain may result. Most of the rain falls on the northeast, windward sides of mountains. Windward slopes receive the highest annual rainfall totals in the region, sometimes more than 200 inches (5,000 millimeters). Lee slopes, to the southwest of the mountains, are typically drier, with annual rainfall less than half that of the windward slopes.

The surface of the Caribbean region is mostly water, so that temperatures are moderated, being neither as hot nor as cold as at the midlatitudes. In addition, the chief ocean currents of the Caribbean arrive from the tropical Atlantic Ocean. These waters help maintain the tropical temperatures and protect the islands from northern climatic influences.

The Greater Antilles and the Bahamas are relatively close to the continent of North America, so in winter they are influenced by cold air masses from the north. Although a cold air mass is warmed on its journey across the warm Gulf of Mexico and Caribbean waters, it can still depress temperatures up to 18 degrees Fahrenheit (10 degrees Celsius) below normal in the Bahamas and Cuba.

Climate Types. The Caribbean region has three distinct climate types, defined primarily by rainfall patterns: tropical wet, tropical wet and dry, and tropical dry.

The tropical wet climate is hot all year and receives more than 80 inches (2,000 millimeters) of precipitation per year. There is no significant dry season. Substantial rainfall occurs in every month, although summer months are wetter. Rain is chiefly orographic. This climate is found on the windward sides of the Greater Antilles and almost all of the Lesser Antilles.

The tropical wet and dry climate is also hot all year. Rain falls chiefly as afternoon convectional thunderstorms. This climate receives two-thirds of its annual rainfall in summer; a four- to six-month dry season is centered on winter. Drought is possible, especially from March to May. This climate occurs on the lee slopes of the Greater Antilles.

The tropical dry climate is found chiefly in the rain shadows to the lee of the highest mountains of the region, especially the highlands of Hispaniola. Annual precipitation totals less than 20 inches (500 millimeters). Smaller pockets of dry climate also are found on the lee sides of Jamaica and Puerto Rico. Additionally, small islands that lack relief, thus lacking the triggers of convection and orographic effect, are usually dry. These include the Bahamas, Turks and Caicos Islands, Cayman Islands, St. Martin, and the Netherlands Antilles off the north coast of South America.

Easterly Waves and Hurricanes. Caribbean climates are affected by easterly waves and hurricanes. Easterly waves are elongated (northeast to southwest) troughs of low pressure that ride the trade winds, mostly in summer. As these troughs move westward, they trigger showers and thundershowers, accounting for much of the total rainfall received by many islands, especially those lacking relief.

In the summer and fall months, for reasons not entirely understood, certain easterly waves may develop into hurricanes, strong rotary cyclonic storms known for high winds, heavy precipitation, and coastal flooding. Most islands are affected by these storms once every three to ten years. Among the devastating effects of hurricanes in the Caribbean are serious floods, major landslides, wind damage to crops and forests, and damage to infrastructure, including tourist facilities.

Influences of Climate. Climate influences many aspects of life in the Caribbean, including agriculture and health. Because there is no winter here, agricultural possibilities are good, depending largely on annual precipitation and altitude. Tropical wet areas are ideal for growing cocoa, bananas, coconuts, nutmeg, and citrus, which are major exports for some islands. Islands with extensive uplands can grow vegetables and flowers, often associated with the midlatitudes. Drier leeward locales are suitable for a variety of crops, including sugarcane, fiber crops, and tobacco, when irrigation is available.

Climate affects health in various ways. As in all humid tropical locales, the lack of frost and abundance of heat and moisture promote a variety of tropical diseases that affect humans, animals, and plants. Yellow fever, malaria, dengue fever, cholera, and typhoid once ravaged the people of the Caribbean, although most have been controlled, except for periodic outbreaks. The extent to which heat affects human performance is still studied and debated.

P. Gary White

For Further Study

Aguado, E., and J. E. Burt. *Understanding Weather and Climate.* Upper Saddle River, N.J.: Prentice-Hall, 1999.

Boswell, Thomas P., and Dennis Conway. *The Caribbean Islands: Endless Geographic Diversity.* Piscataway, N.J.: Rutgers University Press, 1992.

Clawson, David L. *Latin America and the Caribbean: Lands and Peoples.* New York: McGraw Hill, 1999.

Macpherson, John. *Caribbean Lands.* Essex, England: Longman, 1984.

Sealey, Neil. *Caribbean World: A Complete Geography.* New York: Cambridge University Press, 1992.

West, Robert C., and John P. Augelli. *Middle America: Its Lands and Peoples.* Englewood Cliffs, N.J.: Prentice Hall, 1989.

Biogeography and Natural Resources

Natural Resources

North America

Resources map Page 391

Natural resources are materials found naturally in the environment that are used or valued by people as a resource. They provide the raw materials—wood pulp, iron, water, petroleum, soil, and food—that are transformed by refining and manufacturing to make things that are used in daily life. Renewable resources can regenerate themselves and will remain available if they are not used faster than they can regrow or regenerate. These include water, fish, timber, and soil. Nonrenewable resources, which cannot be replaced after they are used, include oil, coal, natural gas, iron, and other minerals.

The United States and Canada contain the greatest concentration of natural wealth in the world. Domestically produced mineral, timber, and agricultural resources that are sold locally and overseas have created economic wealth. The countries of North America also import natural resources from other countries. The United States has only about 5 percent of the world's population, but as the world's leading manufacturing country, it consumes about 40 percent of the resources annually consumed in the world. Some of what the United States consumes is imported, mainly raw materials for use by industry, but much is mined, cut, refined, and produced in the country. Canada and Mexico also have abundant renewable and nonrenewable resources and contribute to the outstanding resource bounty of the North American continent.

Renewable Resources: Water. The humid eastern portions of North America receive much more rainfall annually than the semiarid interior and the more arid western portions of the continent. However, even the arid regions may have freshwater resources available, either from surface rivers or from underground water in aquifers (porous rock beds into which water seeps and slowly flows underground).

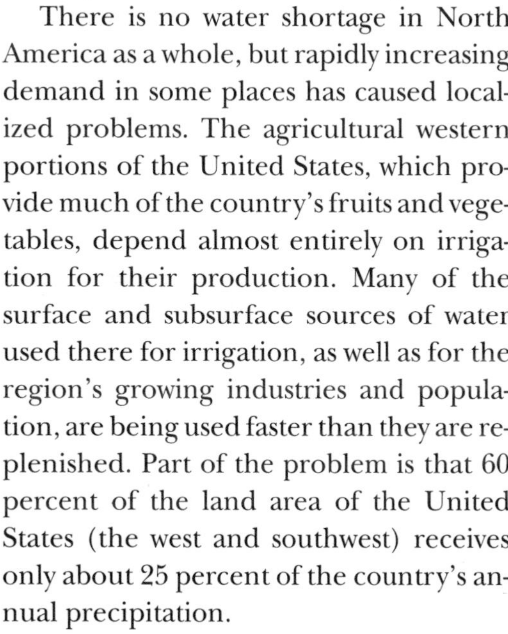

There is no water shortage in North America as a whole, but rapidly increasing demand in some places has caused localized problems. The agricultural western portions of the United States, which provide much of the country's fruits and vegetables, depend almost entirely on irrigation for their production. Many of the surface and subsurface sources of water used there for irrigation, as well as for the region's growing industries and population, are being used faster than they are replenished. Part of the problem is that 60 percent of the land area of the United States (the west and southwest) receives only about 25 percent of the country's annual precipitation.

Many underground sources of water, like the vast Ogallala Aquifer, have for decades been used at a faster rate than that at which water seeps back in. The western U.S. water table has been declining by 3

The Ogallala Aquifer

The Ogallala Aquifer—an enormous underground reservoir of water-soaked sand, silt, and gravel stretching from South Dakota to western Texas—has for decades been pumped (on average) twice as fast as it can be replenished by rainfall and surface runoff. From the 1940's to 1980, the aquifer's average water level declined nearly 10 feet (3 meters).

Because the aquifer underlies such a large region and because human activity at the surface varies across the high plains that overlie it, some places have been drained more rapidly, while other areas have remained unchanged. Some parts of the aquifer experienced a rising water level of more than 15 feet (4.5 meters) between 1980 and 1990, but even larger areas, mostly from western Kansas to northern Texas, declined by the same amount during that time.

The Ogallala Aquifer varies in thickness from 1,300 feet (400 meters) in Nebraska to just a few inches in parts of Texas. It contains about as much water as does Lake Michigan, but its annual overdraft, or water removed in excess of water replaced, is about the same as the annual flow of the Colorado River. Most of the excessive pumping from this aquifer has been done to irrigate crops. The withdrawal has been most excessive where irrigation is heavy but the aquifer is not deep. In parts of Texas, declines have exceeded 100 feet (30 meters) over the last half of the twentieth century. Around Lubbock, Texas, the rate of withdrawal has been fifty times the natural rate of recharge.

As the water table declines, the cost of pumping water from greater depths increases the cost to farmers irrigating their crops, which gradually forces farmers to abandon the practice of irrigation. This has already happened in parts of Nebraska, Kansas, Oklahoma, Colorado, and Texas. If the aquifer were completely drained, it could take six thousand years to refill naturally.

feet (1 meter) each year in some places. Above-ground water sources are also endangered. The U.S. Water Resources Council has found water shortages to be imminent in the Rio Grande basin and the lower Colorado River basin. The Colorado River, which is drained for irrigation by seven arid and semiarid states, has become little more than a trickle of water laden with salts by the time it reaches Mexico. The Missouri River basin also has begun to experience water shortages. The eastern United States is not exempt from water shortages, especially in the heavily urbanized and industrialized Northeast. In this more humid area of the continent, the problem is usually one of water quality, rather than quantity.

Colorado River Pages 388, 517

The danger of absolute water shortage in Canada as a whole is remote; however, local shortages occur in parts of the country. The semiarid western prairie region, an area with low precipitation and high evaporation of moisture, is most susceptible to shortages. Some areas face shortages because local facilities for water purification, storage, and distribution are lacking. Additional factors are that 60 percent of Canada's surface runoff is carried by rivers that flow north toward the Arctic Ocean and away from the more populated area near the U.S. border, and more than one-third of Canada's average annual precipitation is in the form of snow, which is not available in winter and can be overabundant in the spring.

Forest Products. Canada and the United States rank first and second, respectively, in world export of forest products, together accounting for one-third of these exports. Because of variations in terrain and climate across the continent, different types of forests are found in various regions. Half of Canada is covered with trees, more than any other country except Russia. Most Canadian forests are coniferous, with softwood, cone-bearing needle-leaf trees such as pine, spruce, and fir. Much of the forest in British Colombia—about half of all timber harvested in Canada—is used for lumber products. Some lumber and most of the pulpwood (used for paper products) comes from the boreal forest in Ontario and Quebec. The boreal forest is the largest forest in Canada and remains the least accessible. Canadian hardwoods (broadleaf trees such as birch, maple, and beech) are in relatively short supply. Canada has 11 percent the amount of hardwood forest that the United States has, and these forests are found mostly in southern Ontario and southern Quebec, near the U.S. border.

The most important forest resources of the United States are the northeast hardwoods, which provide most of the hardwood lumber for furniture, paneling, and cabinets produced in the country; the western timberlands of the mountain and coastal forests between the Pacific coast and the Rocky Mountains, which accounts for most of the construction lumber produced in the country; and the southeast mixed forests, which are harvested mostly for pulpwood, although the region also produces some hardwood and softwood lumber.

Forests Pages 392, 505

Fish and Aquatic Products. The United States and Canada rank fourth and sixteenth in the world in total fish catch. In the United States, commercial fishing is concentrated in five fishing regions: the northwest Atlantic (off the coast of the New England and mid-Atlantic states), which accounts for 28 percent of the national catch by weight; the central Atlantic and Gulf of Mexico, with 28 percent; the northeast Pacific/Alaska region with 26 percent; the central Pacific with 13 percent; and the southeast Pacific/southern California and inland sources with 3 percent. Inland sources are fish and other

Overfishing in Atlantic Canada

The Canadian government has appealed to the world community to try to save what remains of its once-rich Atlantic cod fishery. The International Law of the Sea bans commercial fishing within 200 nautical miles of shore, but Canada has claimed a 300-nautical-mile Exclusive Economic Zone maritime boundary to curtail foreign commercial fishing trawlers.

At one time, large schools of northern cod were treated as an inexhaustible resource. A dramatic fall in the tonnage of fish caught since the late 1980's, a rise in the number of young fish being netted, and warnings from scientists finally brought action. In 1993 Canada banned all offshore cod fishing for two years to allow stocks to rebuild. A similar reduction in Atlantic salmon fishing went into effect in 1992. In both cases the Canadian government paid fishermen not to catch fish. The newly unemployed cod fishermen received the equivalent of 317 U.S. dollars weekly for ten weeks while not fishing. Salmon fishermen received up to 50,000 U.S. dollars to turn in their licenses in order to preserve salmon stocks for future commercial and sport fishing.

The Canadian government has also tried to convince commercial cod and salmon fishermen to fish for the more plentiful crabs, scallops, and Arctic char. However, foreign "factory ships," mostly trawlers from Russia and Japan, continued capturing migratory cod that swam into international waters beyond Canada's Exclusive Economic Zone. Scientists do not know when the fish stocks will be restored.

aquatic creatures caught in freshwater rivers and lakes, or raised and harvested in hatcheries.

About 60 percent of the commercial fish harvest in Canada comes from the northwest Atlantic region, around the eastern Maritime Provinces. The remainder is collected off the western coast of British Columbia and from inland sources. The Gulf of Mexico, the Caribbean Sea, the Pacific Ocean, and the Sea of Cortés offer abundant tropical and subtropical fishing grounds for Mexico.

In Canada and the United States, the most important fishing grounds historically have been around the Grand Banks area of the northwest Atlantic (the New England and Maritime Provinces region). As late as the mid-1980's, Canadian waters there accounted for 86 percent of the commercial tonnage of fish and other aquatic resources harvested in that country, although by 1999 it was closer to 60 percent.

In the United States, this region previously accounted for 36 percent of the national catch. Since the late 1980's, there has been a notable decline in the quantity and size of fish harvested from these important fishing grounds, especially with the dramatic reduction of Atlantic salmon and northern cod fish stocks. If the value of the products harvested is considered, rather than total weight of the harvest, the highest-ranking states and provinces are Alaska and British Columbia (salmon, crab, lobster), California (lobster, salmon), Texas-Louisiana (shrimp), Massachusetts-Connecticut-Rhode Island (lobster, shrimp, tuna), and Nova Scotia and Newfoundland (lobster and salmon).

Fertile Soil. An essential resource, soil is potentially renewable because new soil is created through the weathering and decomposition of bedrock beneath the surface, even as topsoil is being washed away from the surface. The most fertile soils and the largest farms in North America are found in the Central Plains of Canada and the United States, and the midwestern United States. This region produces most of the continent's wheat, corn, sorghum, milo, and other grains, and annually produces a huge surplus that is exported to countries all over the world.

The eastern United States and Canada have relatively smaller farms, which produce fruits, vegetables, cotton, tobacco, peanuts, and soybeans. Some valleys of the U.S. intermountain west are productive where irrigated.

Volcanically derived soils found in parts of Mexico are highly productive and, because of the tropical and subtropical climates of Mexico, can be farmed throughout the year. The United States is the most agriculturally productive country in the world and produces far more food each year than is consumed within the country. Some of the food surplus is stored, but most is sold to other countries or given away through food aid programs.

Nonrenewable Resources: Oil. North America is one of the world's largest producers of oil. The United States, Canada, and Mexico together accounted for about 20 percent of the global output of oil during the 1980's and 1990's. However, North America has less than 9 percent of the world's proven oil reserves, while the Arabian Peninsula has 40 percent. About half of the continent's oil reserves are found in Mexico, mostly around the Gulf Coast.

Most oil in the United States and Canada is produced in northern Alaska, the Texas-Louisiana Gulf coastal region, the midcontinent district from eastern Kansas to western Oklahoma and Texas, and along the Front Range of the Canadian Rocky Mountains, in central and northern Alberta. Lesser oil fields are found in southern California, west central Appalachia, central Alabama, the northern Great Plains, and the central and southern Rocky Mountains.

During the 1970's the United States and Canada began exploiting their Arctic territories—Alaska, the Yukon, and the Northwest Territories—more heavily. In 1977 the Trans-Alaska pipeline was opened, pumping oil from Alaska's North Slope 800 miles (1,288 km.) south to the warm-water port of Valdez, Alaska, where it is shipped off by tankers. This source provided about 25 percent of U.S. needs and accounted for about 5 percent of world oil production in the late 1990's.

The United States and Canada also have great oil reserves not counted as proven reserves. This oil, which has the consistency of gooey tar, is found within sandstone or shale bedrock and has not been profitable to extract. These vast tar sands in Alberta, Canada, and oil shale in Colorado and Wyoming could be exploited if extractive technology reduced the cost of mining them. The amount of oil stored in these alternative deposits is believed to rival the proven reserves of the Arabian Peninsula.

Natural Gas. The fossil fuel experiencing the fastest growth in consumption worldwide is natural gas. North America is one of the world's largest producers of natural gas, with almost 8 percent of the world's reserves. Natural gas previously was used only near the areas where it was produced, but since a process was discovered to liquefy it, it can be transported more easily. The distribution of natural gas follows the pattern of oilfields, because oil and natural gas are usually found in similar geologic formations

Coal. Coal was important in the rise of North America as an industrial power and was the chief source of energy for industrial and electrical production until the 1960's, when oil began to be used more than coal. Because the United States is the world's largest producer of coal and has the greatest coal reserves, and because coal now can be liquefied and burned like gasoline, the use of coal as an energy source has grown rapidly. The United States doubled its use of coal for producing electricity in the last quarter of the twentieth century. Many of the newer sources of coal discovered and exploited in the United States were found in thick, near-surface deposits.

One of the most important coal-producing regions of North America is the central Appalachia highlands, which produces about half of U.S. coal in underground mines; however, it is declining in importance because its high-sulphur coal

A Gas Resource from Old Mines

Methane gas once was an explosion hazard in eastern Oklahoma's underground coal mines, but new technologies and more knowledge are leading to greater exploration for this resource. Coalbed methane gas—almost unused in the 1980's—accounted for 5.9 percent of U.S. natural gas production in 1997. Production of methane from the coal seams of eastern Oklahoma dates to 1926, when a vertical well was drilled in Pittsburg County, but methane gas was considered more of a hazard than a resource. Gas and dust were factors in mine explosions and disasters killing over five hundred people from 1885 to 1945. Oklahoma gas producers have become especially interested in coalbed methane, because coal deposits have a shallow reservoir that can store three to four times more methane per volume of rock than a sandstone gas reservoir of similar thickness. More than eight hundred coalbed methane gas wells were completed in eastern Oklahoma by the end of 1999.

requires expensive treatment to meet federal clean air standards. The midcontinent coalfields, a large arc of high-sulphur coal found largely in surface or near-surface deposits between eastern Oklahoma and southern Illinois, are also declining in importance as the western coalfields are exploited. The western coal region, centered on the Great Plains and the intermountain region of the western United States and Canada, near their border, is growing in importance because its vast, low-sulphur coal supplies in thick, near-surface seams are ideal for profitable strip mining.

Iron Ore. Iron ore is the primary ingredient in steel, which is necessary for industrial construction, railroads, highways, commercial buildings, and other features of developed countries. The United States and Canada are both major producers and consumers of iron ore, most of which comes from the upper midwest states, such as Michigan and Minnesota, central Alabama, and Ontario province in Canada. The United States and Canada are the world's seventh and eighth largest producers, respectively, of iron ore.

Other Minerals. Many other nonenergy minerals are mined and refined in North America, including gold, silver, copper, nickel, uranium, cadmium, mercury, lead, zinc, and molybdenum. The continent's minerals are consumed by the diverse manufacturing industries of North America and sold to other countries. North America's most important regions for nonenergy minerals are the Canadian Shield in eastern Canada; the volcanic and metamorphosed mountainous areas, including the western Rocky Mountain region; and the Appalachian Mountain region of the United States.

Human Geography of Natural Resources. Abundant resources helped to build and develop the continent's waterway, railroad, and highway transportation networks; transportation, in turn, helped to open up the coal and oil fields, and to exploit and distribute the abundant wealth of fuels, metals, timber, and other resources. Because natural resources are so involved in the development of landscapes and the progress of society, there is a close relationship between resources and human settlement patterns, economic growth, and industry. These variations in the human geography of the continent result, in part, from spatial variations in the location of natural resources.

Resources and Settlement. One of the most formidable barriers to the settlement of North America was the lack of water in the semiarid and arid lands of the west. Although the technology to secure more water resources now exists, allowing for dense settlement and even agriculture on arid lands, water supply still influences human settlement. Water must be found locally or transported, via canal or pipe, before new neighborhoods can be built or towns and cities can expand. Many settlements in North America began as sites of mining activity, lumber camps, or fishing villages, later growing into larger towns and cities.

Resources and Industry. Industry developed at sites across the continent that had favorable access to sources of energy needed for industrial power. The first manufacturing industries in the new United States of America—iron works and textile mills—were sited along the edge of the New England upland and the Appalachian Piedmont. There, rapidly running rivers could be diverted to turn water wheels, whose energy could move the gears and levers of industry. More diverse types of refining and manufacturing facilities later were sited around the coal fields of the eastern and western Appalachian Mountains in Pennsylvania, and still later, around the earliest oil and gas fields in western Pennsylvania.

As the settlement frontier pushed westward, new energy resource deposits were discovered and tapped, and new industries sprang up around the coalfields in Indiana, Illinois, and eastern Michigan. The principal industrial region of the United States and Canada emerged around Great Lakes port settlements that were ideally situated between the coal fields of Appalachia—the energy for industry—and a large source of iron ore—the raw material for steel and related industrial products—in northern Minnesota and southern Ontario. Newer industrial regions emerged around the oil fields of Oklahoma, Texas, and southern California, and the Gulf Coastal Plain in Louisiana, Texas, and Mexico. Later, the energy provided by hydropower in the Pacific Northwest encouraged industry in that region.

Future of Resources in North America. The North American continent was blessed with vast forests, good agricultural land, and extensive deposits of industrial and energy resources. These resources usually have been concentrated in large enough quantities to make long-term extraction economically feasible. Most of the sites that were historically the richest in raw materials have continued to support timber, agricultural, drilling, or mining operations. The continental and offshore mineral storehouse still contains outstanding resource reserves that could attract future exploration and exploitation as new extractive technologies are developed. Possible regions for future resource developments are the humid conifer forests of the southeastern United States, oil and gas supplies in the Arctic, oil shale deposits in Colorado and Wyoming, and tar sands in the Canadian province of Alberta.

Dale R. Lightfoot

For Further Study

Birdsall, Stephen S., John W. Florin, and Margo L. Price. *Regional Landscapes of the United States and Canada.* 5th ed. New York: John Wiley & Sons, 1999.

Getis, Arthur, and Judith Getis. *The United States and Canada: The Land and the People.* Chicago: William C. Brown, 1995.

Guinness, Paul, and Michael Bradshaw. *North America: A Human Geography.* Totowa, N.J.: Barnes and Noble, 1985.

Klee, Gary A. *Conservation of Natural Resources.* Englewood Cliffs, N.J.: Prentice Hall, 1991.

McKnight, Tom. *Regional Geography of the United States and Canada.* 2d ed. Upper Saddle River, N.J.: Prentice Hall, 1992.

Miller, G. Tyler. *Living in the Environment.* 4th ed. Belmont, Calif.: Wadsworth, 1985.

National Geographic Society. *Water: The Power, Promise, and Turmoil of North America's Fresh Water.* Washington, D.C.: National Geographic Society, 1993.

Paterson, J. H. *North America.* 9th ed. New York: Oxford University Press, 1994.

Zwingle, Erla. "Wellspring of the High Plains." *National Geographic* (March, 1993): 80-109.

The Caribbean

The natural resources of the Caribbean are severely limited. In terms of nonrenewable resources, the Greater Antilles is richer in minerals than the Lesser Antilles. Cuba has the most diversified mineral resources, including nickel, iron ore, chrome, cobalt, copper, petroleum, manganese, and marble. Nickel, used in the production of military hardware, is Cuba's most important mineral. It is also mined in the Dominican Republic, where it is an important export.

The Dominican Republic, Jamaica, and Guyana have extensive deposits of bauxite, the ore used for aluminum production. Since 1990, however, only Jamaican mines have operated. Some bauxite is mined and processed locally into alumina and sold mainly to the United States and Canada. Most bauxite refining occurs in North America because processing it requires considerable energy. Jamaica was once the world's largest supplier of bauxite, with several foreign companies operating in the island. Now Jamaica must compete with high-grade ores from Australia, Brazil, and French Guinea. Jamaica also mines gypsum, marble, sand, gravel, and industrial lime.

Haiti's mineral resources, including bauxite, copper, gold, iron, silver, sulphur, and tin, are underdeveloped. Its bauxite mine closed in the 1980's. Haiti is the poorest country in the Western Hemisphere, and its high population growth rate has resulted in too many people for the weak resource base.

The Dominican Republic produces small quantities of gold and ferro-nickel. Amber and dore (an alloy of silver and gold) are also produced and are major exports. Oil in the southwest awaits exploration. Small amounts of manganese, lead, copper, and zinc are found throughout most of the Caribbean islands.

Energy Resources. The Caribbean region is devoid of most energy resources, except in Trinidad. Trinidad has an oil economy that fluctuates according to oil prices. Trinidad's petroleum and natural gas reserves brought prosperity to the island in the 1970's. Oil production began around La Brea Pitch Lake and then moved offshore. When oil prices dropped in the 1980's, Trinidad's economic development slowed, and the per capita gross national product dropped sharply. La Brea Pitch Lake is also important because it is the world's largest natural source of asphalt. The output of asphalt from the lake has decreased, but natural gas and petroleum are still major resources there. Barbados and Cuba also produce small amounts of petroleum.

Firewood is an important fuel source in the Caribbean region, especially among the rural poor. Even though it is looked upon as old-fashioned and inefficient, many peasants also convert it into charcoal for use in cooking foods.

Water Resources. Precipitation varies from island to island. As a rule, low-lying islands such as Aruba, Bonaire, and Curaçao do not receive much rainfall, because the moisture-laden air does not rise high enough to cool and produce rainfall. Therefore, they receive less than 25 inches (625 millimeters) of rain each year. This causes severe water shortages, which affect industry and the tourist trade. Aruba has a large desalinization plant to produce its water supply. Agriculture is limited by the lack of water. Antigua, Barbuda, and Anguilla are flat, semiarid, limestone islands that often experience drought conditions. They frequently must ship water in to meet their needs.

Other Caribbean islands, such as St. Kitts-Nevis and Montserrat, have high central volcanic cores. The Windward Islands are especially mountainous. These volcanic peaks and mountains force moisture-laden winds to rise, cool, and drop their precipitation on the islands. Water is generally in sufficient supply for tourism and agriculture there.

Precipitation varies markedly within the islands themselves. Heavier rains generally fall on the northeast (windward) sides of the islands and lighter rain on the southwest (leeward) sides. Montego Bay, Jamaica, receives an average of 51 inches (1,250 millimeters) of rainfall each year. Kingston, on Jamaica's southern coast, receives only 31 inches (750 millimeters) yearly because precipitation is blocked by the mountains. Irrigation is necessary for agriculture in southern Jamaica. This type of variation in rainfall is found in many Caribbean islands.

While the islands of the Caribbean region are limited in natural resources, they are rich in natural beauty, pleasant climates, and spectacular sunsets. Their sandy beaches and coral reefs draw a large tourist trade and may be the most valuable resource the Caribbean region possesses. Sailing, scuba diving, and hiking are attractions for tourists who want to do more than just relax on the beach. For example, one can hike up trails into the rain forest of an extinct volcano, the Quill, on the island of Saint Eustatius. On the Turks and Caicos Islands, one can snorkel and dive among the ruins of shipwrecks. Trinidad and Tobago are more dependent on industrializing their nonrenewable resource base but are gradually developing tourism as a resource, too. The writings of Ernest Hemingway have made Cuba's deep-sea fishing famous, and Cuba's picturesque scenery and vibrant culture make Cuba an increasingly attractive tourist destination.

Carol Ann Gillespie

For Further Study

Blouet, Brian W., and Olwyn M. Blouet. *Latin America and the Caribbean: A Systematic and Regional Survey.* 3d ed. New York: John Wiley & Sons, 1997.

Bolioli, Oscar L. *The Caribbean: Culture of Resistance, Spirit of Hope.* New York: Friendship Press, 1993.

Boswell, Thomas P., and Dennis Conway. *The Caribbean Islands: Endless Geographic Diversity.* Piscataway, N.J.: Rutgers University Press, 1992.

Clawson, David L. *Latin America and the Caribbean: Lands and Peoples.* New York: McGraw Hill, 1999.

Knight, Franklin W., and Colin A. Palmer. *The Modern Caribbean.* Chapel Hill: University of North Carolina Press, 1989.

Flora and Fauna

North American Flora

The world's major biomes are all represented in the diverse vegetation of North America. Forest is the native vegetation of almost half of mainland Canada and the United States. Before European settlement, the forest was nearly continuous over the eastern, and much of the northern, part of the continent. Grasses covered a large part of the continental interior. Desert vegetation is native in the Southwest, tundra in the far north. Over much of the continent, however, human activity has virtually eliminated native vegetation.

Coniferous Forests of the West. Along the Pacific coast, from Alaska to northern California, evergreen, coniferous forest grows luxuriantly, watered by moisture-laden winds blowing inland from the ocean. This lowland forest includes some of the largest and longest-lived trees in the world. North of California, characteristic trees include Sitka spruce, western hemlock, and western red cedar. Douglas fir, one of the major timber species in North America, is also common. The northwest coastal coniferous forest is sometimes called temperate rain forest because, in its lushness, it resembles the tropical rain forests. Many of the trees of the coastal forest have been cut for timber.

Forests Pages 392, 442, 505

In California, the dominant coastal conifer species is the coast redwood. The tallest tree in the world, coast redwood reaches 330 feet (100 meters) and can live two thousand years.

Coniferous forest also grows along the Cascade Mountains and the Sierra Nevada. Trees of the Cascades include mountain hemlock and subalpine fir at high elevations, and western hemlock, western red cedar, and firs somewhat lower. Sierra Nevada forests include pines, mountain hemlock, and red fir at high elevations; and red and white firs, pines, and Douglas fir somewhat lower. Ponderosa pine is dominant at low mountain elevations in both of these Pacific ranges.

The giant sequoia, long thought to be the largest living organism on earth, grows in scattered groves in the Sierra Nevada. (The largest organism actually may be a very old tree root-rot fungus that covers 1,500 acres in Washington State.) Although shorter than the coast redwood, the giant sequoia is larger in trunk diameter and bulk. It can reach 260 feet (80 meters) tall and 30 feet (10 meters) in circumference.

Coniferous forest also dominates the Rocky Mountains and some mountainous areas of Mexico. In the Rockies, Englemann spruce and subalpine fir grow at high elevations, and Douglas fir, lodgepole pine, and white fir somewhat lower. Ponderosa pine grows throughout the Rockies at low elevations and is a dominant tree in western North America.

Boreal Coniferous Forest. Just south of the Arctic tundra in North America is a broad belt of boreal, coniferous, evergreen forest. It is often called taiga, the Russian name for similar forest growing in northern Eurasia. However, in large areas of northeastern Siberia, the dominant tree is larch, which is deciduous, shedding its leaves each autumn, whereas the North American taiga is mostly evergreen. Taiga is the most extensive coniferous forest in North America, covering nearly 30 percent of the land area north of Mexico. It grows across Alaska and Canada and southward into the northern Great Lakes states and New England. White spruce and balsam fir dominate much of the Canadian taiga. Taiga has little shrub or understory vegetation, but the ground is commonly carpeted with small plants.

Eastern Deciduous Forest. A forest of mainly broad-leaved, deciduous trees is the native vegetation of much of eastern North America. Narrow fingers of this forest, growing along rivers, penetrate westward into the interior grasslands. European settlers cut most of the eastern forest, but second-growth forest now covers considerable areas. The plants are closely related genetically to plants of the temperate deciduous forests in Europe and Asia. In contrast, the plants of other biomes in North America are generally not closely related to the plants that occur in the same biomes elsewhere in the world, although they look similar.

Deciduous forest Page 441

In the eastern deciduous forest, maple and oak are widespread—maples especially in the north, oaks in the south. There are major subdivisions within the

Vermont's maple trees make the state the nation's leading producer of maple syrup. (Vermont Department of Tourism & Marketing/Andre Jenny)

forest. These include oak and hickory forest in Illinois, Missouri, Arkansas, and eastern Texas, and also in the east—Pennsylvania, Virginia, and West Virginia—where oak and chestnut forest formerly predominated; beech and maple forest in Michigan, Indiana, and Ohio; and maple and basswood forest in Wisconsin and Minnesota. The forest in parts of Michigan, Wisconsin, Minnesota, and New England contains not only deciduous trees but also evergreen conifers, including pines and hemlock. Vast native pine stands in the Great Lakes states have been cut for lumber.

Rain forest Page 392

Plant diseases have changed the composition of the eastern forest. American chestnut was once an important tree, but has now nearly disappeared due to an introduced fungal disease. Dutch elm disease is similarly devastating American elms.

Other Forests. The southeastern United States, excluding the peninsula of Florida, once supported open stands of pine and also mixed evergreen and deciduous forest. The mixed forest included a variety of pines, evergreen species of oaks, and deciduous trees. In much of Florida, the native vegetation is a mixture of deciduous and evergreen trees that are subtropical rather than temperate. In many parts of the Southeast, people have replaced the native vegetation with fast-growing species of pines for timber production.

In Mexico, tropical rain forest and savanna are prominent on the west coast, in the south and east, and in Yucatán. On the south coasts of Mexico and Florida, swamps of mangrove trees are common.

Central Grasslands. The central plains of North America, a wide swath from the Texas coast north to Saskatchewan, Canada, were once a vast grassland, the prairie. The climate there is too dry to support trees, except along rivers. Fire is important for maintaining grasslands. From west to east, there is a transition from the more desertlike short-grass prairie (the Great Plains), through the mixed-grass prairie, to the moister, richer, tall-grass prairie. This change is related to an increase in rainfall from west to east. Grasses shorter than 1.5 feet (0.5 meter) dominate the short-grass prairie. In the tall-grass prairie, some grasses grow to more than 10 feet (3 meters). Colorful wildflowers brighten the prairie landscape.

Grassland soil is the most fertile in North America. Instead of wild prairie grasses, this land now supports agriculture and the domesticated grasses corn and wheat. The tall-grass prairie, which had the best soil in all the grassland, has been almost entirely converted to growing corn. Much of the grassland that escaped the plow is now grazed by cattle, which has disturbed the land and aided the spread of invasive, nonnative plants.

Other outlying grasslands occur in western North America. Between the eastern deciduous forest and the prairie is savanna, a grassland with scattered deciduous trees, mainly oaks. Savanna also occurs

Invasive Nonnative Plants

An estimated one-fifth to one-third of the plant species growing in North America north of Mexico originated in other continents. Although the large majority of these plants cause no problems, more than three hundred plants, according to one estimate, reproduce so rapidly that they displace native plants. About half of these invasive plants were brought to North America to beautify gardens, and their spread threatens North American wildlands. California and Florida appear to be the states on the North American mainland most affected by invasive nonnative plants.

over much of eastern Mexico and southern Florida.

Scrub and Desert. In the semiarid and arid West, the natural vegetation is grass and shrubs. Over a large part of California, this takes the form of a fire adapted scrub community called chaparral, in which evergreen, often spiny shrubs form dense thickets. The climate, with rainy, mild winters and hot, dry summers, is like that around the Mediterranean Sea, where a similar kind of vegetation, called maquis, has evolved. However, chaparral and maquis vegetation are not closely related genetically. Human beings have greatly altered the chaparral through grazing of livestock and other disturbance.

Giant saguaro cactus. (PhotoDisc)

The North American deserts, which are located between the Rocky Mountains and the Sierra Nevada, cover less than 5 percent of the continent. Shrubs are the predominant vegetation, although there are also many species of annuals. Desert plants are sparsely distributed, and many have either small leaves or none at all. Cacti and other succulent plants are common.

In southern California, Arizona, New Mexico, west Texas, and northwestern Mexico, there are three distinct deserts. These are all hot deserts, like Africa's Sahara. The Sonoran Desert stretches from southern California to western Arizona and south into Mexico. A characteristic plant of the Sonoran is the giant saguaro cactus. To the east of the Sonoran, in west Texas and New Mexico, is the Chihuahuan Desert, where a common plant is the agave, or century plant. North of the Sonoran Desert, in southeastern California, southern Nevada, and northwestern

The Joshua tree of California's Mojave Desert is actually a member of the lily family. However, it can reach 50 feet (15 meters) in height and looks much like a true tree. (PhotoDisk)

Arizona, is the Mojave Desert, where the Joshua tree, a tree-like lily, is a well-known plant. It can reach 50 feet (15 meters) in height. Creosote bush is common in all three deserts. To the north, the Mojave Desert grades into the Great Basin Desert, which is a cold desert, large and bleak. The dominant plant of the Great Basin Desert is big sagebrush. Plant diversity there is lower than in the hot American deserts.

Deserts dominated by grasses rather than shrubs once occurred at high elevations near the Sonoran and Chihuahuan Deserts. Much of this area has been overtaken by desert scrub, including creosote bush, mesquite, and tarbush. Grazing by cattle may have been a factor in this change. Desert is very fragile. Even one pass with a heavy vehicle causes lasting damage.

Tundra. Tundra vegetation grows to the northern limits of plant growth, above the Arctic Circle, in Canada. The flora consists of only about six hundred plant species. In contrast, tropical regions that are smaller in area support tens of thousands of plant species. Tundra is dominated by grasses, sedges, mosses, and lichens. Some shrubby plants also grow there. Most tundra plants are perennials. During the short Arctic growing season, many of these plants produce brightly colored flowers. Like desert, tundra is exceptionally fragile, and it takes many years for disturbed tundra to recover.

Sagebrush in New Mexico. (PhotoDisc)

Tundra also occurs southward, on mountaintops, from southern Alaska into the Rocky Mountains, the Cascades, and the Sierra Nevada. This alpine tundra grows at elevations too high for mountain coniferous forest.

Coastal Vegetation. Along the coasts of the Atlantic Ocean and the Gulf of Mexico, the soil is saturated with water and is very salty. Tides regularly inundate low-lying vegetation. The plants in these salt marsh areas are not diverse, consisting mainly of grasses and rushes. Marshes are a vital breeding ground and nursery for fish and shellfish, and play an important role in absorbing and purifying water from the land. Coastal marshes are being lost to development at a rapid rate.

Jane F. Hill

For Further Study

Braun, E. Lucy. *Deciduous Forests of Eastern North America.* New York: MacMillan, 1950.

Ellis, Gerry, and Karen Kane. *America's Rain Forest.* Minocqua, Wis.: North-Word Press, 1991.

Kricher, John C. *A Field Guide to the Ecology of Western Forests.* The Peterson Field Guide Series. Boston: Houghton Mifflin, 1993.

MacMahon, James A. *Deserts.* The Audubon Society Nature Guides. New York: Alfred A. Knopf, 1985.

Madson, John. *Where the Sky Began: Land of the Tallgrass Prairie.* Rev. ed. Ames: Iowa State University Press, 1996.

Randall, John M., and Janet Marinelli, eds. *Invasive Plants: Weeds of the Global Garden.* Handbook 149 in Twenty-First Century Garden Series. Brooklyn, N.Y.: Brooklyn Botanic Garden, 1996.

Sayre, April Pulley. *Tundra.* New York: Twenty-First Century Books, 1994.

Information on the World Wide Web

The Web site of the Flora of North America Project, a project listing and describing all the identified species of plants in North America, excluding Mexico, features an on-line database of plants that is updated as new information is gained. The project is the first comprehensive account in many years of the continent's approximately twenty-one thousand plant species that grow outside of cultivation. The series includes information on plant names, relationships, characteristics, and geographic distribution. (www.fna.org)

North American Fauna

The wildlife of North America can be grouped within two large regions: the Nearctic realm, which covers most of North America from the Arctic to northern Mexico; and the Neotropical realm, which covers southern Mexico and all of Central America. Species in the Nearctic region are similar to those of Eurasia and

North Africa, and originally reached North America from Eurasia by passing over the Bering Strait land bridge that once connected Siberia and Alaska, about 60 million years ago. Species in the Neotropical zone are distinctly different from Nearctic wildlife, and reached Central America and Mexico by gradual movement up the isthmus of Panama from South America.

Seals
Page 381

North America's fauna also can be grouped by regions that reflect such climatic influences as latitude, the position of mountain ranges and oceans, and the plants and trees that grow in that area (grasslands, desert, forest, or tundra). Generally, arctic animals are found to the far north, and on the highest slopes of mountains. As one goes farther south, or farther down the sides of mountains, the animals to be found will be those of the forest, grasslands, or desert environments.

Fauna map
Page 443

Arctic Tundra. Animals of the far north are similar to those found in Eurasia, and are well adapted to their cold, treeless environment. Many of these animals evolved from Ice Age species as the glaciers that once covered North America slowly retreated northward. They are large in size and thickly furred, allowing them to maximize conservation of body heat. Large herbivores such as musk oxen and caribou graze on grasses, lichens, and mosses and are, in turn, a food source for polar bears and arctic wolves. Smaller predators such as the arctic white fox feed on arctic hares and small rodents such as voles, lemmings, or the arctic ground squirrels that subsist upon the small shrubs, berries, and grass seeds of the tundra.

Polar bear
Page 378

Seals and whales proliferate in the Arctic seas. Birdlife in the Arctic tundra is nearly absent in the winter months, with the exception of willow ptarmigans and snowy owls. In the three to four months of summer, several bird species use the region as a breeding ground where young can be hatched and fed with the abundant insect life that emerges during the long and warmer days of summer. Among these migratory species are many varieties of waterfowl, including Canada geese, snow geese, whooping swans, trumpeter swans, phalaropes, plovers, and arctic terns.

Boreal Forests. Farther south, below the tree line, coniferous northern for-

Adapting to Extremes

The extremes of climate in North America have caused many animals to adapt in interesting ways. In the far north, animals such as polar bears, musk oxen, and caribou tend to be large in size, so that their external skin area is minimized in relation to their internal portions, allowing the least possible heat loss to the cold air. Many arctic animals have both inner and outer layers of fur, trapping their body heat in the insulating layer. The feet of arctic animals are thickly furred and quite broad, allowing the animals to move over snow without sinking into it.

Animals of the southern deserts have equally effective ways of adapting to the extreme dryness and heat of their environment. They collect and store food when it is abundant after a rare rainfall and then survive long periods of drought on the surplus. They obtain water from the vegetation they eat, rather than from lakes or streams. Many desert animals are pale in color, reflecting back the heat of the sun and blending in with the surrounding landscape. Desert animals are largely nocturnal, moving about only in the cool of the night, after the moist dew falls.

Endangered North American Mammals

Common Name	*Scientific Name*	*Range*
Bat, Indiana	*Myotis sodalis*	Eastern and Midwestern U.S.A.
Bobcat, Mexican	*Lynx rufus escuinapae*	Central Mexico
Bison, wood	*Bison athabascae*	Canada, northwestern U.S.A
Ferret, black-footed	*Mustela nigripes*	Western U.S.A., western Canada
Fox, northern swift	*Vulpes velox hebes*	U.S.A. (northern plains), Canada
Jaguar	*Panthera onca*	U.S.A., Mexico
Otter, southern sea	*Enhydra lutris nereis*	West Coast, U.S.A., south to Mexico
Pronghorn, Sonoran	*Antilocapra americana sonoriensis*	U.S.A. (Arizona), Mexico
Puma, eastern	*Puma concolor conguar*	Eastern North America
Seal, Hawaiian monk	*Monachus schauinslandi*	U.S.A. (Hawaii)

Source: U.S. Fish and Wildlife Service, U.S. Department of the Interior.

ests of fir, spruce, cedar, hemlock, and pine provide shelter and food for the moose, mule deer, and snowshoe hares that browse on the needles of these trees. Squirrels, chipmunks, and porcupines also thrive in the forests of the far north. Predators of this region include martens, fishers, lynx, wolves, weasels, red foxes, and wolverines. Ponds, rivers, marshes, and swamps are common in this habitat, and provide homes for beavers, muskrats, river otters, minks, and such common fish species as whitefish, perch, pickerel, and pike.

Bird species native to the boreal forest include jays (Canada, blue, and gray), thrushes, finches, nuthatches, loons, osprey, ravens, and crows. A wide variety of songbirds (warblers) and some hummingbirds nest in the boreal woods in the summer months.

Hardwood Forests. The eastern half of North America, from southern Canada to Florida, was once thickly covered by deciduous forests of maple, oak, beech, ash, sycamore, hickory, and other trees that shed their leaves in the winter. Where this forest remains, it provides food for a wide variety of mammals, including black bears, red foxes, racoons, red and gray squirrels, minks, muskrats, jackrabbits, cottontail rabbits, groundhogs, chipmunks, mice, moles, bobcats, skunks, ermine, opossums, and porcupines. Fish species common to the rivers of eastern and southeastern North America include catfish, suckers, and gar. Several species of salamanders and turtles live in the marshes, streams, and rivers of the deciduous forests, especially in the Appalachians. Waterfowl such as kingfishers, herons, ducks, and grebes also live along the waterways of the hardwood forest region.

Moose Page 442

Grasslands. The prairies in the center of North America provide abundant grasses and other herbaceous plants for many small mammals and grazing animals. Jackrabbits, badgers, prairie chickens, and small rodents such as pocket gophers, prairie dogs, and Richardson's ground squirrels, feed on grass and roots, as do such larger herbivores as pronghorn antelopes and the American bison. The numerous small rodents and the openness of the grasslands provides optimal habitat conditions for such raptors as owls, hawks, and falcons. Waterfowl nest in the many

The once-great herds of buffalo that roamed the Plains were nearly exterminated after railroads began bringing in more hunters. (Library of Congress)

seasonal watering holes (sloughs) that dot the prairies, although farm drainage and extended periods of drought have greatly reduced this habitat. Seeds and insects are plentiful in the grasslands, supporting such bird species as grouse, quail, partridge, and finches.

Rocky Mountains. The high mountains that run along the western side of North America are inhabited by a number of unique species. Bighorn sheep, Rocky mountain goats, mule deer, and elk graze on the grasses of the foothills and slopes of the mountains. Kodiak bears, grizzly bears, and mountain lions prey upon the grazing animals, and bald and golden eagles subsist upon the ground squirrels, marmots, voles, shrews, and pikas that live in the grasses and scattered forests of the lower mountain slopes. Dipper birds feed from the fast-running mountain streams and are found nowhere else on the continent.

Southwestern Deserts. A large number of animals have adapted to the lack of vegetation and water that exists in much of the southwestern United States and Mexico. Kangaroo rats, pocket mice, jackrabbits, armadillos, peccaries, ring-tailed cats, and ground squirrels all survive in that hostile environment. Predators include bobcats, desert foxes, badgers, and coyotes.

The most prolific forms of wildlife in the arid deserts of southernmost North America are the reptiles, including many different species of lizards, rattlesnakes, toads, and iguanas. Because they can only be active when the outside air temperature provides warmth for basic body functions, reptiles and amphibians are quite rare in the most northern parts of the continent but thrive in the arid and hot southern parts of North America. Roadrunners are a major bird predator of these reptiles, along with eagles and hawks.

Neotropical Forests. The tropical rain forests of Central America and southern Mexico have an astonishing variety of wildlife. The forest canopy has abundant bird life in the form of macaws, parrots, turkey vultures, and flycatchers. Monkeys of many varieties (spider, howler, squirrel, and capuchin) as well as sloths and tamarinds also live in the canopy, feeding on the many fruiting trees. On the floor of the forest, many varieties of ants, spiders, beetles, and chiggers provide food for smaller predators such as anteaters and various species of bats. A number of animals indigenous to South America have adapted to and thrive in Central America, including tapirs, capybaras, pacas, jaguars, ocelots, and agoutis.

Coastal Regions. The beaches, shores, lagoons, and marshes that line the North American continent are home to many kinds of animals that feed upon the ocean life or the intertidal plants and animals that live in the midzone between fresh and salt water. Many different kinds of migratory waterfowl exploit the small crustaceans and mollusks that live at the water's edge, including sandpipers, stilts, curlews, and flamingos. Seals, sea otters, and walruses are found on both coasts in the north of the continent, while Steller's sea lions and California sea lions are found only on the Pacific coast. The lagoons of the southern Atlantic coast and the Gulf of Mexico are home to alligators, pelicans, egrets, and spoonbills.

Helen Salmon

For Further Study

Allen, Thomas B., ed. *Wild Animals of North America.* Washington, D.C.: National Geographic Society, 1995.

Brooke, Michael, and Tim Burkhead, eds. *The Cambridge Encyclopedia of Ornithology.* New York: Cambridge University Press, 1991.

Casey, Peter N. *Birds of North America.* New York: Exeter Books, 1984.

Jones, David. *North American Wildlife.* Vancouver, British Columbia: Whitecap Books, 1999.

The American alligator can be easily identified by its broad snout. (PhotoDisc)

Klein, Stanley. *The Encyclopedia of North American Wildlife.* New York: Facts On File, 1986.

Lewis, Thomas. *Wildlife of North America.* Southport, Conn.: Hugh Lauter Levin Associates, 1998.

Sherrow, Victoria, and Sandee Cohen. *Endangered Mammals of North America.* Brookfield, Conn.: Twenty-First Century Books, 1995.

Whitaker, John O., ed. *National Audobon Society Field Guide to North American Mammals.* New York: Alfred A. Knopf, 1997.

Information on the World Wide Web

The National Geographic Society's "Wildlife Matters" Web site provides information on endangered or threatened wildlife species, interactive explorations of wildlife photography and biodiversity maps, and discussion of conservation issues. (www.nationalgeographic.com/wildlife/)

Caribbean Flora and Fauna

Flowers
Page 444

Most of the Caribbean region has been affected by human activities. Deforestation began with the development of sugarcane culture in the seventeenth century. When forests are cut for farmland, soil erosion and depletion often occur. Jamaica, Haiti, and many of the smaller islands have suffered acute ecological degradation. Thorn scrub and grasses have replaced native forests that were cleared for farming. This new vegetation does not protect the ground from the Sun and provides little protection against moisture loss during drought. Livestock grazing also has contributed to ecological degradation.

Martinique
Page 570

These complex and fragile island ecosystems are finally being appreciated and protected. Most islands recognize that they must balance development with protection of the natural environment. Many have established active conservation societies and national wildlife trusts for this purpose.

Flora. The Caribbean region is noted for its diverse and varied vegetation. Flowers thrive in the moist, tropical environments found on many islands. Hibiscus, bougainvillea, and orchids are just a few of the endless varieties found here.

The only rain forest left in the Caribbean Islands is a small area in Guadeloupe. However, many of the islands still have large stands of good secondary forest that are being harvested selectively by commercial lumber companies. Gommier, balata, and blue mahoe are some of the valuable species of trees cut commercially. Such tropical hardwoods as cedar, mahogany, palms, and balsa also grow on many islands. Martinique has some of the largest tracts of forest (rain forest, cloud forest, and dry woodland) left in the Caribbean.

While the Caribbean rain forest is not as diverse as those of Central and South America, it still supports numerous plant

Bougainvillea. (Digital Stock)

species. Several of these plants are endemic to the region. For example, Jamaica has more than three thousand species with eight hundred endemic to Jamaica. Orchids and bromeliads are stunning examples of climbing and hanging vegetation in the rain forests of the Caribbean. Huge tree ferns, giant elephant ear plants, figs, and balsam trees are also found in these tropical island rain forests.

Plantations of commercial timber (blue mahoe, Caribbean pine, teak, and mahogany) have been established in many locations. These plantations reduce pressure on natural forest, help protect watersheds and soil, and provide valuable wildlife habitat. Much of the original forests of the Caribbean have been cut down to make room for sugar plantations and for use as fuel. Haiti, once covered with luxurious forests, is now on the verge of total deforestation. Soil erosion and desertification have turned the country into an ecological disaster. St. Kitts, on the other hand, is one of the few places in the world where the forest is actually expanding. It provides abundant habitat for exotic vines, wild orchids, and candlewoods.

Closer to the coasts, dry scrub woodland often predominates. Some trees lose their leaves during the dry season. The turpentine tree is common to the dry scrub forests. It is sometimes called the tourist tree because of its red, peeling bark. Tree bark and leaves are often sold in the marketplaces and used for herbal remedies and bush medicine.

Along the marshy coastal waters of many of the islands are dense mangrove swamps. Mangroves grow roots that are thick and stand above the water line. These wetlands provide habitat for the manatee and American crocodile and for huge numbers of migratory birds and resident birds such as the egret and heron.

Manatee
Page 444

Dominica, one of the Windward Is-

Bats are one of the few mammal species to spread among Caribbean islands without human help. (PhotoDisc)

lands, is known as the Nature Island of the Caribbean. Most of the southern part of the island (17,000 acres) has been designated the Morne Trois Pitons National Park, which became a World Heritage Site in 1998. Elfin forests of dense vegetation and low-growing plants cover the highest volcanic peaks and receive an abundance of rain. The trees, stunted by the wind, have leaves adapted with drip tips to cope with the excess moisture. Lower down, the slopes are covered with rain forest. Measures are being taken to protect this forest from cutting for farmland or economic gain, because it is a valuable water source and a unique laboratory of scientific research. On many Caribbean islands, tourism is a vital source of income for the islanders, awareness of the need for conservation is increasing, and forests are being protected.

FAUNA. Mammals are not good colonizers of small islands, so there is a scarcity of species in the Caribbean. Most of the more commonly seen species (opossum, agouti, mongoose, and some monkeys) were introduced by man. Bats are the exception to this rule: They migrated to the Caribbean Islands on their own. The mongoose was imported by the colonists to kill snakes and the rats in the sugarcane estates. It never achieved its purpose because it hunts during the day, and rats are nocturnal. Unfortunately, the mongoose has contributed to the extinction of many species of ground-nesting birds, lizards, green iguanas, brown snakes, and red-legged tortoises.

The green vervet monkeys of Barbados, Grenada, and St. Kitts and Nevis were introduced from West Africa by the French during the seventeenth century. Many of them are exported for use in medical research because they are relatively free of disease.

Many islands have their own endemic species of birds, such as the Grenada dove and the Guadeloupe woodpecker. The islands are important stepping-stones in the migration of birds through the Americas. As a result, this region is a popular area for ornithologists and is home to several important nature reserves. Many species of parrots, macaws, and hummingbirds thrive in this region.

Trinidad and Tobago, close to the South American mainland, have no endemic species of their own, yet together they have more species of birds—an estimated 433—than any other Caribbean island. There are also 622 recorded species of butterfly. The Asa Wright Center is one of the most important bird-watching sites in the world.

Lizards and geckos are found on most of the Caribbean islands. There are many species of snakes, turtles, and iguanas scattered throughout the islands. Many are restricted to one island; Jamaica has at least twenty-seven endemic species. Most of the reptiles found in the Caribbean region are harmless to man, although snakes and geckos are superstitiously feared by the locals. The fer de lance snake is venomous, but its bite is seldom fatal. It lives in isolated areas of dry scrubland and river valleys. Iguanas are found in declining numbers on many islands. These herbivores spend their time hiding in trees and low scrub and trying to avoid contact with humans. The Antilles iguana and the rare, harmless racer snake are in grave danger of extinction in the Caribbean region. Scientists are actively engaged in several projects to learn about and protect these endangered species.

Marine turtles—including the loggerhead, leatherback, hawksbill, and green turtles—are found throughout Caribbean waters. The females come ashore on isolated sandy beaches between the months of May and August to lay eggs. There are programs in place to protect the turtles from poachers on many of the islands. The iguana, marine turtle, and many other species are now protected on reserves in the Caribbean region.

Amphibians such as toads and frogs are common in a variety of shapes and colors. The Cuban pygmy frog is called the world's smallest frog; Dominica's crapaud, or mountain chicken, is one of the largest.

Carol Ann Gillespie

For Further Study

Blouet, Brian W., and Olwyn M. Blouet. *Latin America and the Caribbean: A Systematic and Regional Survey.* 3d ed. New York: John Wiley & Sons, 1997.

Bolioli, Oscar L. *The Caribbean: Culture of Resistance, Spirit of Hope.* New York: Friendship Press, 1993.

Clawson, David L. *Latin America and the Caribbean: Lands and Peoples.* New York: McGraw Hill, 1999.

Knight, Franklin W., and Colin A. Palmer. *The Modern Caribbean.* Chapel Hill: University of North Carolina Press, 1989.

Endangered Caribbean Species

Common Name	*Scientific Name*	*Range*
Blackbird, yellow-shouldered	*Agelaius xanthomus*	Puerto Rico
Crocodile, American	*Crocodylus acutus*	U.S.A. (Florida), Mexico, Caribbean, Central and South America
Iguana, Jamaican	*Cyclura collei*	Jamaica
Parrot, Bahaman or Cuban	*Amazona leucocephala*	Cuba, Bahamas, Caymans
Seal, Caribbean monk	*Monachus tropicalis*	Caribbean Sea, Gulf of Mexico
Toad, Puerto Rican crested	*Peltophryne lemur*	Puerto Rico, British Virgin Islands

Source: U.S. Fish and Wildlife Service, U.S. Department of the Interior.

Human Geography

PEOPLE

NORTH AMERICA

In the late fifteenth century Christopher Columbus sailed across the Atlantic Ocean in search of Asia. When he reached land, he thought he had arrived in India. Therefore, he called the people he encountered "Indians." Soon, European explorers realized that they had found a world that was new to them, and the origin of its inhabitants aroused considerable interest.

After the Spanish priest José de Acosta studied the problem in the late sixteenth century, he concluded that not only were the people of the Americas like human beings elsewhere, but also the plants and animals were similar to those found in other parts of the world. For example, North America and Eurasia (Europe and Asia) both had oak trees, pine trees, deer, rabbits, bears, and wolves, among other common species.

Acosta initially thought that the animals might have arrived in America by boat, along with humans. However, many of the animals were dangerous, and it is unlikely that people would have brought such creatures with them deliberately. Both animals and humans, Acosta therefore suggested, must have arrived in North America by a land connection. North America was not attached to Eurasia in the Atlantic so, Acosta reasoned, human beings must have come to the continent by a connection with Asia in the northern Pacific. More than four hundred years later, most scholars still agreed with this.

ARCHAEOLOGICAL EVIDENCE. In Europe during the second half of the ninteenth century, many early human remains were found. It was learned that early people, especially the so-called Neanderthal man, had a long history in Eurasia. These people lived during the Pleistocene epoch, or Ice Age, and they hunted such now-extinct mammals as the mammoth, giant bison, ground sloth, and woolly rhinoceros.

Human settlers arrived in the Americas long after they were established in Eurasia. For many years, it was believed that the first humans arrived in the Americas long after the end of the Ice Age, in fact, not much earlier than the beginning of the common, or Christian, era. This idea was shattered in the 1920's and 1930's, when stone projectile points were found embedded in the remains of extinct Pleistocene mammals in the southwestern United States. Early people in the Americas also had blades, flakes, choppers, scrapers, knives, hammerstones, and bone tools. These people often are referred to as the Llano culture, after the Llano Estacado of New Mexico and Texas where many of the artifacts were found.

The oldest artifacts are known as Clovis, from materials found near Clovis, New Mexico. Clovis remains date from about

The Pleistocene Epoch

The Pleistocene epoch, or Ice Age, lasted from about 1.8 million to ten thousand years before the present. It is thought that approximately every forty thousand years, the amount of radiation from the Sun that is received at approximately 65 degrees north and south latitude changes. When the Sun's radiation level decreases, the climate becomes colder and glaciers advance; when it increases, the climate becomes warmer and glaciers retreat. As glaciers advance, they absorb a great deal of water and cause the sea level to drop hundreds of feet. Melting ice during warm interglacial periods causes sea levels to rise. Early migrants to North America lived under these changing conditions during the Pleistocene epoch.

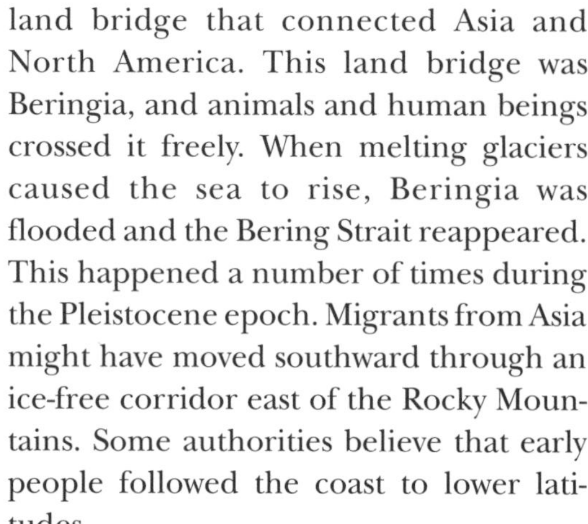

10,000 B.C.E., which is late in the Pleistocene epoch. These people are sometimes referred to as Big Game Hunters, after the large animals that they pursued. They are also known as Paleo-Indians since they are believed to be the ancestors of the present Native Americans.

Archaeologists generally agree that the Clovis date of 10,000 B.C.E.is the earliest date for which there is firm evidence of humankind in North America. Many people argue that humans were in North America far earlier; however, the archaeological establishment stands by the Clovis date of twelve thousand years ago. Archaeologists concede that humans might have been in North America much earlier, but argue that conclusive proof is lacking.

Bering Strait map Page 445

Although the specific time of the first immigrants' arrival in North America is in dispute, it is generally accepted that they came from Asia by way of Beringia. Asia and North America now are separated by the narrow Bering Strait. When sea level dropped during the Ice Age, however, the Bering Strait vanished and left a broad land bridge that connected Asia and North America. This land bridge was Beringia, and animals and human beings crossed it freely. When melting glaciers caused the sea to rise, Beringia was flooded and the Bering Strait reappeared. This happened a number of times during the Pleistocene epoch. Migrants from Asia might have moved southward through an ice-free corridor east of the Rocky Mountains. Some authorities believe that early people followed the coast to lower latitudes.

Other Evidence. Scholars in fields other than archeology have studied early human beings in North America, and some of their work supports the views of archeologists. There is an interesting argument from the field of linguistics (the study of languages). The traditional view has been that there are about sixty Native American language families in North America and one hundred in South America. One study, however, asserts that there are only three language families in both continents. The Eskimo-Aleut family, spoken in Alaska and northern Canada, arrived there four thousand to five thousand years ago. Speakers of languages in the Na-Dene family of western Canada and the southwestern United States migrated from Asia somewhat earlier. All remaining languages of North and South America are placed in the Amerindian family, which arrived from Asia more than 12,000 years ago. These three families are related to language families of Eurasia. Therefore, this study implies that there were three major migrations from Eurasia.

Geneticists who study physical features acquired from heredity have examined remains of early people in the Americas. Africa was the original home of humankind, and from there humans colonized the rest of the world. By analyzing genetic differences among populations, one can estimate when various groups became separated from one another. One study suggests that Asians began settling North America about thirty thousand years ago.

A genetic study based on DNA, the basic material that transmits the hereditary pattern of all living things, also supports the likelihood of three migrations from Asia to North America. The earliest one, called the first Paleo-Indian migration, crossed Beringia from twenty thousand to forty thousand years ago. After arriving in the Americas, these people diversified. They correspond to the Amerindians.

The Na-Dene speakers of western Canada and the Southwest followed the same route to North America five thousand to ten thousand years ago. A third migration occurred from six thousand to twelve thousand years ago. These people were not related genetically to the population of Siberia, that part of Asia from which the other migrations seem to have originated. Instead, this group is more like the populations of East Asia and Polynesia. Rather than crossing Beringia, this second wave of immigrants might have reached America by crossing the Pacific Ocean by boat. The genetic studies tend to reinforce the linguistic and archaeological research.

Ongoing Controversies. Although the majority of archaeologists believe that there is no firm evidence for the presence of humans in North America more than twelve thousand years ago, some disagree. Research from Monte Verde in southern Chile reveals that the site was inhabited at least one thousand years before Clovis. Early remains of a settlement there were found preserved in a peat bog. The site appears to have been occupied by twenty to thirty people for a year or so. Among the artifacts recovered were the remains of shelters, animals hides, food (including some mastodon meat), fires, and a child's footprint. A number of prominent archaeologists who examined the site think that it is genuine. If human beings were in South America more than a thousand years before Clovis, others must have passed through North America considerably earlier.

Early human artifacts have been found in other coastal areas, and it has been suggested that people followed the coast as they moved south. The interior route east of the Rocky Mountains in Canada would have been forbidding, but the coast was not. There, people might have constructed primitive craft and used them to journey down the coast. Coastal areas are appealing because they have a relatively mild climate and provide abundant food in the form of fish, shellfish, sea mammals, and the like.

Materials that have been found in California have led some researchers to believe that humans were there long before Clovis. A number of skeletons from the San Diego area have been dated, the oldest at about forty-eight thousand years old. However, the reliablity of the dating technique employed in this study—protein racemization—is questioned by many authorities. Charcoal from fires, bones, shells, and primitive stone tools also have been found in the San Diego area. Examination of the weathering of the stone artifacts and the age of the surface and soil in which they were found has led some researchers to claim that humans might have been in that area 100,000 years ago. Critics, however, argue that the stone artifacts were fashioned by nature, and there is no precise dating for the finds. Primitive, highly weathered stone artifacts also have been found at various sites in the California desert, particularly the Calico Mountains. Again, some scholars think they might be 100,000 or more years old, but others insist that the so-called artifacts were shaped by natural processes.

The Dating Controversy. The traditional view has been that the first humans who arrived in North America twelve thousand or so years ago were thoroughly modern. All humans of recent times are classified as *Homo sapiens sapiens.* Earlier peoples included *Homo erectus* and more primitive varieties of *Homo sapiens.* For example, the famed Neanderthal people of Eurasia are *Homo sapiens,* but not *Homo sapiens sapiens.* Because these people arrived from Asia, they and their present Native American descendants are believed to be Mongoloid (Asian) in race. This has been challenged. If the first migrants arrived in North America 100,000 years ago as some believe, they could not have been *Homo sapiens sapiens,* since they did not exist then. Some very primitive skulls have been found in Nebraska, Minnesota, and Brazil that are obviously extremely old. They display the prominent brow ridges of the Neanderthal people of Europe, although these might be defined as Neanderthal-like and not classic Neanderthal.

Negritoids, related to the small, dark-skinned people who still occupy remote sections of Africa, Asia, and the western Pacific, might have been in North and South America. If they were in Asia, they could have reached America by way of Beringia. The Botocudo tribe of South America is very negritoid in appearance. If they were in South America, they could have been in North America as well.

There might have been an Australoid presence in North America. Australoids are related to the people of Australia. The native peoples of California shared many traits with the Australian Aborigines, including certain physical characteristics, male pubertal rites from which women were driven away with a device known as a bull roarer, and hunting with throwing spears and curved throwing sticks. The ancestors of the Australian aborigines came from Asia, and some might have migrated to North America as well as Australia

How the First People Came. How could these people have gotten to North America? The earliest Negritoids, Australoids, and possibly Europoids could have arrived by way of Beringia, as did others. (The term "Europoids" refers to people somewhat similar to those of Europe, who were present in East Asia in the remote past. The Ainu of Japan are a contemporary example.) People related to modern Polynesians might have reached North or South America by boat. Certain elements of the Native American population are genetically related to East Asians and Polynesians, and might have entered the Americas by way of the Pacific Ocean, rather than Beringia.

In addition, some Europeans might have migrated across the Atlantic Ocean to North America. This does not mean that modern Native Americans are not of ultimate Asian origin. It appears that Asians did enter North America, and their direct descendants are the present Native Americans. However, the ancestors of modern Native Americans might have been neither the first nor the only people to enter North America.

Dispersion Throughout the Hemisphere. Once humans arrived in North America, they spread out across the continent. By the end of the Pleistocene epoch, about 10,000 years ago, many large mammals had become extinct, including the mammoth, mastodon, giant bison, camel, and ground sloth. It has been suggested that the Big Game Hunters contributed to the extinction of Pleistocene fauna. Modern human beings are not the first people to have had an adverse impact on the environment.

As time passed, other animals were hunted and plants were gathered and eaten. Stone weapons were still used, and the atlatl was employed to propel large darts, or spears. These devices gave extra leverage, which allowed spears to be thrown with great force. The bow-and-arrow was a rather late invention.

Early Agriculture. Southern Mexico and Cental America became a major center of plant domestication. From there, some crops were diffused to North America and were grown as far north as the upper St. Lawrence River Valley in eastern Canada. The most important were maize (corn), beans, and squash. Tobacco was also grown in North America, but it came from South America and not Mesoamerica. The bottle gourd was cultivated and used as a water container and for other purposes. The bottle gourd is a native of Africa, and its presence in the Americas thousands of years ago is a mystery. Acorns, nuts, and the like were placed on a *metate,* a stone slab, and ground with a *mano,* a hand-held stone. The soil was prepared with digging sticks and hoes. Livestock were absent; the only domesticated animal was the dog.

Population Estimates. Recent estimates of the population in 1492 in what is now the United States and Canada vary from a little under four million to nearly ten million. The actual number was probably closer to the lower figure. California and a few other regions had relatively large populations. Agriculture was absent there, but abundant resources allowed for a sizable number of inhabitants. The interior Southwest supported a moderate population among the Pueblos and other sedentary tribes. The Southeast was rather populous and had permanent towns. A few other areas, generally coastal, supported substantial populations. Vast stretches of North America, especially the arid and very cold realms, had very few inhabitants.

The Vikings were in North America about 1000 C.E., and the continent might have been visited by ancient Chinese, Phoenicians, Carthaginians, Romans, and others. These early contacts, if they took place, had little or no significance for the peopling of North America. The vast transformation of North America came with arrival of Europeans after 1492.

John A. Milbauer

For Further Study

Carter, George F. *Earlier than You Think: A Personal View of Man in America.* College Station: Texas A&M University Press, 1980.

Dillehay, Tom D., and David J. Meltzer, eds. *The First Americans: Search and Research.* Boca Raton, Fla.: CRC Press, 1991.

Ericson, Jonathan E., R. E. Taylor, and Rainer Berger, eds. *Peopling of the New World.* Los Altos, Calif.: Ballena Press, 1982.

Fagan, Brian M. *Ancient North America: The Archeology of a Continent.* 3d ed. New York: Thames and Hudson, 2000.

_______. *The Great Journey: The Peopling of Ancient America.* New York: Thames and Hudson, 1987.

Renfrew, Colin, and Paul Bahn. *Archeology: Theories, Methods, and Practice.* 2d ed. New York: Thames and Hudson, 1996.

Trigger, Bruce G., and Wilcomb E. Washburn, eds. *The Cambridge History of Native Peoples of the Americas.* Vol. 1. Part 1. *North America.* Cambridge, England: Cambridge University Press, 1996.

Mesa Verde Page 445

The Caribbean

The first human inhabitants of the islands of the Caribbean were Caribs and Arawaks. Christopher Columbus arrived in 1492 and was followed by many Spaniards who exploited the Native Americans for labor. Danish, Dutch, English, and French explorers, planters, and settlers came later. European diseases decimated the Arawaks and Caribs. As a result, the Europeans turned to African laborers, sometimes as indentured servants, but more often and increasingly as slaves brought in captivity, mostly from the West African coast and Angola. Chinese and Indian indentured servants were eventually brought to some islands.

Native Americans. The earliest evidence of human colonization of the Caribbean is found in Cuba, Haiti, and the Dominican Republic, where sites have been dated to around 3500 to 4000 B.C.E. These migrants probably came from the Yucatán peninsula. There is evidence of subsequent migration, the most far-reaching of which occurred between 500 and 250 B.C.E. It seems to have come from the Orinoco drainage and the river systems of South America's northeast coast, mostly from present-day Venezuela.

When Europeans arrived, they found the Caribbean to be densely inhabited by diverse indigenous groups. They came to view the Caribbean as having two kinds of people, Caribs and Tainos (Arawaks), but it probably was more ethnically complex than that. From 1492 to 1660, European diseases and the effects of forced labor decimated and almost eliminated the native peoples of the Caribbean. It has been estimated that the native population of Hispaniola (modern-day Dominican Republic and Haiti) was well in excess of 3 million in 1496. By 1508 the population was only 100,000. This was the general pattern for the tropical Caribbean islands and the coasts of the Americas. Carib peoples still exist, though, on parts of the islands of Dominica and St. Vincent.

Sugar and Settlers. Europe's demand for sugar drove the particulars of settlement in much of the Caribbean. The Dutch supplied much of the initial workforce and knowledge and were responsible for the firm implantation of sugar and slavery in the Caribbean. By 1640 the English had fifty-two thousand whites on their islands of Barbados, Nevis, and St. Kitts. This contrasts sharply with twenty-two thousand at the same time in the settlements of New England. By the end of the 1650's there were fifteen thousand white Frenchmen in Martinique and Guadeloupe. At first the whites grew tobacco, but a shift to sugar began in 1645 and sugar was dominant by the 1670's. As a result, African slaves became the majority of the British islands' population. In Barbados, there were more than fifty thousand African slaves by the end of the 1600's, while the white population had declined to about seventeen thousand. Similar changes occurred in the French islands, but at a slower pace.

In Jamaica sugar developed more slowly, but by the 1680's, the island's sugar industry began to expand. Slaves began arriving at the rate of more than thirty-six hundred per year in the 1680's. By 1768 the slave population in Jamaica had reached 167,000 while the white population had grown to only 18,000. St. Domingue (Haiti), a French possession, developed in a manner similar to that of Jamaica. By 1740 St. Domingue had 117,00 slaves, about 13,000 free persons of color, and a similar number of white Frenchmen. In 1791 the slaves rose in revolt and eliminated the white population, and modern-day Haiti came into being.

In the late eighteenth century, the estimated slave populations in the West Indies were as follows: French West Indies, including Haiti, 575,000; British West Indies, 467,000; the Spanish West Indies, 80,000. In the early 1860's the slave population in Cuba was 370,553 and in Puerto Rico, 41,738. The slave population altered Cuba's culture for some time, so that it resembled Haiti. Subsequent immigration from Spain in the late nineteenth century shifted Cuba's culture back to being distinctly Spanish.

United States Virgin Islands. In 1666 Denmark occupied St. Thomas. Five years later, a colony was founded there to supply the mother country with cotton, indigo, and other products. Slaves from Africa were first introduced to St. Thomas in 1673 to work the cane fields. The first regular consignment of slaves did not arrive until 1681. In 1684 the Danes claimed neighboring St. John and colonized the islands with planters from St. Thomas in 1717. In 1733 they purchased St. Croix from the French. By 1742 there were nineteen hundred African slaves on St. Croix alone. The United States purchased the islands in 1917.

Indentured Servants. The emancipation of slaves throughout the West Indies in 1834-1838 resulted in a severe labor shortage on the sugar plantations. This need was met by the subsidized immigration of laborers from India and China. British Guiana (Guyana) and Trinidad received the majority of the indentured laborers. During the 1850's and 1860's, 142,000 Chinese went to Cuba. Many of the Chinese came from Canton. In the twentieth century there has been free movement of Portuguese, Syrians, and Lebanese to Trinidad and the Greater Antilles, such as Cuba and Hispaniola.

Dana P. McDermott

For further study

Bergad, Laird W., Fe Iglesias Garcia, and Maria Del Barcia. *The Cuban Slave Market, 1790-1880.* New York: Cambridge University Press, 1995.

Johnson, Howard, ed. *After the Crossing: Immigrants and Minorities in Caribbean Creole Society.* Totowa, N.J.: Frank Cass, 1988.

Klein, Herbert S. *African Slavery in Latin America and the Caribbean.* New York: Oxford University Press, 1986.

Look Lai, Walton. *Indentured Labor, Caribbean Sugar: Chinese and Indian Migrants to the British West Indies, 1838-1918.* Baltimore: Johns Hopkins University Press, 1993.

Wilson, Samuel M., ed. *The Indigenous People of the Caribbean.* Gainesville: University Press of Florida, 1997.

Virgin Islands Page 582

Population Distribution

North America

Population map Page 447

Patterns of settlement in modern North America are the result of more than one thousand years of influence and change. Europeans, Africans, and Asians all left their mark on a continent that had been dominated by different indigenous nations. At the end of the twentieth century, North America was home to more than 400 million people of different cultures dispersed throughout Greenland, Mexico, Canada, and the United States.

The United States had the largest group—about 273 million. Mexico had the second-largest population, approximately 100 million people. Canada was much smaller, with around 31 million residents. The island of Greenland had about 60,000 inhabitants, although its total land area is bigger than Mexico. In terms of gross distribution, almost seven of every ten North Americans lived in the United States.

Canada and United States are sometimes collectively called Anglo-America, reflecting their common British heritage. Mexico, by contrast, has a strong Spanish heritage. Greenland is actually part of the Kingdom of Denmark; however, most Greenlanders are Inuit, descendants of the Thule.

Geographic Patterns of Modern Settlement. The population in North America is not spread evenly; it is quite clustered. Most North Americans live in cities and their surrounding suburbs, or in smaller towns. At the end of the twentieth century, 75 percent lived in urban areas—a big change from two centuries earlier, when only 5 percent lived in a city.

In Greenland, almost all the population lives in the towns and villages along the western coast. In contrast, much of Mexico's population is found in a wide band extending west-to-east across the middle third of the country. Toward the east coast is Mexico City, home to more than 26 million people—over one-quarter of the total Mexican population. This city is projected to become the world's largest urban agglomeration by 2010.

In the United States, about two-thirds of the cities with more than 1 million people are located east of the Missouri River. Rural (farming) areas there also have more people per square mile than in the western half of the United States. The largest urban concentration is in the area that stretches from Washington, D.C., to Boston, Massachusetts, including Washington, D.C. (4.6 million people), Baltimore (2.5 million), Philadelphia (6 million), New York (20 million), and Boston (5.6 million).

In Canada, almost 90 percent of the population lives within 100 miles (160 km.) of the United States border. More than 60 percent of all Canadians are concentrated in southern Ontario and along Quebec's St. Lawrence River Valley. This corridor, extending from Windsor (near Detroit, Michigan) to Quebec City is nicknamed Main Street, because of its linear shape and the fact that so many people live along it. The biggest cities on that corridor are Toronto (4.2 million people), Montreal (3.3 million), and the capital city, Ottawa (1 million).

Along the west coast of Anglo-America are several big cities, extending from San Diego and the Los Angeles area (15.5 million) in California to Vancouver (1.8 million) in Canada. Beyond the coastal area, much of the western and northern parts of North America are sparsely settled. This is mostly due to the nature of the landscape and the climate.

IMPACT OF EUROPEAN SETTLEMENT. The earliest discovery of North America by foreign explorers is believed to have been by Norse seafarers known as Vikings. Erik the Red established a Viking colony in Greenland in the 980's and Leif Eriksson became the first European to land in North America, in 1000. The Vikings built a colony in the northernmost tip of Newfoundland on the east coast of Canada, but it was later abandoned.

Toronto Page 507

Montreal Pages 573

Around 1600 Europeans began building settlements in North America again,

Fanciful modern depiction of Viking navigator Leif Eriksson, whose voyage to Labrador around the year 1000 makes him the earliest-known European to reach North America. (Library of Congress)

and many of those became modern major cities. However, Native Americans, Eskimos, and Inuit already had built communities, and had lived here for at least twelve thousand years before the Europeans arrived. These different nations lived throughout North America, from the Arctic Ocean to the southern border of Mexico. Contact with European diseases and the disruption of traditional lifestyles and homelands dramatically reduced their populations.

By the seventeenth century, a number of European countries were beginning to explore and settle North America, drawn by the great variety of raw materials and resources there—fish, furs, minerals, lumber, and good soil for crops.

The clusters of European colonies, mainly along the Atlantic coast of North America, resulted in different cultural regions. The French were in the northern areas; English Puritans dominated southern New England, around Boston; the Dutch, and later the English, were around New York; and English Quakers settled around Philadelphia. Both England and France established plantations in the southeastern region, the English in Virginia and South Carolina, and the French along the Gulf of Mexico. The Southeast also became the destination for many Africans, brought across the Atlantic Ocean as slaves to work on the plantations. These large farms grew crops like cotton and tobacco, which were in big demand in Europe.

Mexico City Pages 448, 571

The Spanish domination of Mexico was based out of the colonial capital of Mexico City, which was the main population center of New Spain. For decades after Mexico gained independence in 1821, the country was politically unstable. In contrast to Canada and the United States, Mexico lost half its territory in wars. These losses, combined with the legacy of Spanish colonial control and its internal land confiscation, 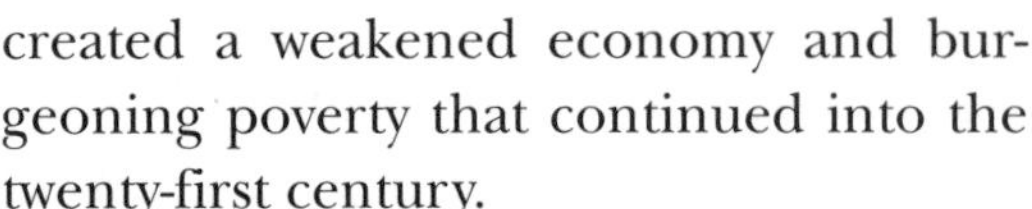created a weakened economy and burgeoning poverty that continued into the twenty-first century.

Distributing Population: The Ability to Move. In North America, overland travel by wagon was difficult because there was no road system such as the network that exists today. It was much easier to move about by boat on the rivers and along the coast. Because of this, the biggest population growth occurred in cities and surrounding areas that were located along the northeast Atlantic coast, the St. Lawrence River, and the Gulf of Mexico. In Anglo-America, New York was the biggest city, with about 100,000 people. Settlements were also built along rivers, such as the Mississippi, that linked the Midwest with the larger cities of the Southeast. River ports such as St. Louis and New Orleans grew quickly because of their location on major waterways.

Boat traffic going down midwestern rivers did not help businesses and cities in the Northeast. Because of competition for trade, northeastern interests built connected river and canal systems. New York business people paid for the construction of the Erie Canal in 1825, which linked the Hudson River at New York to Lake Erie at Buffalo. A second canal system went from Philadelphia and Baltimore to Pittsburgh and the Ohio Valley; there, Cincinnati and Louisville became important port cities.

Those new transportation routes meant that much of the better agricultural lands within the eastern half of United States and the Great Lakes area in Canada could be settled, because farmers could get their crops to markets in the bigger cities. As a result, most of the Midwest and Southeast were settled in the mid-ninteenth century. Many of the new settlers came from Europe and Britain, and a large slave population was forcibly brought from West Africa.

Continued on page 457

The expression "fall colors" derives from the color changes that deciduous trees and shrubs undergo in the fall seasons, as their leaves die and change their colors. By contrast, evergreen trees and shrubs—some of which can be seen in this photograph—retain both their leaves and their green color year-round. (PhotoDisc)

Typical fall colors. (PhotoDisc)

Conifers predominate in high Sierra Nevada locations. (Corbis)

The largest member of the deer family, the moose is found mainly in North America's colder climates in Alaska, Canada, and parts of the northwestern United States. (PhotoDisc)

Habitats and Selected Vertebrates of North America

Manatees can be found in the marshy coastal waters of Florida and many Caribbean islands, whose mangrove swamps provide ideal habitats. (PhotoDisc)

Flowers thrive in the moist, tropical environments of Caribbean islands. Hibiscus, bougainvillea, and orchids are just a few of the endless varieties found here. (Clyde L. Rasmussen)

Colorado's Mesa Verde National Park contains a large number of impressive Puebloan ruins, dating from 550 to 1300 C.E. (PhotoDisc)

Bering Strait Migrations

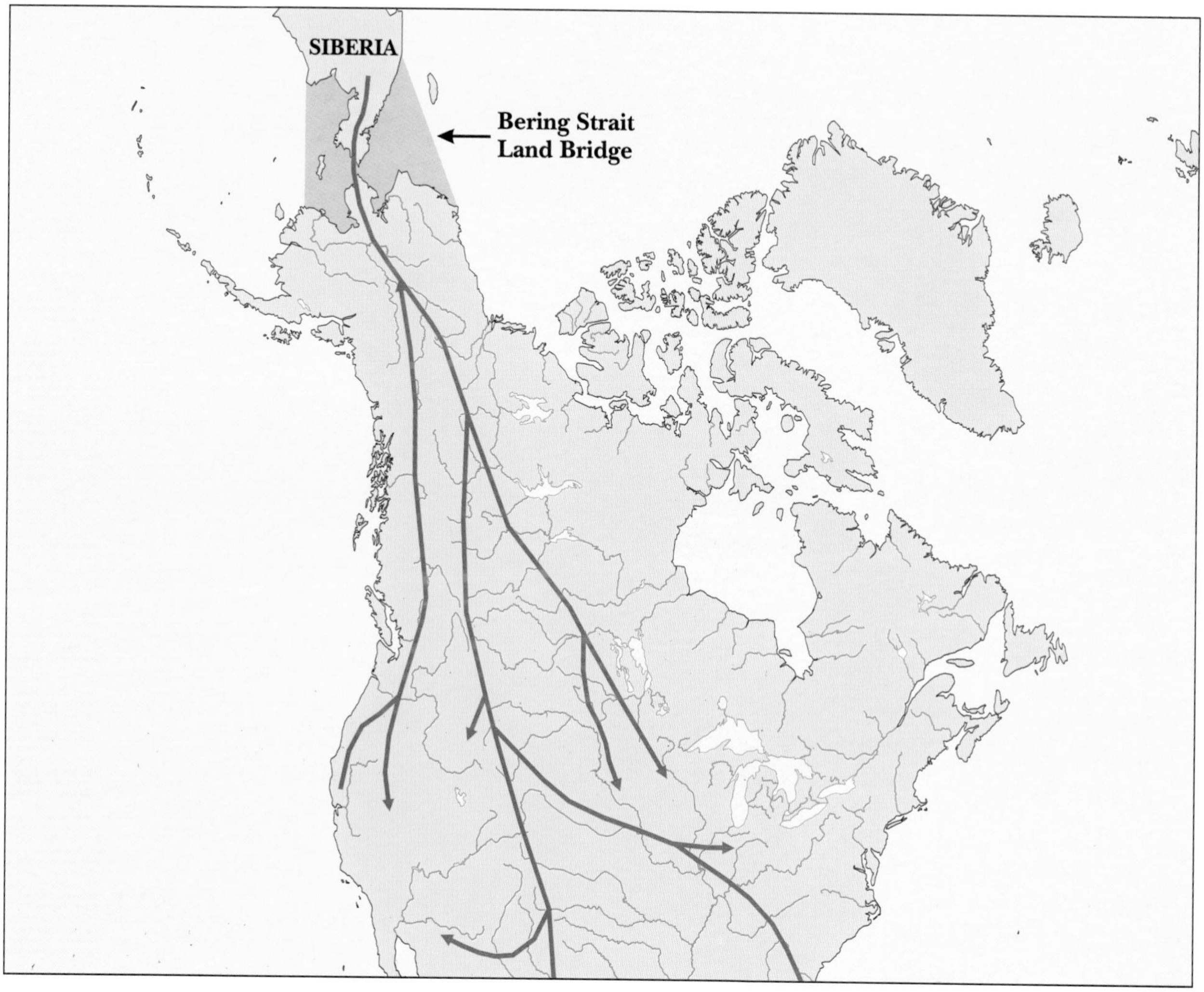

SIBERIA

Bering Strait
Land Bridge

Contemporary depiction of the village of San Francisco as it appeared shortly before the discovery of gold in California transformed it into a major city. (Corbis)

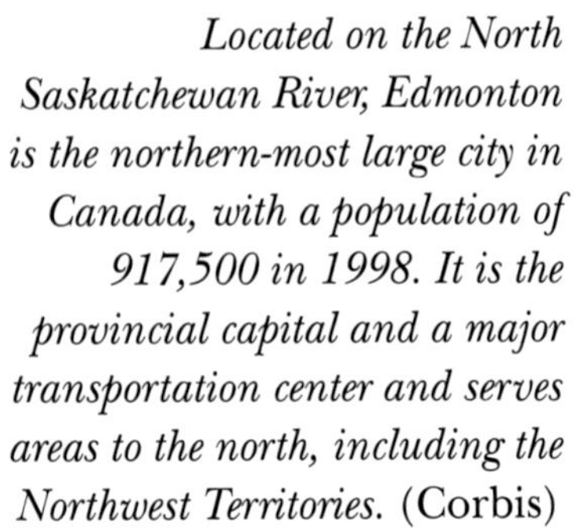

Located on the North Saskatchewan River, Edmonton is the northern-most large city in Canada, with a population of 917,500 in 1998. It is the provincial capital and a major transportation center and serves areas to the north, including the Northwest Territories. (Corbis)

Population Densities of North American Countries
(Based on Mid-1999 Estimates)

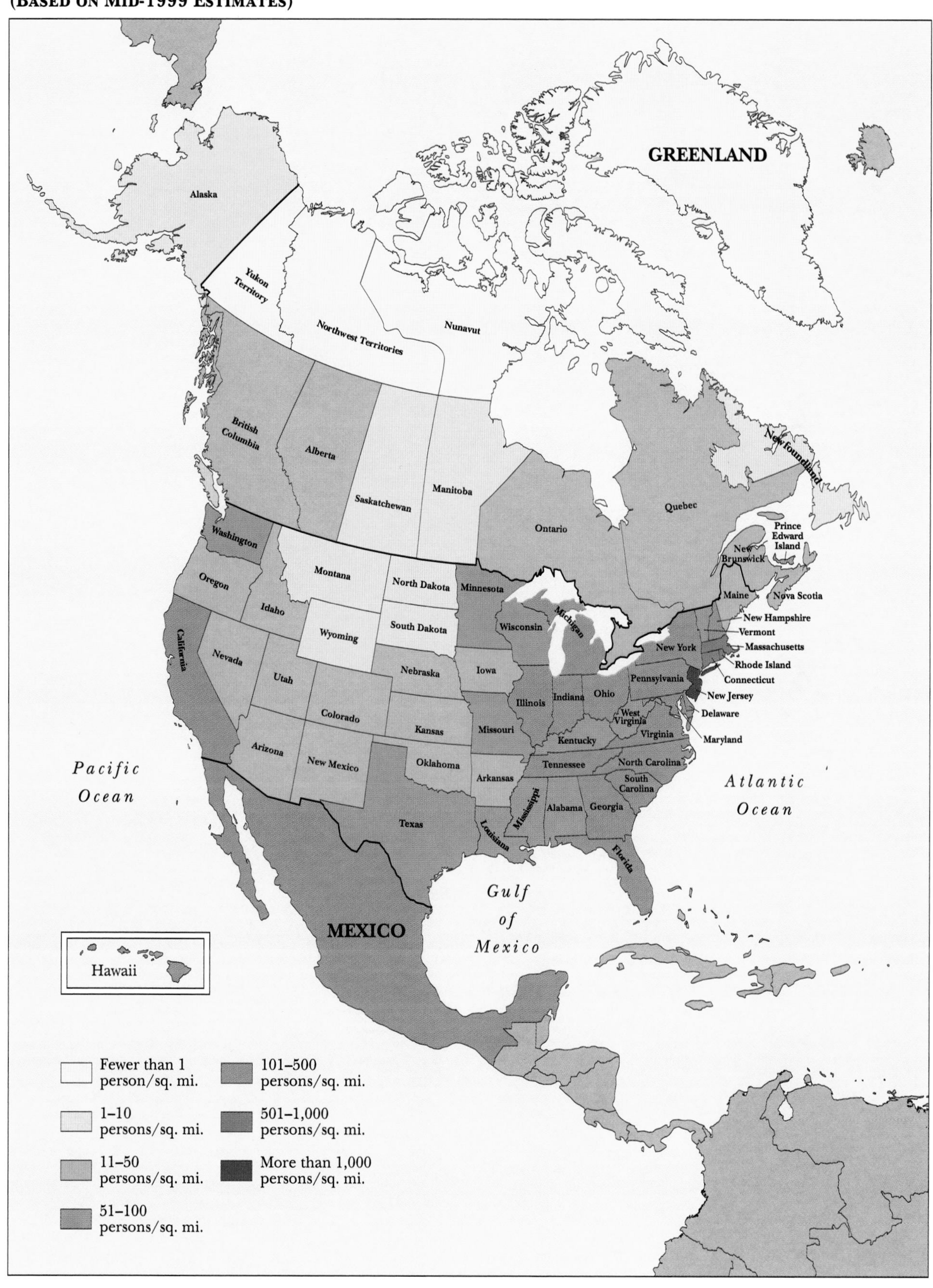

Rapid population growth has made Mexico City one of the most crowded cities in the world. (Corbis)

Population Densities of Caribbean Countries
(Based on Mid-1999 Estimates)

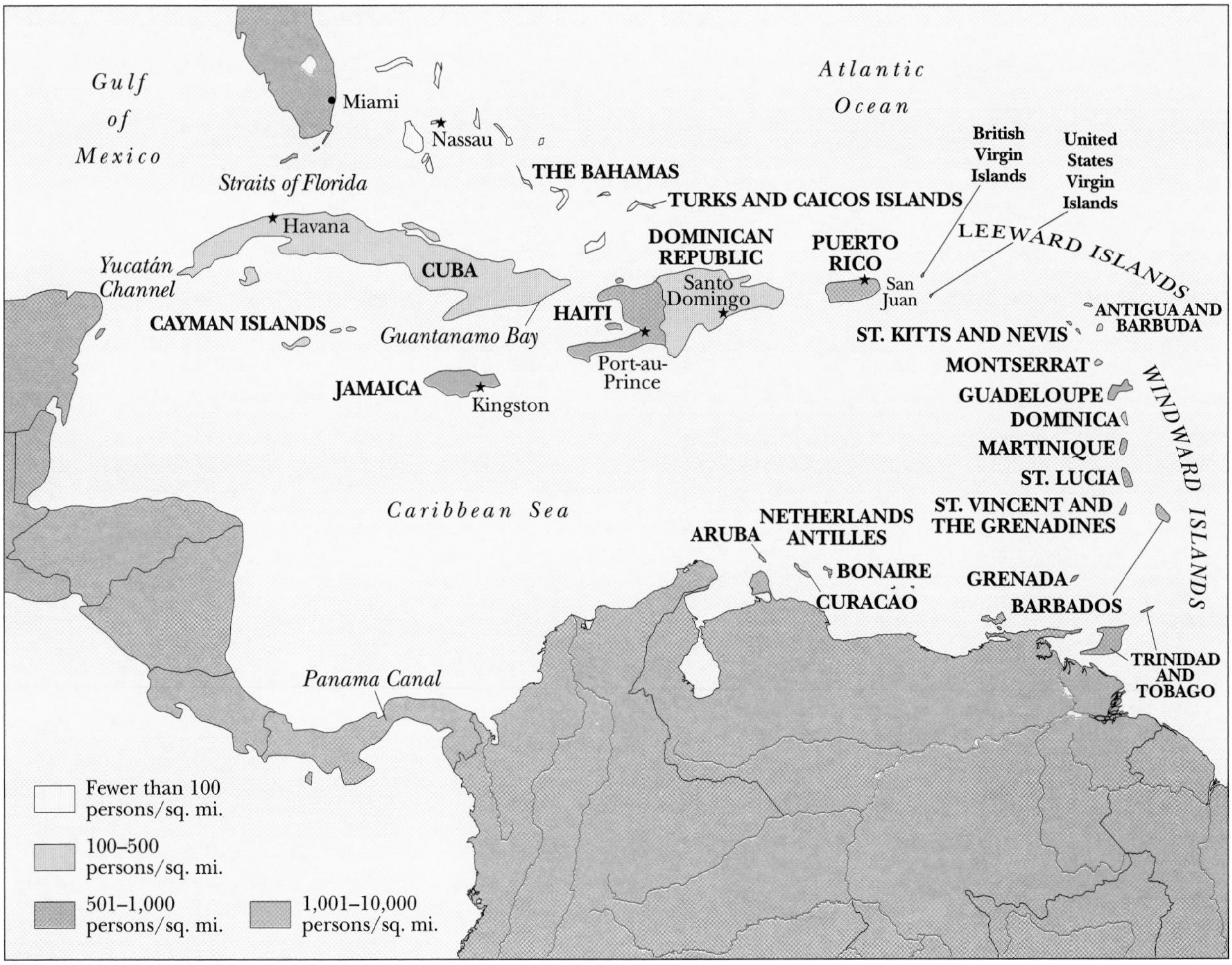

Gulf of Mexico
Atlantic Ocean
Miami
Nassau
THE BAHAMAS
Straits of Florida
TURKS AND CAICOS ISLANDS
British Virgin Islands
United States Virgin Islands
Havana
LEEWARD ISLANDS
Yucatán Channel
CUBA
DOMINICAN REPUBLIC
PUERTO RICO
Santo Domingo
San Juan
CAYMAN ISLANDS
Guantanamo Bay
HAITI
ANTIGUA AND BARBUDA
ST. KITTS AND NEVIS
Port-au-Prince
MONTSERRAT
JAMAICA
Kingston
GUADELOUPE
DOMINICA
MARTINIQUE
WINDWARD ISLANDS
ST. LUCIA
Caribbean Sea
NETHERLANDS ANTILLES
ST. VINCENT AND THE GRENADINES
ARUBA
BONAIRE
GRENADA
CURACAO
BARBADOS
Panama Canal
TRINIDAD AND TOBAGO
Fewer than 100 persons/sq. mi.
100–500 persons/sq. mi.
501–1,000 persons/sq. mi.
1,001–10,000 persons/sq. mi.

Quebec City, the capital of Canada's Quebec province, about 82 percent of whose people are French-speaking. (Corbis)

Monolithic statues erected by the Toltec civilization at Tula (about forty miles northwest of present Mexico City). The Toltecs dominated Mexico from about the tenth through the twelfth centuries. (Corbis)

Mardi Gras, New Orleans's annual pre-Lenten carnival, is a reflection of the city's cultural and historical ties to the Caribbean and Latin America. (Louisiana Office of Tourism)

Trinidad's annual pre-Lenten carnival celebration is the largest and liveliest in the Caribbean region. (Clyde L. Rasmussen)

Voyages of Columbus, 1492-1502

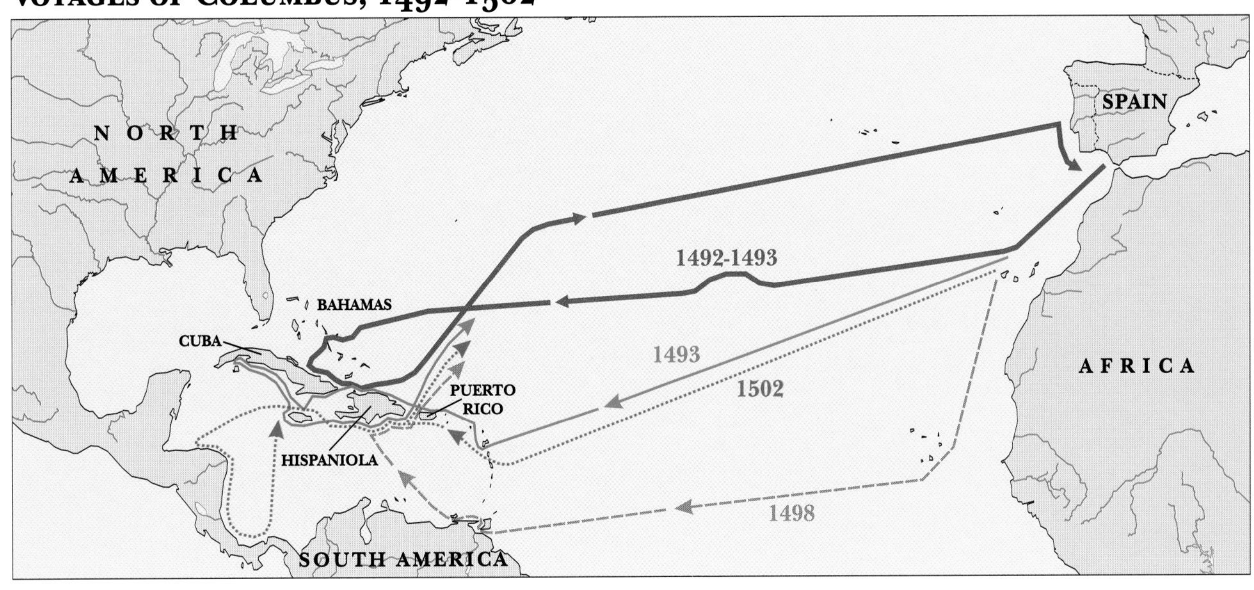

Major Voyages to the New World After Columbus

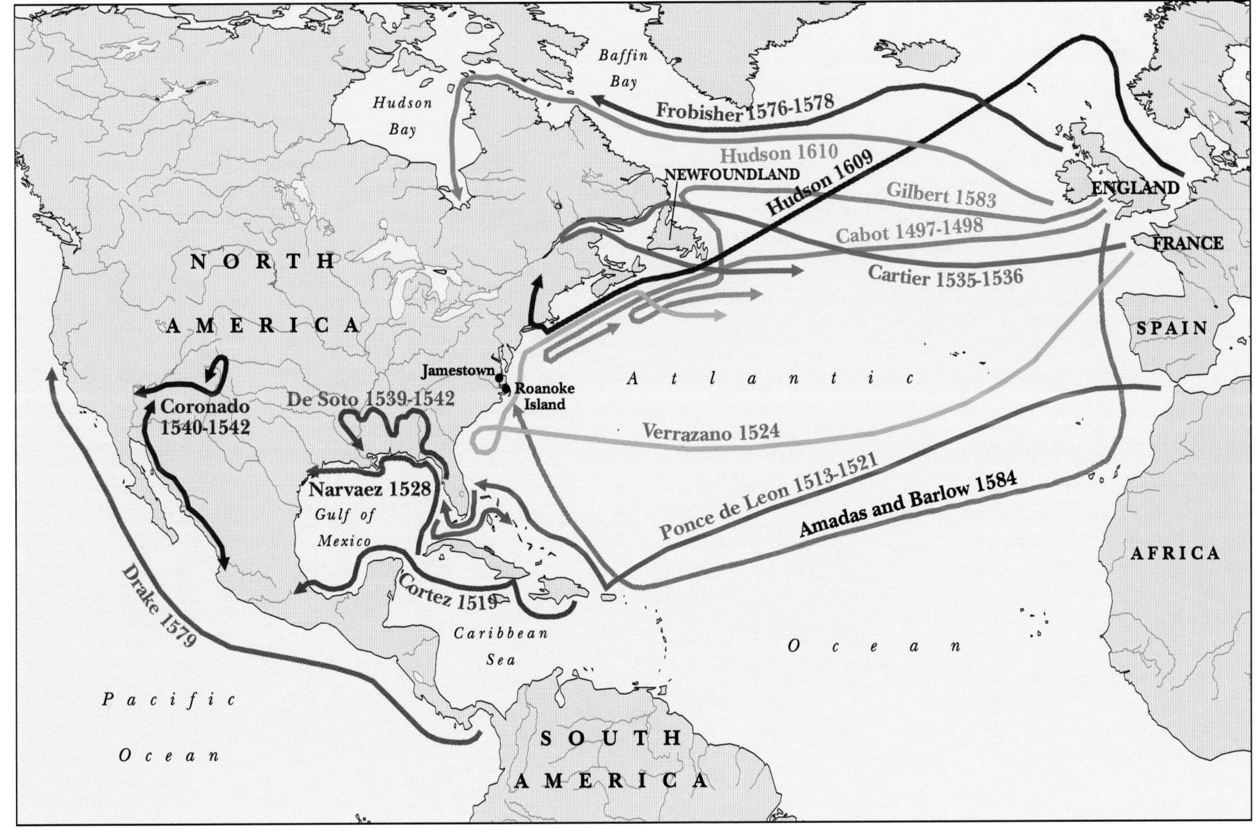

Political Divisions Within Canada, United States, and Mexico

Key to States
(shown by numbers on map)

1 Aguascalientes	**6 Tlaxcala**
2 Guanajuato	**7 Distrito Federal**
3 Querétaro	**8 Morelos**
4 Hidalgo	**9 Puebla**
5 Mexico	

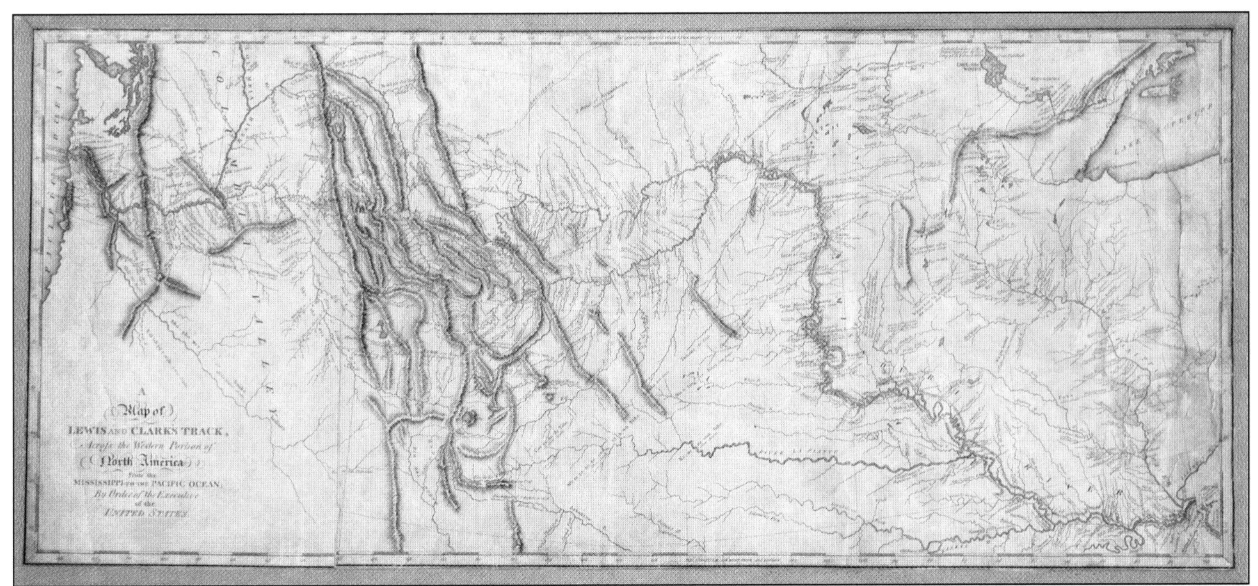

Early nineteenth century map of the Lewis and Clark Expedition's route. (Corbis)

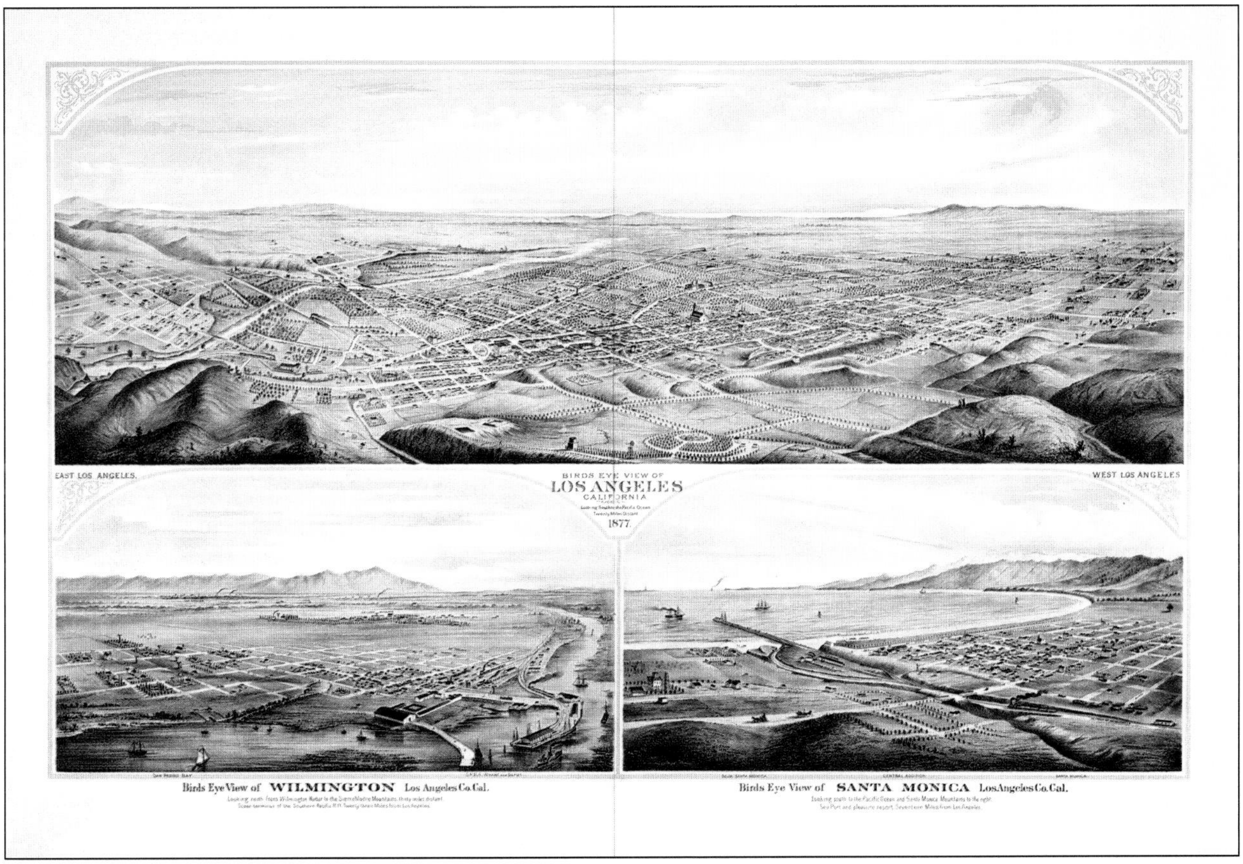

In 1877 Los Angeles revealed few signs of the immense growth it was to undertake in the twentieth century. (Corbis)

Thanks largely to its central location in a network of railroad lines, Chicago grew from virtually nothing to a major metropolis in the mid-nineteenth century. (Corbis)

The middle of New York City's Manhattan is dominated by Central Park, a green belt that occupies 840 acres (340 hectares). The park was created by the city in the middle of the nineteenth century, during an era of urban reform. (Corbis)

Major Urban Centers in North America

Selected Agricultural Products of North America

In Canada, a population of fewer than 300,000 Native Americans and Europeans in 1760 grew to 3.2 million by 1860. In the United States over this same hundred-year period, the population grew from about 2.5 million to more than 30 million. New York alone had around 1 million people. However, most people at that time did not live in cities: In the United States, only 25 percent were city-dwellers; in Canada, it was less than 12 percent.

By the middle of the nineteenth century, the Industrial Revolution had begun to cause great change, not only in where people lived and what their jobs were, but also in where population growth went in North America. An important invention that changed the population distribution in North America was the railroad. Much of this new technology came from England, and it was especially influential in Anglo-America. The impact of rail in Mexico was minor, and in Greenland it was nonexistent. With the new railroad technology, anywhere a track could be laid meant easy movement. This opened up much more of the United States, in particular, for people to settle.

New York City Page 575

San Francisco Page 446

Cities, towns, farms, and mines were built throughout the western half of United States. The discovery of gold near San Francisco in 1849 helped speed up the building of a rail line to the West Coast. Rail reached the Pacific Ocean in 1869. In Canada, the transcontinental railway was completed in 1885. It went from the east coast to the west coast near the present-day Canada-United States border. It strongly influenced where population settled in the western half of Canada. The number of people who live west of the Missouri and Mississippi Rivers and east of the Rocky Mountains is much less than live in the eastern half of North America, but without the railroad, these regions might not have seen much settlement until the twentieth century.

By 1920 most of Anglo-America's remaining agricultural lands were settled. Population in the United States reached just more than 106 million, of which 51 percent lived in urban areas. In Canada, there were about 8,750,000 people (37 percent urban). New York reached 4.75 million, making it the biggest city in either country. In Mexico, population continued to grow, but poverty and inequality were major factors

The Influences of Geography, History, and Technology

The present patterns of population distribution in North America are the result of myriad factors. However, the primary determinants are different for Greenland, Mexico, and Canada and the United States. Geography has played a particularly critical role in Greenland, where the physical landscape effectively restricted settlement to the coastal areas. The rugged landscape has limited the influence of historical colonization and the impacts of transportation improvements.

History explains the continuing legacy of Spanish conquest in Mexico. Ongoing problems of land ownership, poverty, and exploitation have strongly influenced the mass migration to Mexico City, and the limited resources available to much of the population to change their situation.

Technology has played a huge role in the exploration and settlement of Canada and United States. The railroad and automobile, more than any other technologies, have shaped population distribution in Anglo-America.

in limiting population distribution and suppressing development. In the relatively short time since Europeans built settlements along the Atlantic coast and Gulf of Mexico, much of North America was changed by settlers, both urban and rural. It was one of the quickest transformations of a landscape in the history of the human population.

NORTH AMERICANS ON THE ROAD. The first half of the twentieth century saw the invention of the car, the building of highways, more factories and businesses in cities, and farms growing more food with fewer farm workers because of new machines. Urbanization increased. Between 1920 and 1960, the sprawling corridor on the eastern U.S. seaboard and Canada's "Main Street" corridor grew in particular. By 1970 70 percent of the people in North America lived in cities, and urban growth continued.

At the end of the twentieth century, Mexico, the United States, and Canada were 74 percent, 75 percent, and 77 percent urban, respectively. One reason that cities can continue to grow outward is because increasing numbers of people own cars. In Mexico City, there were almost 4 million cars. In United States, there were more than 190 million car registrations—about 1 car for every 1.3 persons. This means individuals can drive to work and do not have to live close to their place of employment. The car and the highway system have created sprawling suburbs. The truck enables industries and businesses also to move the suburbs. Fewer people and fewer jobs are in the inner city or in the downtown area; more farmland is being converted into suburbs.

THE NEW DESTINATIONS. In Anglo-America since the 1960's, almost one of every five persons moves every year. With the car and truck, this becomes quite easy. The moving of people from region to region is called migration. There have been major trends in migration in the United States and Canada during the twentieth century. The most ongoing trend has been for people to move westward, which has occurred for at least two hundred years. Since 1960, some of the fastest-growing U.S. states have been in the west and southwest, including California, Texas, Arizona, and Nevada, and some of the fastest-growing Canadian provinces have been the westward ones of Alberta and British Columbia. The states and provinces west of the Rocky Mountains had at least 50 percent more people in the year 2000 than in 1960.

The cities in the U.S. South, extending from Texas to the Carolinas, have also been destinations for many people. This region is often called the Sunbelt. In the early 1970's, large numbers of people began moving there from the Midwest and Northeast. In part, this is because of the growth of high-technology businesses that have been established there, such as petrochemicals, aeronautic industries, computer-related businesses, and the space program. At the same time, some of the old factories in the Midwest and Northeast—where many jobs existed from the late nineteenth century to the 1960's—became obsolete and closed. The West Coast continued to be a popular destination, fueled in part by the growth in computer industries and the entertainment business.

Migration is a serious problem in Mexico. There, the geographic pattern involves the movement of rural populations to cities—primarily Mexico City. Rural-to-urban migration has caused high rates of urbanization in a country that already experiences high population growth. It is estimated that each day in Mexico City, at least one thousand babies are born and at least one thousand people arrive from rural areas. As a result, the city increases by about 750,000 people every year. It seems

Information on the World Wide Web

Population.com, a Web site sponsored by the World News Network, collects current articles, resources, and directories relevant to world population and population statistics. (www.population.com)

The World Factbook 2000 Web site, maintained by the U.S. Central Intelligence Agency (CIA), features worldwide population information and individual country profiles. (www.odci.gov/cia/publications/factbook)

impossible to provide enough new housing, new jobs, new schools, clean water, and sewerage capacity for such a rate of growth.

Timothy J. Bailey

For Further Study

Birdsall, Stephen S., John W. Florin, and Margo L. Price. *Regional Landscapes of the United States and Canada.* 5th ed. New York: John Wiley & Sons, 1999.

Greenfield, Gerald S., ed. *Latin American Urbanization.* Westport, Conn.: Greenwood Press, 1994.

Paterson, John H. *North America.* 9th ed. New York: Oxford University Press, 1994.

Peters, Gary L., and Robert P. Larkin. *Population Geography.* 6th ed. Dubuque, Iowa: Kendall, 1999.

Preston, David A., ed. *Latin American Development.* 2d ed. New York: Longman, 1995.

The Caribbean

With a total population of about 38 million people in the year 2000, the Caribbean region has roughly the same number of people as California and Washington State combined. However, the Caribbean's people are unevenly distributed among the many islands of its independent nations and colonial dependencies. This uneven distribution is closely linked to the centers of production of the region's main agricultural products: sugar, coffee, and tobacco, as well as the locations of port cities largely developed to export these products.

The Caribbean's most populous nation occupies its largest island: Cuba, whose 1999 population was about 11.1 million people. With an area of 42,754 square miles (110,860 sq. km.), Cuba has a population density of about 260 residents per square mile (100 per sq. km.). Its total area is similar to that Tennessee, but Tennessee has half the number of people and is thus half as crowded.

Population map Page 447

Population Densities. The average population density for the Caribbean region as a whole is roughly 400 people per square mile (158 per sq. km.). By contrast, the United States has an average population density of about 70 people per square mile (27 per sq. km.). However, while the Caribbean is the most densely populated region in the Western Hemisphere, its countries show a wide range of individual population densities. The region's most densely populated island nation is Barbados. It had about 274,000 people living on its 166 square miles (430 sq. km.) in 1999. Its population density of about 1,650 people per square mile (637 people per sq. km.) is twice that of the Caribbean's next most densely populated nation, St. Vincent and Grenadines. The country with the lowest population density is the Bahamas, with about 55 people per square mile (21 people per sq. km.).

The Caribbean's second-largest country, in both area and population, is the Dominican Republic, with 8,442,533 inhabitants on 18,793 square miles (48,730 sq. km.). Its population density is about 450 people per square mile (173 people per sq. km.). The Spanish-speaking Dominican Republic shares the island of Hispaniola with French- and Creole-speaking Haiti. With 10,702 square miles (27,750 sq. km.), Haiti has only 57 percent of its neighbor's area, but its population of 6,867,995 is more than 80 percent than that of the Dominican Republic, making it 40 percent more crowded.

No other Caribbean islands approach Cuba, the Dominican Republic, and Haiti in the size of their populations. Puerto Rico, a dependency of the United States, is next biggest, with about 3,916,000 residents. Independent Jamaica has 2,652,689 people on an island a tenth the size of Cuba. Trinidad and Tobago is the only other nation with a population of over a million, with about 1,086,908 people on a small group of islands covering just under two thousand square miles. Haiti, Jamaica, and Trinidad and Tobago all have population densities of the same order of magnitude—more than double that of Cuba.

Among the Caribbean's other island nations and colonial dependencies, the next largest in population are French-ruled Guadeloupe (425,317) and Martinique (415,724), the Bahamas (287,548), Barbados (259,248), Netherlands Antilles (209,888), St. Lucia (155,678), St. Vincent and the Grenadines (121,188), and the U.S.-ruled Virgin Islands (120,917). All remaining countries and territories had populations of less than 100,000 in 1999.

Major Population Clusters. The Caribbean has four major population concentrations of people. The largest is found on the central and southern portions of the island of Hispaniola (divided into Haiti and Dominican Republic), roughly connecting the cities of Port-au-Prince and Santo Domingo. The three remaining large clusters include northwest Cuba (including the city of Havana), Puerto Rico (including San Juan), and Jamaica (including Kingston).

While country population totals and population clusters are highest on the larger Greater Antilles islands of Cuba, Hispaniola, Puerto Rico, and Jamaica, high-densities can be found on many of the smaller islands of the Lesser Antilles.

Kristopher D. White

For Further Study

Blouet, Brian W., and Olwyn M. Blouet. *Latin America and the Caribbean: A Systematic and Regional Survey.* 3d ed. New York: John Wiley & Sons, 1997.

Boswell, Thomas P., and Dennis Conway. *The Caribbean Islands: Endless Geographic Diversity.* Piscataway, N.J.: Rutgers University Press, 1992.

Clawson, David L. *Latin America and the Caribbean: Lands and Peoples.* New York: McGraw Hill, 1999.

Culture Regions

North America

The culture regions of North America extend from the Arctic Circle, through Canada and the United States, to Mexico and include many people, languages, and lifestyles.

Greenland. Although citizens of Greenland are also Danish citizens, Greenland is a part of North America. Connected by a submarine ridge to North America, Greenland lies only 16 miles (26 km.) from the Canadian island of Ellesmore. About two-thirds of Greenland's 840,000 square miles (2.18 million sq. km.) is within the Arctic Circle and 84 percent of Greenland's land area is covered by thick sheets of ice. These facts indicate the types of cultural groups and activities that could flourish in Greenland. Only about 1 percent of the island is used for agriculture. At its southernmost point, the island provides pasture for sheep and reindeer, which are raised for meat, wool, and milk.

About 80 percent of Greenland's fifty-five thousand people are of Inuit heritage, although over the years there has been an intermixing of Inuit and Europeans, mostly Danes, who have emigrated to the island. The Inuit of Greenland, like those of Canada and Alaska, have had a traditional lifestyle adapted to a cold climate where there is little vegetation, and people must seek much of their livelihood from nature itself. Many people fish the coastal waters and rivers. Greenland's chief exports are canned and frozen cod, prawns, and other marine life, as well as zinc and lead from the island's mines.

Greenland has neither metropolitan areas nor superhighways. Of its 120 localities, only about 65 have populations of more than one hundred. Nuuk, the largest city and capital, has a population of only thirteen thousand. Near the coastal areas are some highways, but much of the year, over much of the land, Greenlanders must travel on iceways.

While Greenlanders have relatively modern lifestyles, they still adhere to many of the values and beliefs that were brought by the Thule culture to Greenland in 900 C.E. The Inuit culture is now found in its pure form only in the Thule District; however, Greenlandic, a three-dialect form of the Inuit language, is spoken throughout Greenland. Inuit folktales and folk arts are part of the culture of Greenland. Dogs remain important to the Inuit, both for transportation and as companions in a cold, isolated climate. Each year Greenland hosts the Arctic Circle Race, an international race for cross-country skiers across 100 miles (160 kilometers) at the Arctic Circle. Greenlanders follow the visiting skiers in dogsleds.

Greenland's culture is also influenced by Scandinavian culture. Erik the Red settled in Greenland around 985. To encourage other Vikings to settle on the island, he named it Greenland to make prospective settlers think it was a land where people could live prosperously. In 1000 Erik's son, Leif Eriksson, introduced Christianity to Greenland. His mother built the first Christian church in Greenland, at Brattahild. Instruction in modern Greenland's schools is conducted in the Greenlandic language, but administrative affairs and most media coverage are conducted in Danish.

Political Boundary map Page 452

NUNAVUT. Just to the west of Greenland lies Nunavut, a Canadian administrative unit that was created in 1999 out of the eastern portion of the Northwest Territories. Nunavut is made up of the traditional lands of the Canadian Inuit, whose language, Inkutitut, is the official language of the government. Most of Nunavut is inhabited by Inuit, although the southern part of the area is a Dene cultural area. The Dene are Native Canadians. The Inuit of Nunavut are closely related to the people of Greenland and are also descendants of members of the Thule culture. While the popular culture of North America has come to Nunavut, as many as 40 percent of its adults do not participate in a wage-based economy. Many follow the traditional cultural beliefs and practice the traditional arts of the Inuit.

The Inuit value the land, sea, animals, weather, human goodness, and sharing. Older people are respected and regarded as cultural experts. Younger Inuit look to older people for guidance about hunting, the weather, astronomy, cultural beliefs, and ethics. While most modern-day Inuit live permanently in their villages, their ancestors were nomadic, moving from place to place to follow game. Many of the remaining elderly lived a nomadic lifestyle in their early years. They have shared their stories with others in their families and villages to keep alive the traditional Inuit lifestyle. In Nunavut, some of the Inuit elders broadcast their stories on the radio in the Inukitut language.

CANADA'S ATLANTIC PROVINCES. South of Nunavut lie Canada's Atlantic Provinces: Newfoundland, Nova Scotia, Prince Edward Island, and New Brunswick. Although some Inuit and Native Canadians from the Micmac group live in Newfoundland, 95 percent of the people there are descendants of immigrants from southwestern Ireland or southwestern England. This heritage, and the fact that Newfoundland is somewhat isolated, have given the culture of the province a special flavor. The English spoken in Newfoundland is much like the English of seventeenth century West County England. The citizens of Newfoundland also cling to Irish traditions. At public gatherings bards and minstrels often do presentations in an Irish manner.

More than 50 percent of the people of Newfoundland live in urban areas. They engage in fishing, processing of seafood, and mining, particularly the extraction of iron ore. Emigration to other parts of Canada and to the United States was high during the last part of the twentieth century.

In 1605 people from France settled at Port Royal in Acadia. This settlement, now know as Annapolis Royal, Nova Scotia, was the first permanent North American settlement of Europeans north of Florida. The French lived and flourished in this area early in the seventeenth century, but, with the Treaty of Paris of 1763, France had to cede their North American lands to Great Britain. Most of the Acadian French refused to swear loyalty to the British government and were deported. Many went to New Orleans, where their culture became known as Cajun. At the beginning of the twenty-first century, about 13 percent of the people of Nova Scotia traced their ancestry to the original Acadians who settled there. These people are often bilingual and generally live on farms as their ancestors did.

About 75 percent of the citizens of Nova Scotia are descendants of British immigrants. They practice the occupations of their ancestors, fishing for lobsters, oysters, clams, and scallops, or dairy farming. Many are of Scottish heritage and there is a strong Scottish cultural influence within the province.

Around Halifax and Shelburne live many descendants of the West Indian slaves who left boats docked in this area during the eighteenth and nineteenth centuries. There are about 14,000 Micmac Indians in Nova Scotia; 3,000 of these live on government-administered lands. About 90 percent of the people of Nova Scotia speak English exclusively; about 8 percent are bilingual, speaking English and French.

Although Prince Edward Island has a rural atmosphere, it is the most densely populated Canadian province. The areas around Charlottetown are urbanized. The majority of the island's inhabitants are descendants of immigrants from the British Isles. Another several thousand people are descendants of Acadians who were not deported in the eighteenth century; they often are French speakers. More than one-third of the citizens of Prince Edward Island are Roman Catholics.

New Brunswick is the only Canadian province that has both English and French as its official languages. The majority of the citizens of New Brunswick are descended from citizens of the British Isles: Some of their ancestors were Loyalists during the American Revolution; others were immigrants from England, Ireland, and Scotland during the nineteenth and early twentieth centuries. There are also French-speaking descendants of Acadians who were not deported in the eighteenth century, African Canadians who are mostly descendants of loyalist slaves, Native Canadians living on government-administered lands, and some Asians who arrived in the latter part of the twentieth century.

Quebec and Ontario. About 82 percent of the people of Quebec are French-speaking, and French is the official language of the province. While people of French heritage dominate the culture of Quebec, people of English heritage dominate the economy. This leads to much tension within Quebec. Many French speakers have attempted to establish their own personal identities in an economy dominated by a culture different from their own. In Quebec, 82 percent of the people live in urban areas. The rates of divorce, suicide, and teenage pregnancy in Quebec are among the highest in Canada. Special singers (*chansonniers*) present music that identifies with the Quebeçois search for political and cultural identity. Radio and television programs are broadcast in both French and English, and there are several newspapers in each language.

Ontario is the political and industrial center of Canada. English is spoken there, since relatively few French ever settled in this province. While Ontario is the industrial center of Canada and its citizens make up 50 percent of the Canadian workforce, in the last part of the twentieth century, many of Ontario's skilled workers crossed the border to work in the United States.

New Brunswick Page 574

Fifty-four thousand Cree Indians live in northern Quebec, mostly on government-administered land. Other Native Canadians live in rural areas of southern Ontario. Large numbers of immigrants from Asia have settled in Toronto.

Montreal Page 573

Toronto, Ontario; and Montreal, Quebec; are major centers for the Canadian performing arts. Their respective theaters, symphonies, and ballet companies rival each other. These two cities are also important in the sporting life of Canada. Ice hockey is the national sport, and both Toronto and Montreal have major ice hockey teams.

Canada's Prairie Provinces. The central provinces of Canada—Manitoba, Saskatchewan, and Alberta—are known as the Prairie Provinces. English is the official language, but all these provinces have many citizens of German, Scandinavian, Ukrainian, and French ancestry. These people have kept their heritages alive through ethnic festivals at which they wear ethnic costumes, sing music of their ancestors' homelands, and prepare and eat the foods of those homelands. During the latter part of the twentieth century, Alberta received many immigrants who came there to work in the rich petroleum fields near Edmonton.

Abundant natural resources are found in the Prairie Provinces. Alberta and Saskatchewan are also prime farming areas. Huge wheat farms and cattle ranches dot the landscape there. Some areas of these provinces have a cowboy culture complete with rodeos and western wear.

The Northwest Territories and the Yukon. There are two large, sparsely populated areas in northern Canada: the Northwest Territories and the Yukon. Major towns in these areas are Yellowknife, capital of the Northwest Territories; Whitehorse, capital of the Yukon Territory; and Dawson, Hay River, Fort Smith, and Inuvik. About 60 percent of the people are of European or mixed European heritage. Some are descendants of people who came searching for gold; others are transients who have come for a variety of employment reasons and do not plan to settle there. Many transients work in the gold and diamond mines of the Yellowknife area.

The people of European descent tend to live in settlements along the Mackenzie River, although a few live in the far northern coastal regions. One such settlement is Inuvik, the administrative center for the western Arctic. Inuvik is literally the "end of the road." People who live there are at the end of the Dempster Highway that connects the western Arctic to Whitehorse, Yukon.

About 10 percent of the people are western Inuit, who live mostly in the far north and east of the Northwest Territory. The western Inuit have many of the same customs and beliefs as other Inuit groups. About 25 percent of the people of these territories are American Indians who call themselves Dene. The Dene comprise several tribes who speak languages from the Athapascan group. The Dene live near Fort Smith and along the Mackenzie River. Many of them were originally fur traders and, as demand for that occupation has declined, have had a hard time finding a way to fit into a wage-based economy.

British Columbia. The Canadian province of British Columbia is a cultural mix. More than 50 percent of its inhabitants are descendants of people from the British Isles, and many towns and streets are named for places in England and for members of British royalty. However, Vancouver has one of the largest Chinese populations outside of China, Taiwan, and Hong Kong. There are also people of Scandinavian, German, and Ukrainian heritage in the urban areas of the province. Most of the people of the province live in the Vancouver-Victoria region in the southwestern corner of British Columbia. Groups of people also live in the north, along the Pacific coast, and in the sparsely populated interior mountainous areas. These include the northern Inuit. The Athapascan live in the northern part of the province. Other Native Canadian groups live along the coast, where they have traditionally made their living by catching fish.

The United States. About one-third of the people of the United States are of a British or Irish heritage; about 25 percent are descendants of people from Germany; about 10 percent are of African American heritage. The remaining U.S inhabitants represent nearly all the languages and cultural groups on the earth. These cultural groups tend to be clustered in various areas. While the public policies of the United States once encouraged people to assimilate and adapt to the dominant, Euro-centered culture, in the last part of the twentieth century, people were encouraged to preserve their cultural backgrounds.

Northeastern United States. The northeastern United States was originally settled by Europeans, mainly from England, the Netherlands, and France. In the year 2000, in such densely populated metropolitan areas as New York and Boston, there are many people of Asian and African heritage. While citizens of the northeastern part of the United States, like the nation as a whole, are largely of the Christian faith, there are many people of the Jewish faith in the New York metropolitan area.

The U.S. culture is held together by a media-generated pop culture, by huge chain stores and large fast-food franchises, as well as by certain basic values: patriotism, belief in freedom, and love of family. The northeastern part of the United States is where many of these values were secured, since the Revolutionary War began there.

U.S. culture is supplemented and enriched by the ethnic neighborhoods, festivals, and foods that are found in the urban areas of the northeast. People of Chinese, Indian, Korean, Arabic, and African American heritage give life to the urban centers in this area. The northeastern part of the United States also is home to world-famous universities such as Harvard University, Massachusetts Institute of Technology, and Yale University.

Middle Atlantic States. The Middle Atlantic states of Pennsylvania, New Jersey, Delaware, and Maryland are highly industrialized areas with large metropolitan centers. Their citizens are generally of European heritage, but, particularly in the urban areas, there are many citizens of Asian and African backgrounds. Baltimore, Maryland, was an incubator for jazz created by African Americans in the middle of the twentieth century.

In the Philadelphia-Lancaster area of Pennsylvania live the Amish, an Anabaptist religious group that immigrated to the United States from Germany. The Amish have led lives isolated from the other citizens of the United States, shunning modern conveniences such as automobiles and electricity, and have been self-sufficient farmers.

Southeastern States. The southeastern states—Virginia, North Carolina, South Carolina, Georgia, and Florida—began as agricultural states. While there is still much farming there at the beginning of the twenty-first century, some of these states, particularly North Carolina and Georgia, are heavily industrialized.

Large urban centers in the southeast include Charlotte, North Carolina; Atlanta, Georgia; and Miami, Florida. Nevertheless, many of the people of the southeast live in small towns or in rural areas where life is slower paced than in large cities. About 25 percent of the population of the Southeast is African American. While in the industrialized north most African Americans live in urban areas, in the southeast many of them live in rural areas on small farms. The African Americans of the Southeast trace their heritage to slaves who worked in the fields and the huge homes of the European planters who settled there in the seventeenth and eighteenth centuries.

In the western mountains of North Carolina live Native Americans, the Eastern Cherokee, who have an Indian reservation there. Members of another Native American group, the Seminole, live in Florida, where they fish and raise cattle. While most members of this group live a lifestyle similar to that of the mainstream U.S. culture, some practice some of the folkways of their ancestors.

Mexicans in the United States. At the beginning of the twenty-first century, hundreds of Mexican immigrants had settled in central North Carolina to work in the meat-packing industry. These immigrants brought with them Mexican culture, foods, and music, changing somewhat the cultural landscape of North Carolina. They also brought special problems to the area, including many children who did not speak English.

Many elderly Americans from northern states, where it is cold and icy in the winter, migrate to Florida for the winter months or have emigrated there to live year-round. Miami, West Palm Beach, St. Augustine, and Tampa have large groups of older people.

Miami Page 572

Cuban Americans are another cultural group of the Southeast. Their original members fled Cuba after Fidel Castro became that country's president, and have preserved their culture as it existed when they left Cuba in the late 1950's and early 1960's. The Cuban Americans of southern Florida have exerted tremendous political power in U.S. politics, managing to get several administrations to keep in place an economic embargo against their homeland because it is led by Fidel Castro and his followers.

Southern Appalachian States. The southern Appalachian states of West Virginia, western Virginia, Kentucky, and

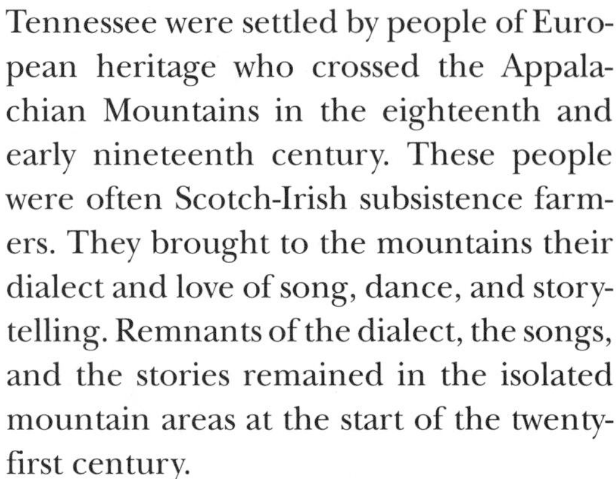

Tennessee were settled by people of European heritage who crossed the Appalachian Mountains in the eighteenth and early nineteenth century. These people were often Scotch-Irish subsistence farmers. They brought to the mountains their dialect and love of song, dance, and storytelling. Remnants of the dialect, the songs, and the stories remained in the isolated mountain areas at the start of the twenty-first century.

Early in the nineteenth century, German and Swiss immigrants traveled up the Mississippi River to the Ohio River and up the Ohio into the Appalachians in order to work processing iron ore mined in the area. At the end of the nineteenth century, coal mining began in the Appalachians, and other groups began to move into the interior of the Appalachians, joining the Scotch-Irish who had made a living on small farms. Immigrants from Poland, Wales, Italy, Austria, and England, and African Americans from southern areas, moved into the Appalachians to become coal miners. Because of the hard life that they endured in the coalfields of Appalachia, the miners of Appalachia became a special cultural group, sharing beliefs and a special way of life.

The culture of the southern Appalachians is a rural culture dominated by love of family and love of church. Fundamental Christianity, in which the Bible is taken as a literal truth, has many dedicated followers there. In a form of Christianity known as snake handling, which is practiced by small congregations in isolated areas throughout the southern Appalachians, followers prove their faith in God by handling poisonous snakes as part of their religious services. In the southern Appalachians, country music was born and is produced. Nashville, Tennessee, home of the Grand Ole Opry, is the country music capital of the world.

Lower South. The southern states of Alabama, Mississippi, and Louisiana have much in common with the southeastern states. Their nineteenth century historical background includes large farms, owned by European settlers and worked by African American slaves. At the beginning of the twenty-first century, these states had large rural populations composed of African Americans and descendants of the people who ran the large plantations. There are still large farms producing cotton, sugarcane, and rice. These farms are now worked by laborers from all cultural groups.

Unlike other southern states, which were settled by the English, Louisiana's original European settlers were Spanish and French; therefore, New Orleans and areas surrounding it have many French streets and place names. The famous New Orleans festival of Mardi Gras is a French celebration. The Creoles, who generally live in New Orleans and surrounding areas, are descendants of the original Spanish and French settlers. Some members of the Creole group are descendants of both the original European settlers and African Americans. Creoles have a special English dialect that incorporates some aspects of the language of their French ancestors. Some Creoles are bilingual, speaking both English and French. Well into the twentieth century, official documents of the Louisiana state government were written in both French and English.

Between 1763 and 1770, the British exiled about eight thousand French settlers from Acadia, which is now Nova Scotia. These settlers, called Cajuns, went to Louisiana, where their descendants now live in the bayou areas around New Orleans. Cajuns speak a special English dialect that has a French influence. Many of the descendants of the Acadians are bilingual, speaking both French and English. About 30 percent of the people in the lower South are of African American heritage. Some of the African Americans living in Louisiana speak a special French dialect.

Midwest. The Midwest comprises the states that make up the interior of the United States. While there are many urban centers in the Midwest—including Chicago, Illinois; Minneapolis-St. Paul, Minnesota; Omaha, Nebraska; and St. Louis, Missouri—the Midwest is characterized by vast stretches of flat land planted in corn to the south and wheat the north. The Midwest was originally settled by people of several European countries, including Ireland, Great Britain, Germany, and Scandinavia.

Minneapolis Page 572

Today the descendants of these early settlers give cultural variety to an area that the casual observer may see as homogeneous. In Iowa and Wisconsin, many descendants of German settlers keep their cultural heritage alive by staging German festivals such as Oktoberfest, by cooking and eating the foods of their ancestors, and by performing German music and dances. In parts of Ohio and Indiana, there are members of the Amish and Mennonite religious groups. Their plain lifestyles are noteworthy when compared to the complex lives that many other Americans live.

Mardi Gras Page 450

In Minnesota and eastern North Dakota, many people of Norwegian and Swedish heritage live. Several thousand Chippewa also live in Minnesota, some on the White Earth Reservation. Other Chippewa live in Michigan, some on reservations. Many Sioux Indians live on the Pine Ridge and Rosebud reservations in South Dakota; others live on the Standing Rock Reservation that straddles the borders of North Dakota and South Dakota.

The Southwest. The southwestern states of Texas, New Mexico, and Arizona have a cultural mix different from that of the East and the Midwest. The first Euro-

The Cochiti pueblo of New Mexico in 1880. Early Spanish explorers gave the name "Pueblo" to the adobe-building peoples of the Southwest because their villages resembled Spanish pueblos. (Museum of New Mexico)

Denver Page 518

Salt Lake City Page 580

Las Vegas Page 569

peans to live in this area were Spanish, and their influence can be seen in the place names, architecture, foods, language, and lifestyle. Immigration from Mexico in the latter part of the twentieth century reinforced the Spanish influences in this area. The blend of the United States and Mexican cultures in such Texas cities as San Antonio and El Paso and such Mexican cities as Juarez has led to the formation of the Tex-Mex culture, characterized by foods, dress, music, and dialect combining Spanish and U.S. cultures.

Native Americans also live throughout the Southwest, on reservations, in towns and cities, or on their own farmland. Many Navajo live in Arizona; some Laguna Pueblo live in New Mexico. The jewelry and pottery of the Native Americans of this area are prized throughout the world.

Rocky Mountain States. The Rocky Mountain area of the United States has densely populated urban areas such as Denver, Colorado; Salt Lake City, Utah; and Las Vegas, Nevada; but much of this area is sparsely populated. Throughout the region are huge sheep and cattle ranches.

One distinctive group found in the Rocky Mountain States is the Mormons, members of the Church of Jesus Christ of Latter-day Saints. This group left the eastern part of the United States in the middle part of the nineteenth century and moved to the Great Salt Lake Desert area in what is now the state of Utah. It was a barren land that no one else wanted. Through their knowledge of land management and irrigation, the Mormons prospered there. Thousands of Mormons live in areas around Salt Lake City and Ogden, Utah, where they practice their special religious beliefs.

Many Native American groups, including the Blackfoot in Montana and the

Cheyenne in Wyoming, live in the Rocky Mountain states, some on reservations.

Pacific States. The Pacific states of California, Oregon, and Washington possess a cultural diversity that is not found to such an extent in other parts of the United States. Since the middle of the eighteenth century, people from Asia have migrated to the United States, although at times in American history both state governments and the federal government tried to hamper this immigration.

Many people who can trace their ancestry to China, Taiwan, Japan, Korea, Vietnam, and other Asian countries live along the Pacific Coast. Some of these people live in ethnic communities in such large cities as Los Angeles and San Francisco. Here they speak the languages of their homelands, eat their native foods, and practice a lifestyle similar to the one they left behind in Asia. Other people of Asian ancestry prefer to live in culturally diverse communities and embrace the mainstream U.S culture.

In Southern California, there are many immigrants from Mexico, as well as descendants of people who immigrated from Mexico in past decades. They have brought the culture of Mexico to California, giving California foods, music, and a special atmosphere it would not otherwise have had.

Throughout the Pacific Northwest there are Native American groups. Some of these people, such as the Coeur d'Alene, live on Indian reservations where their native culture is kept alive through the work of tribal councils and the knowledge handed down from older people to younger. Other Native Americans live in the towns, cities, and rural areas of this region.

The origins of San Francisco's Chinatown go back to the mid-nineteenth century gold rush days, when thousands of Chinese men came to California to help build the railroads and work the mines. (PhotoDisc)

Mexico. A variety of societies ruled Mexico before Spain began occupying the region in 1519. The Olmecs, Maya, and Aztecs all developed brilliant civilizations noted for their advanced arts and sciences, monumental architecture, and large-scale political systems. Mestizos (people of mixed Spanish and native blood) form the majority of Mexico's population. In their efforts to create a new society in Mexico, the Spanish government and its partner, the Roman Catholic Church, permitted a measure of continuity with the indigenous past. Local officials administered Mexico through the indigenous institutions, wherever such existing customs and practices did not conflict with the demands of church and state. Racial mixing fostered cultural mixing, producing a blending of Spanish and indigenous culture that is unique in Latin America.

About three quarters of Mexicans live in cities. Mexico has one of the largest Roman Catholic populations in the world. About 90 percent of its nearly 100 million people call themselves Catholics—despite their government's twentieth century history of anticlericalism. The absorption of indigenous spiritual traditions into Catholic practices has made it easier for native poeples to embrace Catholicism.

Annita Marie Ward

For Further Study

Garreau, Joel. *The Nine Nations of North America.* New York: Avon, 1981.

Getis, Arthur, and Judith Getis. *The United States and Canada: The Land and the People.* Chicago: William C. Brown, 1995.

Guinness, Paul, and Michael Bradshaw. *North America: A Human Geography.* Totowa, N.J.: Barnes and Noble, 1985.

Paterson, John H. *North America.* 9th ed. New York: Oxford University Press, 1994.

Zelinsky, Wilbur. *The Cultural Geography of the United States: A Revised Edition.* Englewood Cliffs, N.J.: Prentice Hall, 1992.

The Caribbean

The culture regions of the Caribbean islands, formed in the wake of the European conquest that began with Columbus in 1492, marked a new phenomenon in the history of Western civilization—a relationship between masters and slaves that resulted not in the imposition of one culture on top of another but in the constant transfusion of numerous traditions derived from Europe, Africa, and the indigenous peoples of America.

The Spanish, English, French, and Dutch colonists created a world whose crux was the sugar plantation. African and native slaves and their offspring, known as "mulattoes" and "mestizos," kept their own customs alive while superficially accepting the domination of the whites. Out of this admixture arose a distinct Caribbean identity, neither black nor white, native nor European, but a unique hybrid. The arrival of immigrants from the Indian subcontinent in the nineteenth century added one more strain.

Culture of the Masters. The colonial masters carved the Caribbean into rival spheres of influence: Cuba, Puerto Rico, and the Dominican Republic formed the Hispanic bloc; Haiti, Guadeloupe, and Martinique composed the French zone; Jamaica, Barbados, Trinidad, and the Windward and Leeward Islands made up the English contingent; the Dutch Antilles rounded out the picture.

Whether Latin or Anglo-Saxon, the conquerors shared certain cultural characteristics, related to the need to protect the sugar plantation complex, that they passed on to their descendants: a monolithic religion (Catholicism, Anglicanism, or Dutch Protestantism) preaching defined notions of social status; military, political, and religious power invested in a planter class that identified more closely with its metropolitan motherland than with the New World; and a formal ban on mixing of the races that was often ignored.

All the Caribbean islands had black and mulatto majority populations by the nineteenth century, and the culture of the masters could not remain undiluted. Mulattoes and mestizos attained a degree of social acceptance then unimaginable in the United States. In the late twentieth century, white upper-class families attended religious ceremonies conducted in praise of African deities and participated in the game of cock-fighting learned from Africans, although both practices were denounced by the officers of the church and state.

Four centuries of Spanish rule left an indelible imprint on Cuban architecture. (Ciro Coelho/mercurypress.com)

Culture of the Slaves. The most devastating legacy of the European conquest was genocide, the eradication of the Carib, Arawak, and other indigenous peoples who occupied the islands until the end of the fifteenth century. The Indoamerican culture, however, was not entirely wiped out. It survives in place names such as Guanabacoa in Cuba and the straw-patched hut called a *bohio,* which shelters peasant farmers. Some Caribbean Indian gods, transformed into saints, have entered the folk religions of the islands. A mestizo culture, borrowing freely from Europe, Indoamerica, and Africa, arose in the sixteenth century. Aspects of that culture that still survive include the white-laced *guayabara* shirt worn in Puerto Rico, and the smoking of tobacco, originally an indigenous crop harvested by African slaves and sold to the Europeans. The music of the Caribbean, meringue and dances such as the mambo, is probably the mestizo product best known in the United States.

The African heritage of the Caribbean is preserved in its purest form in Haiti, which makes up half the island of Hispaniola. The religion called voodoo, which involves ritual magic and the physical possession of believers by spirits, can be traced directly to the West Coast of Africa. The Haitian people, nearly all descended from slaves imported by the French and Spanish, developed their own language, Creole, that preserves a largely African vocabulary while using French grammar.

The other half of Hispaniola, the Dominican Republic, is the best example of a Caribbean mulatto culture, blending African with European. Race mixing has gone on for so long and to such an extent that almost every Dominican might be classified as a "mulatto." African languages are no longer spoken in the Caribbean, but Dominican Spanish carries its own Creole inflection. Voodoo there blends almost perfectly with Roman Catholicism, producing a cult of saints to whom believers attribute magical powers without invoking their African origin.

Anglo-Caribbean Culture. Two elements make the English-speaking Caribbean islands stand out from the rest. One is an Anglophile (English-loving) elite that, regardless of skin color, turns its eyes to London and tries to recreate the glory days of the British empire in miniature form, whether by playing the game of cricket or by strictly adhering to mainstream British Protestantism. This fixation with the colonial metropolis has resulted in a more disparaging attitude toward race mixing, although a not insignificant portion of the population is mulatto. The poems of Nobel Prize-winning author Derek Walcott cannily reconstruct the dilemma of race and culture in the English-speaking islands. An Afro-American culture survives there largely in opposition to the elite culture, as evidenced by the continued popularity of reggae music and religious sects such as the Rastafarians in Jamaica.

Trinidad carnival Page 450

Another unique feature of the Anglo-Caribbean is the sizeable presence of generations of women and men descended from migrants from preindependence India, including the areas that are now Pakistan and Bangladesh. Torn between nostalgia for a homeland most have never known and a language and set of customs imposed by the British, East Indians in the Caribbean have produced their own subculture, mining elements of the Hindu, Muslim, and English elements of their heritage. In the novels and essays of Trinidad-born author V. S. Naipaul, the contradictions of East Indian identity in the New World are beautifully explored.

Julio César Pino

For Further Study

Davis, Wade. *The Serpent and the Rainbow.* New York: Simon & Schuster, 1985.

Knight, Franklin W. *The Caribbean: Genesis of a Fragmented Nationalism.* 2d ed. New York: Oxford University Press, 1990.

Minority Rights Group, eds. *No Longer Invisible: Afro-Latins Today.* London: Minority Rights Publications, 1995.

Naipaul, V. S. *The Middle Passage: Impressions of Five Societies—British, French, and Dutch—in the West Indies and South America.* London: Andre Deutsch, 1962.

Sarduy, Pedro Perez, and Jean Stubbs. *AfroCuba: An Anthology of Cuban Writing on Race, Politics, and Culture.* New York: Ocean Press, 1993.

Walcott, Derek. *Collected Poems, 1948-1984.* New York: Farrar, Straus & Giroux, 1986.

Information on the World Wide Web

The AfroCubaWeb site features current news about Afro-Cuban history, literature, music, and the arts. (www.afrocubaweb.com)

Exploration

North America

The first explorers of North America were the peoples who crossed from Asia to present-day Alaska several thousand years ago. They became the original population of both North and South America. Their cultures developed and thrived for many centuries, completely unknown to the peoples of Europe. Finally, Europeans began to discover America, although accounts of the early expeditions are shrouded in myth and legends.

Early Legends and Explorations. Legendary accounts begin in the sixth century with the supposed voyage of St. Brendan, Bishop of Clonfert in Ireland. Although Brendan is credited with reaching the western limits of the known world, written accounts of his exploits did not appear until the tenth century. It is impossible to know what those limits were, either the Canary Islands off the coast of Africa or the east coast of North America.

The next legend is that of the Seven Cities. When Muslim Arabs conquered Spain in 711 C.E., it was said that seven Christian bishops and their congregations fled west across the Atlantic Ocean and founded seven cities. This story was passed down orally for centuries. After Spanish maps of North America began to appear in the sixteenth century, the seven cities were identified as the pueblos of New Mexico.

The last major legend is the account of the Welsh adventurer Madoc in the late twelfth century. Written accounts about four hundred years later, after the colonization of America by Europeans, claimed that Madoc and a large group of settlers in ten ships landed on the east coast of North America. Later reports of "white Indians" who spoke the Welsh language in Tennessee, Kentucky, and on the upper Missouri River have been linked to the adventures of Madoc.

Historically, European exploration of North America began in the ninth and tenth centuries, when Norse adventurers from Norway discovered and colonized Greenland. The colony, established by Erik the Red in 986 C.E., survived for about five hundred years before vanishing for unknown reasons. About the year 1000, Leif Eriksson, the son of Erik, led a party south and west of Greenland. After landing on Baffin Island and in Labrador, his party established the colony of Vinland, probably in what is now Newfoundland. Either tragedy or a return to Greenland ended this settlement after about twenty years, but the forests of Labrador continued to provide timber for Greenland for many years. Accounts of Vinland written in the thirteenth century provided little aid to later Europeans.

Spanish Discoveries. In 1477 Christopher Columbus, a native of Genoa, Italy, joined an English trading expedition to Iceland. Any plans he might have had to get to Asia by crossing the North Pole ended after he experienced the harsh conditions of this voyage. Columbus then developed his grand design of reaching Asia by sailing west across the Atlantic Ocean, but he miscalculated the size of the world. He thought that a journey of 2,400 miles (3,860 km.) would take him to Japan. The actual distance is about 10,600 miles (17,055 km.), with the American continents blocking the path. In 1492 Columbus secured the financial backing of the Spanish monarchs, Ferdinand and Isabella, and sailed west. After his landing on San Salvador in the Bahamas, he made three more trips, still with the hope of reaching Asia. Columbus's voyages opened the New World to further exploration and colonization, and began the modern era.

Columbus map Page 451

In 1513 Vasco Nuñez de Balboa crossed the Isthmus of Panama—the connecting link between North and South America—and discovered the vast Pacific Ocean that still separated Europeans from Asia. The first Spanish attempt to explore the North American mainland was by Juan Ponce de León, who had sailed with Columbus on his second journey and had discovered Puerto Rico. León made two trips, in 1513 and in 1521, to Florida, which he first thought was an island rather than a peninsula. He explored both coasts, naming the peninsula for the fact that he landed first on Easter Sunday ("Pascua de Florida"—the Feast of Flowers) and for the abundant and beautiful vegetation of the area. León was killed by local people in 1521.

In 1526 Vasquez de Ayllon established the first Spanish settlement in the New World, near the mouth of the Savannah River in Georgia. Hardships such as native hostility and disease soon led to the abandonment of this colony.

EARLY INTERIOR EXPLORATIONS. The next step for the Europeans was to investigate the size, shape, and human geography of the New World. In 1524 Giovanni da Verrazano, an Italian, was commissioned by King Francis I of France to find a Northwest Passage through or around North America to Asia. Verrazano became the first European to sail into New York Bay. In 1535 Jacques Cartier, also commissioned by Francis I, discovered the St. Law-

Jacques Cartier was the first European to explore the St. Lawrence River and the region around present-day Montreal and Quebec. (Library of Congress)

PONCE DE LEÓN AND THE FOUNTAIN OF YOUTH

The Spanish explorer Juan Ponce de León was motivated by legends about a fountain of youth in which elderly people bathing themselves became young again. Legends of such fountains had existed in Europe for many centuries. In Florida in 1513, León and his men sampled every brook, spring, and puddle they could find, but found no such fountain.

rence River, immediately raising hopes of a Northwest Passage. Cartier travelled about one thousand miles into the Appalachian mountains and valleys. He eventually reached the present-day sites of Quebec and Montreal, but he was stopped at the Lachine Rapids south of Montreal, far short of his goal of reaching the Pacific Ocean.

The next expedition was by the Spanish explorer, Hernando De Soto. In 1539 De Soto was made the governor of Florida, which at the time meant the entire southeastern corner of North America. Although he was authorized to explore and colonize the area, De Soto's major goal was to find gold. He began his exploration at Tampa Bay with about six hundred men and traveled up the Atlantic Coastal Plain. As far north as Ayllon's abandoned settlement, De Soto faced opposition from the native inhabitants. Moving inland, he entered the southern section of the Appalachians. Here he made contact with people who had not yet met the Europeans and initially were friendly to the Spanish.

After crossing the Appalachian Mountains, De Soto discovered the Hiwassee River, a tributary of the Tennessee River and part of the vast Mississippi River system. Now facing native hostility, he continued west into the central lowlands. He died in 1541, after discovering the Mississippi River near Memphis, Tennessee, and he was buried in the river. Although De Soto had found the legendary town of Chisca, where Memphis now stands, he found no gold.

Another Spaniard, Francisco Coronado, began an expedition north from Mexico at about the same time as De Soto's. Like De Soto, he was searching for gold. With Coronado were 336 soldiers and several hundred Native Americans. The group entered the desert basin of Arizona, followed the Colorado River, and became the first Europeans to view the magnificent Grand Canyon. After crossing the Rocky Mountains, Coronado found himself on the Great Plains of North America. Here the Europeans saw for the first time the huge herds of buffalo, numbering in the millions, that roamed the plains. Coronado traveled as far east as Kansas before turning back to Mexico. Like De Soto, he had found no gold.

Grand Canyon Page 519

Search for the Northwest Passage. In 1607 the search for a Northwest Passage was renewed by Henry Hudson from England. In the most determined search yet, Hudson sailed up the west coast of Greenland as far as 80 degrees 27 minutes north latitude, far north of the Arctic Circle, before realizing that there was no hope of crossing the Arctic Ocean. Still, he believed that only a narrow isthmus separated the Atlantic and Pacific Oceans. On

In 1610 navigator Henry Hudson was abandoned by his crew on the great Canadian bay later named after him. (Library of Congress)

another voyage in 1609, this time financed by the Dutch East India Company, Hudson discovered the Hudson River in New York Bay. After sailing up the river about 150 miles, he realized that this route, like all earlier routes, did not reach the Pacific Ocean.

In 1608 Samuel de Champlain of France founded Quebec. The following year, he discovered the lake in upper New York to which he gave his name, and he later mapped Lake Huron. Champlain did more than any explorer to that time to make this area of North America known to Europeans.

Jamestown Page 583

The next phase of the search for a Northwest Passage came when the French began exploring the Mississippi River-Great Lakes section of the central lowlands. In 1634 Jean Nicolet reached Green Bay on the west side of Lake Michigan. This exploration involved the rich fur trade that the French were developing, but it also included the possibility that the Mississippi River might be a route to the Pacific Ocean. In 1669 Father Claude Dahlon, a Roman Catholic priest and a trained geographer, ascended the Fox River and portaged to the Wisconsin River, but did not reach the Mississippi River.

The journey of Louis Joliet and Jacques Marquette, beginning in 1673, followed Dahlon's route and reached the mighty Mississippi River. They descended the river as far as the mouth of a tributary, the Arkansas River, before confirming their growing realization that the Mississippi flowed south to the Gulf of Mexico rather than west to the Pacific Ocean. In 1682 another French adventurer, Robert La Salle, followed the same route and reached the Gulf at present-day New Orleans.

Later Explorations. English exploration of the Atlantic Coastal Plain began at Jamestown, Virginia, in 1607. By 1700 they had moved west to the fall line on the eastern slope of the Appalachian Mountains. After taking over French claims to North America in 1763, the English explored and settled the Mississippi River-Great Lakes and Ozark sections of the central lowlands. A major step toward exploring the unknown regions of this territory came in 1775, when Daniel Boone built the Wilderness Road through Cumberland Gap in the southern Appalachians. This opened up the valleys of the Tennessee, Kentucky, and Ohio Rivers all the way to the Mississippi River.

Frederic Remington's 1906 painting of Meriwether Lewis and William Clark resting near the mouth of the Columbia River, at the end of their journey of exploration. (Library of Congress)

In 1803 the Louisiana Purchase added the vast Great Plains west of the Mississippi River to the new United States. President Thomas Jefferson authorized Meriwether Lewis and William Clark to explore this territory. Their famous

Sacajawea

A member of the Shoshone nation, Sacajawea was born in about 1786 in present-day Idaho. After being captured by an enemy tribe, she was sold to a French fur trader and became his wife. In the winter of 1804-1805, Lewis and Clark met Sacajawea and her husband in North Dakota and hired them as guides for their expedition. Carrying her infant son on her back, Sacajawea, with her knowledge of the area and of the local languages, became a valuable asset to the expedition, especially when they met the Shoshone. Sacajawea died about 1812. In 1999 the U.S. mint honored Sacajawea by issuing a new one-dollar coin featuring her image.

expedition left St. Louis, Missouri, in May, 1804, and returned in September, 1806. They had followed the Missouri River to its source, crossed the Continental Divide in the Rocky Mountains, and followed the Columbia River to the Pacific Ocean. Journals kept by every member of this expedition provided valuable information about the physical geography, animal and plant life, and human geography of the area.

Lewis and Clark map Page 453

Many other expeditions explored the west. In 1806 Zebulon Pike, searching for the source of the Arkansas River, discovered the peak in Colorado that bears his name. Sylvester Pattie and his son explored the Intermontane Region west of the Rockies and the Gila River area of the southwest. In 1832 Benjamin Bonneville went through the South Pass of the Rockies in Wyoming and paved the way for the famous Oregon Trail. John C. Frémont and others explored the Great Basin around the Great Salt Lake and then across the Sierra Nevada to the Pacific coastlands of Cali-

The Oregon Trail—cut by Benjamin Bonneville from Missouri over the Rocky Mountains to Fort Vancouver on Oregon's Columbia River—was the main route west for pioneers settling the American frontier during the 1840's and 1850's. (Library of Congress)

fornia. Future exploration and development revealed that North America was rich in natural resources. Lumber, iron ore, coal, copper, silver, and the gold that the early Spanish had sought, were all found in abundance. To these were added the rich oil deposits in many areas of North America.

Glenn L. Swygart

For Further Study

The De Soto Chronicles: The Expedition of Hernando De Soto to North America in 1539-1543. Tuscaloosa: University of Alabama Press, 1993.

Furtwangler, Albert. *Acts of Discovery: Visions of America in the Lewis and Clark Journals.* Urbana: University of Illinois Press, 1993.

Goelzmann, William, and Glynder Williams. *The Atlas of North American Exploration.* New York: Prentice-Hall, 1992.

Hubler, Clark. *America's Mountains: An Exploration of Their Origins and Influences from the Alaskan Range to the Appalachians.* New York: Facts on File, 1995.

Morgan, Ted. *Wilderness at Dawn.* New York: Simon & Schuster, 1993.

Severin, Timothy. *Explorers of the Mississippi.* New York: Alfred A. Knopf, 1968.

The Caribbean

The European explorers who first sailed to the Caribbean did not expect to discover it. At first they assumed that the sea and its islands were merely way stations on their Atlantic passage to Asia. Gradually, however, the fact that the Caribbean was a partly enclosed sea itself became apparent.

The Caribbean's indigenous people included the Caribs (from whom the name of the sea was later derived) and the Arawaks. The Arawak umbrella also covers local groups such as the Taino and the Ciboney. It is not known exactly when the Caribs and Arawaks arrived in the Caribbean basin. Historians generally believe the Arawak arrived around 300 C.E., the Caribs a millennium later.

When Christopher Columbus sailed out of Palos, Spain, in August, 1492, most learned Europeans already knew that the world was round. However, they believed—and correctly—that Asia was about 15,000 miles (24,000 km.) to the west of Europe's farthest western reaches. They therefore believed it was not worth the effort to sail west, instead of making the long overland trek from west to east. Columbus, a sailor from Genoa who was employed by the king and queen of Spain, thought that the world was smaller than it actually is. As a consequence, he thought that the east-to-west distance from Europe to Asia was considerably shorter than was actually the case. Finding evidence in various geographical texts to back him up, he persuaded the Spanish monarchs to finance his voyage.

Columbus's expedition included three ships: *Nina, Pinta* (captained by Martin Alonzo Pinzón), and *Santa Maria.* The ships stopped at Gomera in the Canary Islands on September 9. This was their last landfall before they reached the New

Nineteenth century engraving of Christopher Columbus, giving thanks to God after making his first landing in the Americas. (Institute of Texan Cultures, San Antonio, Texas)

World. After a voyage of slightly longer than four weeks, Columbus's expedition reached landfall on an island that Columbus called San Salvador (24 degrees north latitude, longitude 75 degrees west). Its Arawak name was Guanahani; it is now called Watling's Island. It is part of the Bahamian chain on the east central edge of the island group, just north of the tropic of Cancer. Two days later, the expedition discovered the nearby island now called Rum Cay. The Spaniards encountered local plant and animal species and also native human populations whom they did not antagonize.

Two Major Islands. The small Bahamian islands, which Columbus believed to lie off the coast of Malaysia, were insufficient finds for Columbus's purposes. Columbus heard from the Arawak people of a large island to the south called Colba (present-day Cuba). From October 20 to December 3, the expedition explored the northeast coast of Cuba. It then moved on to Hispaniola, Columbus giving the island its name (Española in Spanish), which means "Little Spain." Thus the two biggest islands in the Caribbean, the anchors of the Greater Antilles, had been found.

The expedition returned triumphantly to Spain in early 1493. Immediately, plans for a second expedition were made; it left Spain in late September, 1493, and made landfall in the Caribbean on November 3. This time, Columbus and crew landed to the south and east of their previous destination, on the island of Dominica. From Dominica, the fleet sailed northwest toward Cuba, sighting many of the Lesser Antilles, stretching in a northwesterly chain from Dominica, and also the much larger island of Puerto Rico. Once Columbus had returned to Cuba, he led a small expedition that probed to the south and discovered Jamaica. Columbus's third voyage, in 1497, was devoted to finding the American mainland, although Trinidad was sighted on the way to Venezuela. At the first Caribbean landfall of his fourth and final voyage in 1502, Columbus's ships discovered Martinique.

After Columbus's return to Spain and death in 1506, the rule of Cuba was entrusted to Nicolás Ovando. In 1506 Ovando sent his talented lieutenant Juan Ponce de Léon to search for gold on Puerto Rico (called Borinquen by its original people). In June, Ponce de Léon landed at Añasco Bay on the west coast of the island, but soon the native Arawaks resisted. Here is one of the few canine adjuncts in the saga of European exploration. Becerillo the dog was Ponce de Léon's beloved personal pet, but he was also a major aid to the Spanish conquest. Becerillo's outstanding sense of smell helped him detect the enemy. He was of crucial help to the Spanish in conquering the island—and demonstrated that exploring new places is not just something done by human beings.

LATER EXPEDITIONS. Not all islands were explored in the first wave, and some seem to have never been inhabited even by indigenous peoples. Some of the Lesser Antilles, of little immediate interest to trade- and gold-hungry explorers, were not extensively probed. Barbados was only sighted by Portuguese explorers on their way to Brazil in the early 1500's, and Europeans did not set foot upon it until the English beached there in 1627.

Outlying islands such as Bermuda were also late to be explored. The first European landfall in Bermuda did not occur until 1505, and the island was only permanently settled by the English in the early seventeenth century. Some islands close to the South American coast (Bonaire, Curaçao, and Aruba) were discovered by Alonso de Ojeda in 1499, but they were deemed useless other than as a source of slaves.

Once the Pacific Ocean was discovered by Vasco Nuñez de Balboa in 1513, the Spanish concentrated most of their efforts on exploring that side of the hemispheric landmass as well as exploring and settling the areas to the south. Although the American continent narrowed at the Panama isthmus, there was no point of direct access to the Pacific in the area of the Caribbean latitudes. People could voyage to the Caribbean from the east, but they could not voyage westward from there. The geographic orientation of the modern Caribbean was thus toward Europe, Africa, and North America—not Asia, to which its first European explorers aspired to journey.

Nicholas Birns

NAMING THE ISLANDS

The names first given to the Caribbean islands by Columbus and other early explorers may be confusing to persons used to present-day nomenclature. The Spanish explorers tended either to retain native place names (for example, Cuba) or to name places with religious meanings, such as the names of saints or other religious words (for example, Trinidad, which means "trinity"). Many of the names given to islands by Columbus have changed. The island Columbus named after Saint Martin of Tours is not the present French/Dutch island Saint Martin/Sint Maarten, but the formerly British-ruled Isle of Nevis. San Jorge, just north of Nevis, is now familiar as Saint Kitts. Although an explorer may have given an island a name, time may not always have retained it.

For Further Study

Fritz, Jean. *Around the World in a Hundred Years: From Henry the Navigator to Magellan.* New York: Putnam, 1994.

Knight, Franklin. *The Caribbean.* New York: Oxford University Press, 1990.

Morison, Samuel Eliot. *The European Discovery of America: The Southern Voyages.* New York: Oxford University Press, 1974.

Paiewonsky, Michael. *Conquest of Eden, 1493-1515:* Chicago: Academy Chicago, 1991.

Rogozinski, Jan. *A Brief History of the Caribbean: From the Arawaks and Caribs to the Present.* New York: Facts on File, 1992.

Sauer, Carl Ortwin. *The Early Spanish Main.* Foreword by Anthony Pagden. Berkeley: University of California Press, 1992.

Information on the World Wide Web

Mitchell's West Indian Bibliography is a comprehensive index of English-language books on the Caribbean, many of which deal with the exploration period. (books.ai/index.html)

The Columbus Page, maintained at Millersville University in Pennsylvania, provides access to a sizable database of information on the Italian explorer. (muweb.millersv.edu/~columbus)

A Web site called "The European Voyages of Exploration: The Caribbean" provides general background information on the voyages after Columbus. (www.ucalgary.ca/HIST/tutor/eurvoya/carib.html)

Political Geography

North America

Political boundary map Page 452

Mexico City Page 571

North America primarily comprises Canada, Mexico, and the United States. Canada started as a French possession, New France, centered in what became Quebec and Quebec City. Conflict between Great Britain and France dominated its history in the sixteenth century. The conflict culminated in the Seven Years' War, known in North America as the French and Indian War (1756-1763), when Great Britain took Canada from France. Great Britain then possessed a colony populated almost wholly by non-English subjects, the Queçois or French-Canadians.

Canada. Scots and some Americans dominated the subsequent European settlement of Canada. There also were armed conflicts between Canada and the United States. During the American Revolution and the War of 1812, U.S. forces invaded Canada in unsuccessful attempts to conquer it. Revolts in 1837 pushed Canada toward self-governance, which eventually resulted in the formation of the Canadian Confederation in 1867, with the British monarch as the head of state. Canada developed a parliamentary government with the prime minister as the head of government.

Spanish horsemen storming the citadels of Tenochtitlán. Hernán Cortés's conquest of the Aztec Empire in the early sixteenth century began three centuries of Spanish rule in Mexico. (Library of Congress)

Mexico. Modern Mexico began with Hernán Cortés's conquest (1519-1521) of the Aztec Empire and its capital city, Tenochtitlán, located on the site of modern Mexico City. Mexico developed into a rich Spanish possession with a vast territory that included present-day California, Nevada, Utah, Arizona, New Mexico, Texas, and parts of Colorado and Oklahoma. In 1810 Father Miguel Hidalgo y Costilla issued a manifesto calling for the end of Spanish rule.

In 1846 the Mexican-American War began, in which Mexico lost roughly half its original territory. In 1861 three European powers occupied Mexico and made Austrian archduke Maximilian, a brother of Emperor Franz Joseph of Austria-Hungary, Mexico's titular emperor. The forces of Benito Juárez, president of Mexico and a Zapotec Indian, overthrew Maximilian in 1867. Dictators subsequently ruled Mexico until 1910, when revolution broke out led by individuals such as Pancho Villa and Emiliano Zapata. For much of the twentieth century, the Institutional Revolutionary Party (Partido Revolucionario Institucional—PRI) ruled Mexico.

United States. The United States began as thirteen British colonies that declared independence in 1776. The country underwent great expansion, subsequent wars with Great Britain (1812-1814) and Mexico (1846-1848), and finally a Civil War (1861-1865). The Civil War settled major issues with regard to slavery and federal supremacy. The country expanded further to the Pacific and, with the Spanish-American War in 1898, entered the world stage as a world power. The United States' form of government is a republic with great autonomy for the diverse states, and a central government with elected representatives and a chief executive, the president.

Governmental Structures. Canada has a federal system of government. Federal legislative authority is vested in the Parliament of Canada, which consists of the sovereign of Canada, the Senate, and the House of Commons. Legislative and executive authority is divided between the central government and the provinces, whose powers are similar in scope to those of the fifty U.S. states. The Parliament of Canada is assigned authority over such matters as control of the armed forces, the regulation of trade and commerce, and currency. The Governor-General who represents the Crown is appointed by the reigning monarch of the Commonwealth upon the advice of the Canadian government. In order to form a government, the Governor-General calls upon the leader of the party winning the most seats in Parliament in a general election. That party leader becomes the prime minister and generally chooses to form the cabinet from among party colleagues who have been elected to Parliament.

Mexico is a federal republic comprising thirty-one states and the Federal District, which is similar to the United States' District of Columbia. Governmental powers are divided between executive, legislative, and judicial branches, but in practice, the president has strong control. The PRI was the dominant political party for more than seventy years. The president is popularly elected and can serve only one six-year term. He is empowered to select a cabinet as well as the governor of the Federal District, the attorney general, diplomats, high-ranking military officers, and supreme court justices, who serve life terms. At the state and local level, governors, unicameral (one-house) legislatures, and

Pancho Villa and "Blackjack" Pershing

In the early 1910's the Mexican revolutionary Pancho Villa raided New Mexico. U.S. general John J. "Blackjack" Pershing was ordered to pursue Villa, even if it meant going into Mexico. Although General Pershing never caught Villa, he later became famous as the leader of the American Expeditionary Force that went into combat in France during World War I.

Seat of the U.S. Supreme Court, whose primacy in the federal government was reconfirmed in December, 2000, when the Court's justices resolved legal issues surrounding the deadlocked presidential election. (PhotoDisc)

mayors are elected by popular vote. Governors serve for six years, deputies for three. States can levy taxes and have all powers not delegated to the federal government, but in fact they have relatively little revenue-generating potential or political power. The military has long been an apolitical force in the country, but its high-ranking officers are appointed by the president and serve at his pleasure.

The United States is also a federal republic, comprising fifty states, the District of Columbia, and the territories and possessions of Guam, Puerto Rico, and the U.S. Virgin Islands. Governmental powers are, as in Mexico, divided between the executive, legislative, and judicial branches. The executive and legislative branches are almost equally strong, but the U.S. Supreme Court can have the final say in many matters, especially those of constitutional importance. Even lower federal courts, the U.S. district courts, and the U.S. circuit courts of appeals can make rulings on constitutionality and find the president, for example, in contempt of court and possibly subject to criminal proceedings.

The fifty states are generally autonomous and have considerable law-making and revenue-generating power. Any powers not expressly granted to federal government are reserved to the states. The governors of the states are popularly elected, as are the state legislatures. Almost all state legislatures are bicameral (two-house). The U.S. military is apolitical. The president is commander-in-chief of all U.S. armed forces, but can only appoint or nominate the Joint Chiefs of Staff, who are subject to Senate approval.

ILLEGAL IMMIGRATION. There is illegal immigration from Mexico to the United States and into Mexico from the Caribbean and, in particular, from Central American countries. Illegal immigrants from Central America usually are using Mexico as a route into the United States. Many illegal immigrants are injured or even die in the attempt to enter other countries. For example, in April, 2000, five illegal Central American immigrants died, and forty-eight others were hospitalized after trying to travel to the United States in two sealed train cars packed with two hundred people. The train was intercepted in the southern Mexican Gulf Coast state of Tabasco.

Illegal immigration of Mexicans into the United States is most often tied to Mexico's economy. Even a small downturn in Mexico's economy can result in a significant increase in illegal immigration across the U.S. border. A 10 percent decrease in the Mexican real wage typically leads to at least a 7.5 percent increase in illegal attempts to cross the United States-Mexico border. A devaluation of the Mexican peso leads to a 3 to 8 percent increase in apprehensions at the border the next month.

Internal Instability and Separatism. Both Mexico and Canada have had internal strife into the late twentieth century. In Canada, the problem is a longstanding one. Quebec remains strongly French or French-Canadian. The Québeçois firmly retain their identity, language, and customs. Many strive for an independent Quebec. This has put great strain on the Canadian governmental structure. Many efforts have been made to encourage Quebec to stay in the Canadian Confederation, including placing the French language on an equal footing with English. The loss of Quebec would geographically isolate the Maritime Provinces of New Brunswick, Nova Scotia, Prince Edward Island, and Newfoundland from the rest of Canada.

Mexican society is sharply divided by income and educational level. Although a middle class is developing in the cities, the principal division is between the wealthy, well-educated elite and the urban and rural poor. From the 1940's through the 1970's, Mexico enjoyed sustained economic growth and political stability. At the close of the 1970's, a petroleum boom produced growth rates of 8 to 9 percent. It seemed that Mexico could be headed toward first-world status, but there were serious flaws in the country's development model. Highly inequitable income distribution left 30 to 50 percent of the population mired in poverty, particularly in the countryside.

The Mexican political system concentrated near-dictatorial powers in the hands of a single-term president. A flawed industrialization model that too long ignored export opportunities, protected industries that did not become competitive, and allowed excessive government indebtedness all contributed to an economic collapse and a 25 to 40 percent decline in living standards during the 1980's. In 1994 there was an uprising of Mayan peasants in Chiapas in southern Mexico. While the Zapatista rebels never posed a threat to the regime, they did focus attention on Mexico's economic and political injustices.

Hundreds of immigrants take their U.S. citizenship oaths in a mass ceremony at Sacramento, California. Every year many more foreign nationals apply for entry into the United States than are admitted. (Ben Klaffke)

The United States has had some problems with regard to Puerto Rico—a Spanish-speaking island that was taken from Spain by the United States during the Spanish-American War (1898). Puerto Rico is a commonwealth, which does not have the status of a state. Its citizens are citizens of the United States but cannot vote in presidential elections; however, Puerto Rico does not have a voting representative in Congress, and citizens of Puerto Rico do not pay U.S. income taxes. At times, violence has occurred. In 1950, Puerto Rican nationalists attempted to assassinate President Harry Truman. Another group of nationalists wounded five U.S. congressmen in 1954.

The United States faces an increasing gap between the "haves" and "have-nots." Europeans often note that two societies seem to be evolving in the United States. While the problem has not been as acute as in Mexico, the gap between the two groups is widening. The "have-nots" include large percentages of African Americans, Native Americans, and Hispanics.

NAFTA. The North American Free Trade Agreement (NAFTA) went into effect in January, 1994, and lowered or eliminated tariffs among its three members, Canada, Mexico, and the United States. The United States had a $1.6 billion trade surplus with Mexico in 1993. Between 1992 and 1997, Mexico increased its exports to the United States by 144 percent, running up $50 billion in surpluses from 1995 through 1997. That surge of Mexican exports may have resulted, in part, from the fact that Mexico devalued its peso shortly after NAFTA went into effect. United States exports to Mexico increased 76 percent between 1992 and 1997, but those were primarily components to be assembled in Mexican factories and re-exported north. U.S. exports to Canada increased from 1993 through 1996, but the trade deficit with Canada doubled from 1993 to 1996, to $21.7 billion, because of a surge of imports from Canada.

NAFTA has been criticized in both the United States and Mexico. Americans have complained that little benefit has come to the United States and jobs have been lost to Canada and Mexico. NAFTA did include worker safety rules for Mexican workers, and the Mexican government has fined some companies for violation of these rules. A key complaint, however, is that pay for Mexican workers has not kept pace with inflation. In 1998 the Mexican minimum wage of twenty-five pesos per day had to rise to thirty-one pesos to match pre-1994 buying power. Multinational companies moved factories to Mexico to take advantage of the cheaper labor and access to U.S. markets.

North America and the World. The relations among the three countries were generally good in the year 2000. The border between Canada and the United States is the longest open border in the world. Except for Canada's French-speaking province, Quebec, the two countries are culturally similar in many ways, and many Canadians have become prominent in the entertainment industry and sports in the United States. The border between the United States and Mexico, however, has continued to be a problem. The tide of illegal immigration and drug smuggling has been so great that the United States makes strong efforts to police the border and choke off illegal immigration and drugs. These efforts seem to be largely unsuccessful: The flow of people and drugs continues.

Internationally, all three countries are members in good standing of almost every major international organization. Mexico is a member of the Organization of Petroleum Exporting Countries (OPEC).

Dana P. McDermott

For Further Study

Birdsall, Stephen S., John W. Florin, and Margo L. Price. *Regional Landscapes of the United States and Canada.* 5th ed. New York: John Wiley & Sons, 1999.

Castaneda, Jorge G. *The Mexican Shock: Its Meaning for the United States.* New York: New Press, 1995.

Collier, Christopher, and James Lincoln Collier. *Hispanic America, Texas, and the Mexican War 1835-1850.* New York: Benchmark Books, 1998.

Dunn, Timothy. *The Militarization of the U.S.-Mexico Border, 1978-1992: Low-Intensity Conflict Doctrine Comes Home.* Austin: University of Texas Press, 1996.

Needler, Martin C. *Mexican Politics.* Westport, Conn.: Praeger, 1995.

Smith, David E. *The Invisible Crown: The First Principle of Canadian Government.* Toronto, Canada: University of Toronto Press, 1995.

Information on the World Wide Web

The complete text of the North American Free Trade (NAFTA) agreement can be found at the Web site of *The Tech,* the student paper of the Massachusetts Institute of Technology. (www-tech.mit.edu/Bulletins/nafta.html)

The Caribbean

The Caribbean region contains thirteen independent and mostly tiny nations: Antigua and Barbuda, the Bahamas, Barbados, Cuba, Dominica, Dominican Republic, Grenada, Haiti, Jamaica, St. Kitts and Nevis, St. Lucia, St. Vincent and the Grenadines, and Trinidad and Tobago. There are also thirteen dependencies—territories ruled by other countries. These include Guadeloupe and Martinique (administered by France); Aruba, Curaçao, and Netherlands Antilles (administered by the Netherlands); British Virgin Islands, Cayman Islands, Montserrat, and Turks and Caicos Islands (administered by Great Britain); and Navassa Island and Puerto Rico (administered by the United States).

By 1993 estimates, more than 60 percent of the people living in the Caribbean were of black African or mixed African and European descent. Thirty-five percent are European. Most of these are people of Spanish descent who live in Cuba, the Dominican Republic, and Puerto Rico. The remaining 5 percent are of East Asian descent. Most of them live in Trinidad and Tobago. The peoples of Haiti and the remaining islands are predominantly of African descent.

Languages spoken in the Caribbean vary as much as the cultures. Although English is the region's predominant tongue, the people of Cuba, Haiti, and a few other countries continue to speak the Spanish and French of their early colonizers. In addition, many islanders speak regional dialects that linguists call patois. This term was originally applied to the bastardized French spoken by colonized peoples, but it has come to apply to any local blend of native and imported languages.

Caribbean identity remains a problem. The region and its islands are known by a variety of names. The most common name for the region, the West Indies, was coined by explorer Christopher Columbus, who believed he had discovered islands off the coast of India. In France and Spain, the islands were called the Antilles. Variants on this name have included the Greater Antilles (the large islands of Cuba, Jamaica, Hispaniola, and Puerto Rico in the west of the chain) and the Lesser Antilles (the smaller islands to the east). Some of them are also known as the French Antilles and the Netherlands Antilles.

INDEPENDENCE. The largest and most heavily populated Caribbean islands were the first to shed their European rulers. France's richest Caribbean colony, St. Domingue, occupied the western portion of the island of Hispaniola. It was the world's leading sugar producer during the mid-eighteenth century. However, its wealth came at the expense of exploiting a slave workforce. Brutal conditions provoked a successful slave uprising. Afterward, the island reverted to its original Arawak name, Haiti, when it became the second independent nation (after the United States) in the Western Hemisphere, as well as the world's first black-ruled republic.

Cuban independence came much later, as a result of the Spanish-American War of 1898, when Cuban rebels sided with the United States against Spain. After defeating Spain, U.S. forces occupied the island until 1902, when Cuba became an independent nation.

Nationalism in Britain's West Indian colonies dates back to 1938 labor riots in Jamaica and the eastern Caribbean, which led to the establishment of self-government and voting rights throughout the region during the next two decades. Jamaica became fully independent in 1962, as did Trinidad and Tobago. Barbados followed in 1966. The Bahamas progressed to internal self-rule under the British during the 1960's and then to independence in 1973. By the late 1960's, six more colonies became "associated states" of Great Britain, which meant they were internally self-governing in all matters save defense and foreign affairs. These six colonies became independent shortly thereafter: Grenada (1974), Dominica (1978), St. Lucia (1979), St. Vincent and the Grenadines (1979), Antigua (1981), and St. Kitts and Nevis (1983).

At the end of the twentieth century, five official British dependent territories remained in the Caribbean: Anguilla, the Cayman Islands, the British Virgin islands, Montserrat, and the Turks and Caicos Islands. Bermuda, a small Atlantic Ocean island group north of the Caribbean, also remained a British dependency.

After winning independence, most former Caribbean colonies elected to keep the British monarch their official head of state. In 1998, however, Barbados became the first former British colony in the Caribbean to end its connection with the British monarchy. Jamaica was expected to follow its example. For the remainder of the nations, however, maintaining a connection with the British monarchy has been an important means of remaining culturally distinct from the nearby United States.

OTHER DEPENDENCIES. The Netherlands Antilles and Aruba are internally self-governing states but rely on the Dutch for defense and foreign affairs. In 1986 Aruba withdrew from the Netherlands Antilles to become an autonomous member of the Kingdom of the Netherlands. Both the Netherlands Antilles and Aruba have resisted full independence.

The islands of Guadeloupe and Martinique (known also as the French Antilles) have also chosen assimilation over autonomy. There status is "overseas departments" of France—which means they have the same legal status as France's mainland departments.

The island of Puerto Rico has chosen a different path. A U.S. territory since 1898, when Spain ceded it to the United States after the Spanish-American War, Puerto Rico was officially designated a "commonwealth" in 1952. Residents of Puerto Rico are U.S. citizens; however, they do not pay federal income tax and cannot vote in national elections. In a 1993 referendum, 48.4 percent of Puerto Rican voters opted to retain their commonwealth status. Another 46.2 percent chose statehood, and the remainder voted for complete independence from the United States.

Economic Unity. There have been many attempts to organize the islands of the Caribbean into regional economic and political organizations. The West Indies Federation was, for example, an attempt by Great Britain to unite its ten Caribbean colonies in one political grouping to prepare them for collective independence in 1958, but it lasted only until 1962. In 1968 Antigua, Barbados, Trinidad and Tobago, and the South American nation of Guyana established the Caribbean Free Trade Area (CARIFTA). It was designed to provide a wider market for industrial products. Anguilla, Dominica, Grenada, Jamaica, Montserrat, St. Lucia, St. Kitts and Nevis, and St. Vincent and the Grenadines joined it later that year. In addition, the Caribbean Regional Development Bank was established in 1969 to make loans to encourage industry.

By 1973 Barbados, Guyana, Jamaica, and Trinidad and Tobago had left CARIFTA to form a customs union known as the Caribbean Community and Common Market (CARICOM). This new union provided for internal free trade and common tariff rates on goods produced outside the union. It also worked toward creating more uniform fiscal, monetary, and other economic policies. By 1975 all the original members of CARIFTA had joined CARICOM.

Martinique Page 570

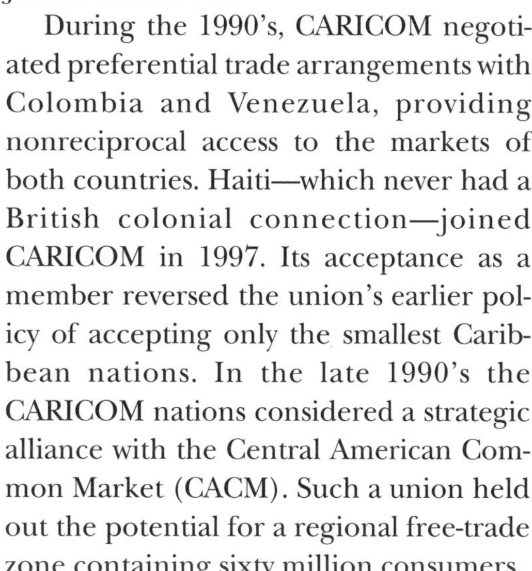

During the 1990's, CARICOM negotiated preferential trade arrangements with Colombia and Venezuela, providing nonreciprocal access to the markets of both countries. Haiti—which never had a British colonial connection—joined CARICOM in 1997. Its acceptance as a member reversed the union's earlier policy of accepting only the smallest Caribbean nations. In the late 1990's the CARICOM nations considered a strategic alliance with the Central American Common Market (CACM). Such a union held out the potential for a regional free-trade zone containing sixty million consumers.

Political Stresses and Strains. Potential regional problems facing the region at the beginning of the twenty-first century included the possible secession of Barbuda from Antigua, ongoing political turmoil in Jamaica, and disputes between Trinidad and Tobago and Venezuela over fishing and oil rights in their overlapping coastal waters. Some factions in Puerto Rico continued to press for U.S. statehood, while others sought complete independence from the United States. Environmental degradation and overpopulation also contribute to the general instability of the Caribbean region.

Cuba and the United States. Perhaps the greatest threat to political stability in the Caribbean region is the ongoing standoff between the United States and Cuba. Since Fidel Castro assumed power in 1959 and established a socialist government, the United States has been uneasy about having a communist nation so close to its shores. The United States severed diplomatic relations with Cuba in 1961. Since then a rigid trade embargo has prevented U.S. companies from doing business with the communist nation.

In 1996 the U.S. Congress passed the Cuban Liberty and Democracy Act (also known as the Helms-Burton Act) to extend and tighten the U.S. embargo against Cuba, with the goal of bringing down the Castro regime. Canada and Mexico immediately prepared counterlegislation as an "antidote" to the measure and considered challenging the U.S. law under provisions of the North American Free Trade Agreement (NAFTA).

Cuba, meanwhile, strengthened its economic ties with other Caribbean islands. Castro began participating in the new Association of Caribbean States (ACS) in 1995. Cuba also began reestablishing formal trade and diplomatic relations with other Caribbean nations.

The United States has officially linked the possibility of its normalizing relations with Cuba to Cuba's establishment of a democratic government. By 1998 the tide appeared to be turning in Cuba's favor. In March of that year U.S. president Bill Clinton relaxed the U.S. trade embargo on Cuba to permit direct charter flights to the island nation, to expedite sales of medical supplies, and to allow Cuban Americans send money to their relatives in Cuba. In 1998 Congress considered two bills that would increase U.S. humanitarian aid to Cuba through religious groups and the Red Cross.

P. S. Ramsey

For Further Study

Anthony, Michael. *Historical Dictionary of Trinidad and Tobago.* Landham, Md.: Scarecrow Press, 1997.

Blouet, Brian W., and Olwyn M. Blouet, eds. *Latin America and the Caribbean: A Systematic and Regional Survey.* 3d ed. New York: John Wiley & Sons, 1997.

Clawson, David L. *Latin America and the Caribbean: Lands and Peoples.* New York: McGraw Hill, 1999.

Sealey, Neil. *Caribbean World: A Complete Geography.* New York: Cambridge University Press, 1992.

South America, Central America, and the Caribbean. London: Europa Publications, 1999.

Suchlicki, Jaime. *Historical Dictionary of Cuba.* Landham, Md.: Scarecrow Press, 2000.

URBANIZATION

NORTH AMERICA

To geographers, urbanization is both a process and a state. The state or extent of urbanization for a region or country at a point in time can be measured by the ratio of city to rural dwellers, by the number of designated "urban areas," or by the proportion of land included in designated urban or metropolitan areas. As a historical process, urbanization is descriptive of the ways in which a society creates high-density population centers that serve multiple needs of the broader community. Urbanization also refers to the ways in which the relationships of cities to rural areas, and of cities to cities, change over time.

In a broader sense, urbanization also can describe the ways in which cities and urban life affect the society and culture of people, changing attitudes, norms, customs, and even language. Urbanization is a matter of interrelationships that develop in complex ways, and numerous factors affect these developments: population changes, technology, economic conditions, and governmental and legal actions. In dealing with a single urban area and its development, one finds that transportation opportunities, communication possibilities, regional economic development patterns, on-site resources (minerals or recreation facilities), and governmental decisions influence success or failure. In examining the process for a region or nation, many of the same factors apply.

Cities map Page 455

EARLY AMERICA. When Europeans first began colonizing North America, only a few of the native inhabitants lived in urbanized cultures. The Mississippian culture centered on Cahokia, several tribes in the Southwest, and the peoples of Mexico's Tenochtitlán had developed population centers of relative sophistication, but the influence these had on their respective regions is unknown. Except for the Tenochtitlán, they did not inspire further urbanization. The Europeans who colonized North America came from societies that were becoming increasingly urbanized, and it was the European pattern of early urban development that would characterize growth in the New World.

European concepts of property rights, the institution of the Christian church, the use of horses and wheeled vehicles, continuing contacts with the mother countries (especially England, Spain, and France), the economic needs or desires of those countries, and a frontier mentality that craved expansion and ignored native claims to land, were dominant factors in the early settling and urbanization of North America.

The most heavily urbanized region was the seaboard from Boston to Philadelphia. With Newport and New York, these four merchant-controlled cities regulated the flow of raw materials to England and the Caribbean, and of manufactured goods into the British colonies. The southern region of the future United States had only Charleston as a major port, and despite the later growth of Savannah and New Orleans, remained relatively underurbanized until after the Civil War. In the Northeast, competition among cities and continuing immigration fueled the growth of new cities as well as the dissatisfactions with England that led to the American Revolution.

While in 1690 an estimated 10 percent of the American population lived in colonial cities, the 1790 census showed an urban population of 5.1 percent. Cities stagnated as trade with England fell off and migration inland increased. New York City, however, soon benefited from special agreements made with transatlantic shippers, and never looked back. By 1840 its population was 250,000, and it was the main port of entry for immigrants from Europe.

The early nineteenth century witnessed the growing population and urbanization of the American interior. Cities required transportation and communication links with other cities, and waterways provided the most efficient channels for both. Canals in Pennsylvania and New York opened up the Great Lakes to the eastern port cities.

Baltimore Page 512

Chicago Pages 454, 507

Excepting Chicago, Indianapolis, and Milwaukee, all the major urban centers of the upper Midwest began between 1790 and 1820. Although initially tied economically and socially to the urban Northeast, these towns of the Ohio Valley and lower Great Lakes soon controlled the rural hinterland around them and created a distinctive frontier culture that played an important role in defining the U.S. identity. These cities, like their eastern elders, were strongly federalist and democratic in outlook and supported national initiatives that aided the urban economies and expansion: national currency, tariffs, and federally supported transportation, especially railroads.

Until the early twentieth century, urbanization meant both the growth of older metropolitan areas and the creation of new ones. The harnessing of steam power revolutionized both processes. In 1840 only 12 U.S. cities had more than ten thousand inhabitants; in 1860, 101 cities had more. Manufacturing that once required river waterpower could locate anywhere, including the cities, where financial and legal resources as well as cheap labor resided. Steamboats made the transatlantic voyage faster and cheaper, and spurred immigration (as did European events such as the Irish potato famine of the later 1840's). Steamboats also enhanced river traffic, as they could defy the current and carry huge loads in both directions.

The development of the railroad had perhaps the widest influence: It increased access to otherwise isolated areas, shortened travel and shipping time, greatly reduced the costs of shipping, brought raw materials to manufacturing sites, created crossroads with river cities like St. Louis and Cincinnati, stimulated the founding and development of cities along its path, and eventually connected the east and west coasts and their cities.

By the 1820's, Baltimore was the United States' third city (after New York and Philadelphia) thanks to the Baltimore and Ohio Railroad. Chicago grew overnight into America's rail center, becoming the terminus for eleven trunk lines. This led to its dominance in meat-packing and other regional manufacturing and service industries. By 1850 U.S. cities were connected by almost nine thousand miles of track, most of which were in the northern states. By 1860 that figure was thirty-one thousand miles; by 1870, fifty-three thousand.

The highly agricultural economy of the U.S. South did not depend on rail transport, and while the Midwest and Northeast were being sewn ever more tightly together, the South remained isolated and underdeveloped. Its lack of urban, industrial, and transportation infrastructure weighed heavily against it during the Civil War. Aggressive capitalization and development followed the war and helped integrate the South into the U.S. mainstream. Atlanta was rebuilt as a major rail hub, and Birmingham created as a center of steel production.

Metropolitan Growth. During the 1840's, the urban proportion of the U.S. population doubled to about 11 percent, and by 1880 had risen to 28 percent. The form as well as the distribution of cities changed. New York City claimed one million inhabitants in 1860, and other eastern cities grew apace as a result of foreign and regional immigration. Cities became more densely populated in part because of the development and spread of tightly

New York City Page 575

Populations of Selected U.S. Cities, 1790-1970

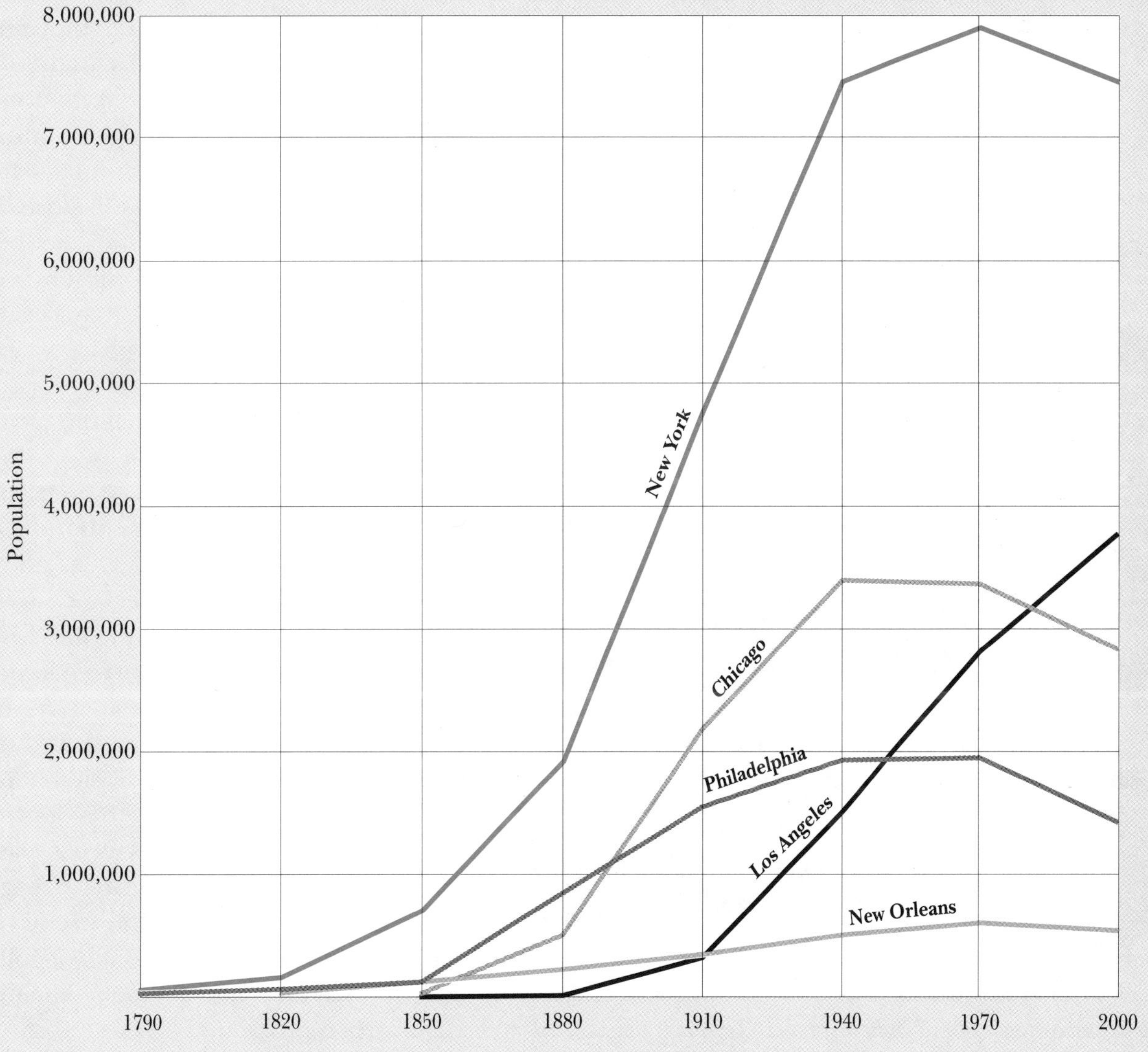

Source: U.S. Census Bureau Statistics.

packed, inexpensive tenements. Elevators and steel-beam construction allowed cities to build upward, further increasing urban densities. Some housing units occupied older, industrial buildings, while specially built "dumbbell" apartments provided cramped but efficient residences. In parts of New York City, densities hit one hundred persons per acre.

Cities also spread out, as both horse-drawn and steam omnibuses carried workers and shoppers into and out of the city along regular routes. These routes connected outlying smaller towns and stimulated growth along them. Central portions of cities grew into "downtowns" or central business districts, with concentrations of manufacturing, services, shopping, and entertainment. People changed residences at increasing rates, in some cities as high as 30 percent per year. In the later nineteenth century, wealthier people occupied the central portions of urban residential space, with the middle classes farther out, and the poor—along with noxious industries—farthest out.

Removal of human and industrial wastes is one of the most difficult problems produced by the concentration of large numbers of people in urban centers. (PhotoDisc)

With high rates of European immigration, ethnic enclaves developed in eastern and, later, midwestern cities. In Greek Towns or Little Italys, customs, traditions, and languages were preserved, and new immigrants found welcoming communities. Along the West Coast, and later further east, Asian communities likewise developed, often in older neighborhoods. In many cities, the pattern of ethnic or racial supplanting is quite clear, with, for example, an Irish neighborhood giving way to Eastern European Jews, then to African Americans who migrated from the South, and, more recently, to Asians.

Such growth and development had their costs. The high concentration of people in small areas meant enormous daily demands for food, water, and sanitation services. Scientific farming meant increased crop yields in the urban hinterland and, combined with rail transport and mechanical refrigeration, served the rising demand efficiently. Provision of potable water often proved more of a problem, but inventive engineers, urban planners, and politicians seemed to manage. Larger-capacity sewers were developed to carry away waste, but air and water pollution, animal dung, and garbage remained major urban problems.

Social problems plagued the growing cities also. Industrialization and new immigrants needing assimilation provoked demand for education. Poverty, transience, and poor housing fostered disease, organized violence, crime, and social pathologies like illiteracy, alcoholism, and child and spousal abuse. Tensions in cities sometimes erupted into ethnic or racial violence, with Catholics giving way to African Americans as targeted victims.

Expansion and Reform. In the West, gold and other mineral strikes drew people to San Francisco, Butte, and Denver; timber and Alaskan gold, to the Pacific Northwest. The railroad connected these coastal centers with the Midwest and East; by 1910, San Francisco and Los Angeles each had more than 250,000 inhabitants, and Denver, Seattle, and Portland more than 200,000 each. Speculators attempted to prompt a land rush to Southern California in the 1880's, but more than a hundred townships remained unoccupied.

The South and Southwest grew slowly, with larger centers like New Orleans and Louisville reliant on connections to the Midwest. In 1910 Atlanta, the major inland southern rail center, had only 154,000 people, and industrial power Birmingham only 132,000. As in the Midwest and still in the East, migration from rural areas was important, but relatively few of the 23.5 million immigrants to America from 1880 to 1920 settled in the South; in 1910, 70 percent of urban Americans still lived in the upper Midwest and Northeast. The South and Southwest both profited mightily from the invention and marketing of air conditioning in the 1930's.

The late nineteenth and early twentieth centuries was the era of urban reform. Both urban political bosses and legitimate urban reformers carried out social and physical improvements that made life more tolerable, and greater attention was given to the physical layout and amenities of cities. From New York with its Central Park to Seattle and its "emerald necklace" of parks, a new breed of land use planners—with grand ideas of The City Beautiful and newly legalized tools for zoning and land use organization—sought to rationalize and aesthetically enhance urban space. Metropolitan comprehensive planning emerged, continuously clashing with property rights and the realities of capitalist land use economics. Later in the century, however, it evolved into regional planning efforts and federally based programming efforts that affected every U.S. city.

Seattle Page 581

San Francisco Pages 446, 508

Los Angeles Page 453

Denver Page 518

Approaching Modernity. In the early twentieth century, the automobile encouraged the spread outward from urban cores, and created the need for complex circulation systems. This freed development from urban transit lines and fostered the further annexation of surrounding towns. City center and periphery became more closely tied, but the spatial separation of disparate population groups became ever greater. Black migration from the South into northern cities peaked between 1910 and 1930, at the same time that foreign immigration dropped off. Territoriality and nativist and racist sentiments flared—sometimes violently—in cities in the 1920's, ensuring that African Americans would be ghettoized for decades to come.

During the Great Depression of the 1930's, rural-to-urban migration decreased, and the era of federal aid to cities began. The federal government's New Deal urban policies revolved around aiding the unemployed, and thousands of federally funded works projects repaired or enhanced the fabric of U.S. cities. Slum clearance and public housing projects eliminated some of the blight, and experimental planned communities for low-income families—like Greenbelt, Maryland (1937)—foreshadowed later, more extensive federal efforts.

The Tennessee Valley Authority and rural electrification movements put many rural people in touch with urban values and culture, especially through the radio, and later, television. Like no other inventions, those devices homogenized U.S. culture around broadcasts that originated in huge cities and reflected their origins. Federal money also funded extensive road, bridge, and cloverleaf construction, which more tightly connected U.S. cities and opened the hinterland. In the 1950's, President Dwight D. Eisenhower's national system of federal freeways continued this trend and created the largest construction project in human history.

POSTWAR DEVELOPMENTS. World War II increased migration to U.S. cities, and federal aid to returning veterans helped millions buy their own homes. Tract housing projects developed on the fringes of large cities and were linked to them with fine roadways. New manufacturing and industries relocated to the suburbs, where land was relatively inexpensive and a younger, eager, increasingly well-educated population was concentrating. Efficient air travel and federal aid to airports revolutionized the movement of people and goods as railroads had done earlier. Inner cities stagnated and declined, while aesthetic and recreational considerations began to dictate the locations of people and businesses.

The flight of affluent whites from central cities, urban pollution, and inner-city problems of poverty, unemployment, poor housing, and failed urban renewal efforts plagued major cities by the 1960's. Many cities exploded in violent riots by urban African Americans in the 1960's. The Democratic administration responded to these problems with its Great Society programs. President Lyndon B. Johnson's War on Poverty sought to alleviate the economic roots of urban problems, and comprehensive and regional planning were revived to coordinate the federal efforts. These measures neither succeeded, nor were they eliminated. President Richard Nixon's failed attempts to create a population flow toward rural areas reflected Republican principles, as did President Ronald Reagan's emphasis on revenue sharing and New Federalism, a turning away from federal control.

Late twentieth century efforts to create transportation efficiencies resulted in more complex road systems but few successful mass transit programs. These have connected cities within regions into megalopolises, such as the "Bos-Wash" corridor (Boston to Washington, D.C.), or Southern California between Los Angeles and San Diego. Efforts at cleansing polluted urban water and air have had positive results. Many inner cities have undergone restoration or revival, both physical and economic, and neighborhoods once abandoned by the middle classes have been gentrified by wealthier people seeking easier access to downtown. Energetic African Americans, Hispanics, and Asian immigrants have revitalized hundreds of neighborhoods, and federal efforts in the 1980's and 1990's generally have sought to subsidize private enterprise rather than supplant it. Finally, the computer revolution points the way to further economic and physical decentralization, especially in the service sector.

CANADA. Like the United States, both Canada and Mexico were settled by Europeans with a tradition of town life. Canada's major cities began as French fur-trading posts along rivers in the southern part of present-day Canada. They grew as defensive positions against an aggressive early nineteenth century United States, and as further resources (timber, wheat farming) were developed. By the 1920's, more than half the population was still rural, and no city exceeded one million inhabitants.

In 2000 most of Canada's population and population centers were located in a 745-mile-long (1,200 km.) corridor—known as Main Street—stretching from Windsor, Ontario, to Montreal, within 200 miles (320 km.) of the U.S. border. Toronto, and to a lesser degree Montreal, dominate the region and, with Vancouver to the west, contain nearly 30 percent of the Canadian population of 31 million (1999 estimate).

Urbanization of the population occurred rapidly in the last half of the twentieth century, largely as a result of mechanized and scientific farming, immigration, industrialization, and the growth of the service sector of the urban economy. By the late twentieth century, more than 75 percent of Canadians lived in cities. Efficient mass transit systems rather than extensive roadways distinguish Canadian from U.S. cities, but sprawling suburbs, malls, and vertical downtown development parallel U.S. patterns of development.

Toronto

Ontario's provincial capital and Canada's largest city was founded as York in 1795, on the site of several forts on Lake Ontario. Pillaged by Americans in 1813, it burned in 1849 but later served as Canada's capital (1849-1851, 1854-1859). Its excellent harbor and central position along the U.S. border made it a natural hub for railroad development in the 1850's. Toronto grew from nine thousand people in 1834 to forty-five thousand in 1861. Immigration from Ireland was important in the 1840's and 1850's, and worldwide immigration has made Toronto one of the world's most cosmopolitan cities at the end of the twentieth century. By 1901 Toronto had doubled its physical size by annexation and boasted a population of 208,000. Twenty years later, both its population and size had more than doubled again. In 1954 a regional Metropolitan Council was established to coordinate planning, as it became one of North America's fastest-growing urban areas.

Toronto
Page 507

Mexico. The Spanish ruled Mexico from small cities and towns, but urbanization is a recent phenomenon. Mexico's population rose from 35 million in 1960 to more than 100 million in the late 1990's. Natural growth, along with migration from the countryside, accounts for the urban explosion. In 1990 73 percent of the population lived in cities, and 32 percent in only fourteen urban areas of over half a million. Guadalajara has 4.5 million

Mexico City
Page 448

Mexico City

The Aztec city of Tenochtitlán amazed the Spanish conquistadores, who destroyed it in 1521. Threaded with canals and efficient sanitation systems, it surpassed both Paris and London in population. Spaniards made the site the capital of New Spain, and it later became the capital of Mexico. The city is located at an elevation of 7,800 feet (2,380 meters) on a lake island in the long Valley of Mexico. Its depletion of underground water is causing it to sink, and its placement on a geological fault line results in major earthquakes, such as the 1985 earthquake that killed 10,000 people. One of every five Mexicans lives in the huge metropolitan area. It was the largest city in the world in 1998, and it suffers from tremendous traffic congestion and pollution, which becomes trapped by temperature inversions. A subway began operation in 1969, and automobiles have been banned from parts of the central city since 1991.

inhabitants; Monterrey, 3 million. In 1992, half of Mexico's fifteen million housing units lacked piped water or flush toilets, despite government efforts that reach back to 1938. All of Mexico's major cities suffer from congestion, poverty, and pollution. Largely uncontrolled suburban sprawl and annexation of surrounding towns characterize physical growth.

Joseph P. Byrne

For Further Study

Chudacoff, H. P., and J. E. Smith. *The Evolution of Urban American Society.* Englewood Cliffs, N.J.: Prentice Hall, 1994.

Davis, Diane E. *Urban Leviathan: Mexico City in the Twentieth Century.* Philadelphia: Temple University Press, 1994.

Findlay, John M. *Magic Lands.* Berkeley: University of California Press, 1992.

Kleinberg, Benjamin. *Urban America in Transformation.* Thousand Oaks, Calif.: Sage Publications, 1995.

Larsen, Lawrence. *The Urban South: A History.* Lexington: University Press of Kentucky, 1990.

Mohl, Raymond A., ed. *The Making of Urban America.* Wilmington: Scholarly Resources, 1997.

Roberts, Gerylynn, ed. *The American Cities and Technology Reader.* New York: Routledge, 1999.

Stelter, G. A. *Shaping the Urban Landscape.* Ottawa: Carlton University Press, 1982.

Teaford, Jon C. *Cities of the Heartland.* Bloomington: Indiana University Press, 1993.

Ward, David. *Cities and Immigrants.* New York: Oxford University Press, 1971.

The Caribbean

At the end of the twentieth century, more than half of the people of the Caribbean region were living in cities—a rate of urbanization exceeding that of the world as a whole. The largest cities of the region are the capitals of the Caribbean's biggest countries: Santo Domingo in the Dominican Republic, Havana in Cuba, Port au Prince in Haiti, and San Juan in Puerto Rico.

Sixty-five percent of the people of Cuba, Puerto Rico, and the Dominican Republic are classified as urban residents. Havana, San Juan, Santo Domingo, and even Port au Prince, the capital of the region's poorest country, Haiti, have populations greater than one million. Social scientists link this increasing urbanization phenomenon to the processes of economic change experienced by the region. It is in great part the product of migration of the rural population to urban centers, particularly to capital cities. People move to large cities expecting to find better social services, increased job opportunities, higher incomes, better education, and other amenities.

Mechanization of agriculture also has contributed to encouraging people to leave the countryside for the cities. New technologies and advanced farming equipment have reduced the demand for agricultural workers. However, the decline in the number of rural residents has caused economic problems in islands where agriculture remains among the most important economic activities. Overall, the rural-to-urban migration has caused labor shortages in the countryside and contributed to an increase in the unemployment rates of the city. Shifting land use from crop production to less-intensive grazing is among the results of the lack of rural labor.

Some Caribbean cities are not prepared to absorb large groups of immigrants. They lack the infrastructure and support agencies necessary to deal with this influx. The contradiction is that most of these nations have designed development programs that favor cities and neglect the countryside. A major problem associated with massive rural-to-urban migration is the emergence of shantytowns. These squalid areas are part of the landscape in cities where government cannot meet the demands of uncontrolled urban growth.

Providing housing for fast-growing urban populations is challenging for Caribbean nations, which are among the poorest in the Western Hemisphere. The housing units that abound in West Indian shantytowns are usually built of cardboard, scraps of wood, and some types of light metals. In more prosperous areas, structures are adapted according to local environmental conditions, and buildings are able to withstand the high winds of tropical storms. For example, apartment complexes in Havana and San Juan are made of concrete and cement. The homes of the Haitian, Dominican, and Puerto Rican middle and elite classes are built with these materials too. In addition, shopping centers can be seen in some suburban communities of the most prosperous Caribbean countries, accentuating in many ways the contrasts within these cities.

Jose Javier Lopez

For Further Study

Blouet, Brian W., and Olwyn M. Blouet, eds. *Latin America and the Caribbean: A Systematic and Regional Survey.* 3d ed. New York: John Wiley & Sons, 1997.

Clawson, David L. *Latin America and the Caribbean: Lands and Peoples.* New York: McGraw Hill, 1999.

Sealey, Neil. *Caribbean World: A Complete Geography.* New York: Cambridge University Press, 1992.

West, Robert C., and John P. Augelli. *Middle America: Its Lands and Peoples.* Englewood Cliffs, N.J.: Prentice Hall, 1989.

Economic Geography

AGRICULTURE

NORTH AMERICA

"Agriculture" originally meant simply the cultivation of fields. In modern usage, however, the word has been generalized to mean the entire process of producing food and fiber by the raising of domesticated plants and animals. In addition, a discussion of modern agriculture in North America cannot be complete without some attention to agribusiness, the system of businesses associated with and supporting agricultural production in an industrialized society.

In North America, agriculture generally has become mechanized and heavily dependent upon an integrated system of supporting agribusinesses, although traditional practices continue in Mexico. In the United States and Canada, most farmers and ranchers depend heavily upon technology, although groups such as the Amish have rejected automation and continue to use animal power for traction. Most farmers practice monoculture, relying upon a single crop for their primary income, and have expanded to very large acreages in order to take advantage of economies of scale. Such farms generally are referred to in terms of the primary crop, for example, a dairy farm, a cattle ranch, or a wheat farm. Some small farms are run by part-time farmers who also have jobs in town.

Agriculture map Page 456

THE FARM CRISIS OF THE 1980'S

In the early 1980's thousands of farmers across the United States were going bankrupt, as were many agribusiness companies that had supported them. Many people decried the death of the U.S. family farm. In response, the American public rallied with such fundraising activities as the Farm Aid concerts, the first of which was held at Memorial Stadium at the University of Illinois at Urbana-Champaign in 1985.

Ironically, the success of U.S. agriculture created the crisis. Because of the efficiency of mechanized farming techniques, massive food surpluses drove prices below the point at which farmers could break even on operating expenses. To make an adequate profit, farmers had to expand their operations to increasingly larger scales. However, because arable land is a limited resource, not all farmers could expand their operations, and many of those who could not were forced out of business. There was grave concern about the possible corporate takeover of U.S. farming, but at the close of the twentieth century, most farms still were owned and operated by individual families, although family farms tended to be far larger than they previously had been.

Wheat harvesting in the state of Washington. (Digital Stock)

Within the United States, there were 2,192,000 farms, cultivating a total of 954,000,000 acres, in the 1990's. These farms produced net returns of $44.1 billion. Although farmers represented less than 2 percent of the U.S. population, they successfully fed the country at a high standard of living, produced grain and other products for export, and still maintained a surplus carryover of as much as 2 percent of the total grown.

Regional Patterns of Cultivation. Modern farming techniques in the United States and Canada require specialization in a single cash crop. Such specialized farms tend to cluster by region, where the climate is appropriate to a given crop. Such factors as average temperature and rainfall, soil quality, and the likelihood of frost determine what crops can be grown successfully in a given region. The supporting agribusinesses—such as implement suppliers, sellers of chemical fertilizers and pesticides, and grain elevators, tend to specialize in the products and activities that support the primary crops of their given area.

Corn
Page 505

Wheat, the most important cereal grain in Western diets, grows in the broad, open lands of the Great Plains, in Kansas, Nebraska, North and South Dakota, and the Canadian provinces of Alberta and Saskatchewan. In the southern part of this region, the primary crop is winter wheat, which is planted in the fall, is dormant during the winter, completes its growth in spring, and is harvested in midsummer. In many of these areas, a farmer then can plant a crop of soybeans, a practice known as double-cropping. The soybeans often can be harvested in time to plant the following year's wheat crop in the fall. Farther to the north, where the weather is too harsh for wheat to survive the winter, farmers plant spring wheat, which completes its entire growth during the spring and summer and is harvested in the fall. Wheat is used to make bread, pasta, and many breakfast cereals, and is an ingredient in numerous other products.

Corn (maize), which originally was domesticated by Native Americans and not known to the rest of the world until after Christopher Columbus's explorations, is the best producer per acre. It requires a longer growing season than wheat, so the area where it can be grown economically is limited. The midwestern states—Iowa, Illinois, Indiana, Ohio—are the principal areas for cultivation of corn and frequently are referred to as the Corn Belt states. Much corn is used as livestock feed, although a considerable amount is processed into human foods as well, often in the form of cornstarch and corn-syrup sweeteners.

Continued on page 521

Tree farm. Concerns about environmental damage done by clear-cutting of virgin forests encouraged many companies to reseed the cut areas with suitable tree species that could be harvested thirty or forty years later. Another form of tree farming, although on a smaller scale, is the production of small evergreens for Christmas trees. (PhotoDisc)

Iowa corn field. (PhotoDisc)

Sugarcane harvest on Trinidad. (Clyde L. Rasmussen)

Rice harvesting in Trinidad. (Clyde L. Rasmussen)

Skyline of modern Chicago, whose early industrial growth was due to the westward expansion of the railroad system, the emergence of catalog retailers, and the city's location on Lake Michigan. (Corbis)

Located on the northern shore of Lake Ontario, Toronto grew rapidly as the building of canals and locks improved travel among the Great Lakes. It eventually became the largest city in Canada. (Corbis)

Opened in 1937, San Francisco's Golden Gate Bridge was long ranked as the world's longest suspension bridge. The building in the foreground is a fort built in the mid-nineteenth century by the federal government to protect the entrance to San Francisco Bay; it is now a national historic site. (Corbis)

Locks on the Mississippi River. The series of locks and dams built by the Army Corps of Engineers on the Mississippi River is the most significant of the Corps's projects. Built in the 1920's and 1930's, this dam system, which also spans the Illinois River, enables barge traffic to move along the rivers. Without the twenty-nine dams located between St. Louis and St. Paul, the river would not be navigable. (PhotoDisc)

Welland Ship Canal, originally known as Welland Canal, was opened in 1829 to connect Lake Erie and Lake Ontario in Canada's Ontario Province. (PhotoDisc)

The most accomplished builders of pre-Columbian North America were the Maya of Mexico and Central America, who built this massive pyramidal temple at Chichén Itzá in the Yucatán Peninsula. (Corbis)

The economic development of North America's vast inland regions was fostered, to a great extent, by the cheap transportation of commodities on inland riverways. (PhotoDisc)

Acapulco, a historic port on Mexico's Pacific coast, became a popular resort town after a highway connected it to Mexico City during the 1950's. In addition to providing attractive sandy beaches, Acapulco offered the spectacle of death-defying cliff divers, who plunged into the surf from heights of sixty feet. (Corbis)

Alaska's largest city is Anchorage, a port on the state's south coast, below the Chugach Mountains. Nearly 40 percent of Alaska's residents live in Anchorage. (PhotoDisc)

Baltimore, the largest city in Maryland. (PhotoDisc)

Canada's oldest national park, Banff National Park in Alberta was founded in 1885; it is famous for its mountain and glacier scenery and its abundant wildlife. (PhotoDisc)

Cabo San Lucas. Rock formations carved by water erosion. (Corbis)

Calgary is the second-largest city in Alberta, Canada. Built on the Bow River in the southern part of the province, it owes much of its development to the local oil industry. (Corbis)

California's Highway 1, along the middle of the state's long Pacific Ocean coastline. (PhotoDisc)

Satellite view of the Gulf of California, looking approximately toward the southeast, across Southern California. Baja California is at the upper right. (Corbis)

Space shuttle launch at Cape Canaveral. Located at the middle of Florida's Atlantic Ocean coast, Canaveral has been the main launching site for the U.S. space program since the 1950's. (PhotoDisc)

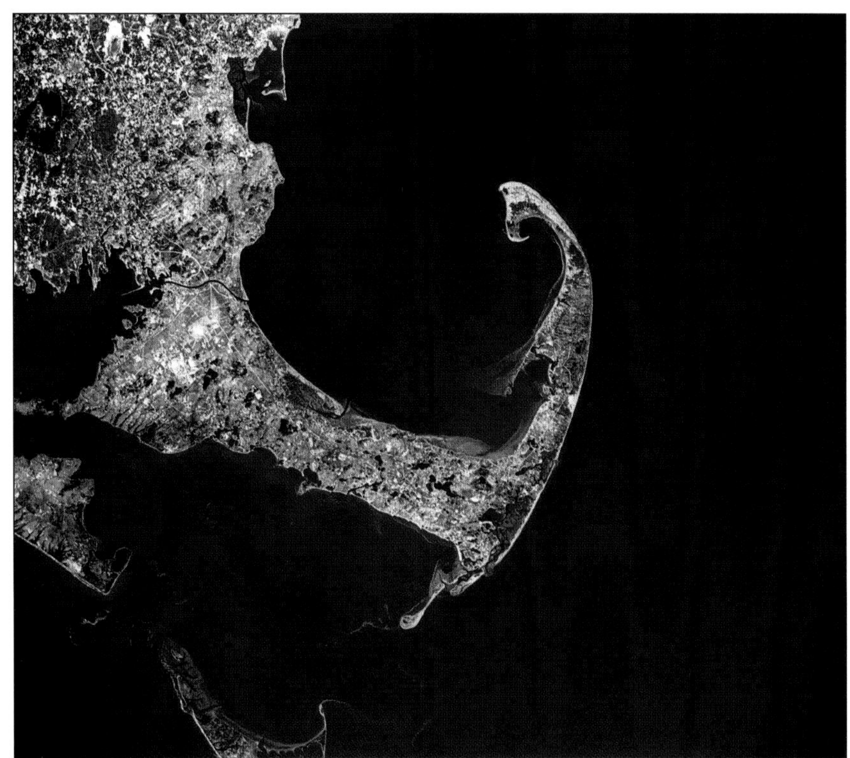

Massachusetts's Cape Cod, a long sandy peninsula that encloses a bay of the same name south of Boston, is the most famous example of a spit and hook in the United States. This picture was taken from the space shuttle Atlantis *in early 1990.* (Corbis)

Rising to an elevation of 14,162 feet (4,317 meters), Northern California's Mount Shasta is one of many extinct volcanoes in the Cascade Range. (Digital Stock)

The Colorado River flows through the Grand Canyon, which it helped to carve. (PhotoDisc)

California's Death Valley is arid because mountains block moisture from reaching it from the sea. The combination of mountain barriers and low elevations makes Death Valley the hottest, driest desert in North America. (Corbis)

Denver, the capital and largest city of Colorado, is nearly a mile above sea level—a fact celebrated in the naming of a major city sport facility Mile-High Stadium. (PhotoDisc)

Florida's peninsula, viewed from space. The large dark spot is Lake Okeechobee. (PhotoDisc)

The Grand Canyon covers nearly two thousand square miles (5,000 sq. km.) in northwestern Arizona. It was made a national monument in 1908 and a national park in 1918. (Corbis)

Houston, Texas's largest city and the center of its commerce. (PhotoDisc)

Los Angeles's Hollywood district is synonymous with the motion picture industry; however, little actual film production work is done within Hollywood itself. Hollywood is part of the city of Los Angeles, but a movement to separate the district from Los Angeles arose at the end of the 1990's. (PhotoDisc)

Rice requires flooded fields for successful cultivation, so it can be grown only in areas such as Louisiana, where large amounts of water are readily available. Because labor costs are the primary limiter in U.S. agriculture, American rice growers use highly mechanized single-field growing techniques rather than the labor-intensive transplantation technique used in Asian countries, where labor is cheap and land is at a premium. Laser levels and computerized controls tied into the Global Positioning System enable farmers to prepare perfectly smooth fields with the slight slope necessary for efficient flooding and drainage. Because the ground is usually wet during tilling and harvesting, the machinery typically used in growing rice is fitted with tracks instead of wheels to reduce soil compaction.

Rye, oats, and barley are other major grain crops, although none form the backbone of an area's economy to the extent that wheat, corn, and rice do. Oats, once a staple feed grain for horses, now is used mainly for breakfast cereals, while most barley is malted for the brewing of beer. Rye typically is used in the production of specialty breads.

Legumes such as soybeans and alfalfa form the next major group of crops produced in North America. In addition to being an important source of protein in human and livestock diets, legumes are important in maintaining soil fertility. Nodules on their roots contain bacteria that help to transform nitrogen in the soil into compounds that plants can use. Because of this, soybeans have also become a regular rotation crop with corn in much of the U.S. Midwest.

Both corn and soybeans can be grown with the same machinery and sold to the same markets, although harvesting corn requires a specialized corn-header that pulls down the stalks and breaks loose the cob on which the corn kernels grow, rather than the generalized grain platform used with soybeans and small grains. Soybeans for human consumption generally are heavily processed and become filler in other foods, although there is a market for tofu (bean curd) and other soybean products for Asian cuisines.

Other crops include edible oil seeds, such as sunflower seeds and safflower seeds, which are generally grown as rotation crops with corn or wheat. Sugarcane is grown in Louisiana and other areas on the coast of the Gulf of Mexico that have the necessary subtropical climate. Many varieties of fruits and vegetables are grown in California's irrigated valleys; Florida grows much of the nation's juice oranges. Other citrus crops are grown in Alabama, Mississippi, and Texas, where these warmth-loving trees will not be damaged by frost. Fruits such as apples and pears, which require a cold period to break dor-

Vineyards in the Sonoma Valley of California, the most productive wine-producing state in the United States. (AP/Wide World Photos)

mancy and set fruit, are grown in northern states such as Michigan and Washington and the eastern provinces of Canada.

Livestock. Several species of animals are raised for their meat and other products in North America. Dairy cattle, which need to be milked twice daily, generally are raised in hilly areas that are not suitable for growing row crops but produce sufficient grazing yield per acre to support the small spreads that dairying requires. Much of Wisconson's agricultural income comes from dairy cattle. In the open country of Texas, by contrast, there is low rainfall and each animal must graze over a large area. This region is suitable for the production of beef cattle, which can range freely with little human intervention until they are of marketable size. Further west, where the grass cover becomes too scant to support cattle, sheep find satisfactory grazing. However, there have often been intense conflicts between sheep and cattle ranchers over marginal areas.

Because hogs require a concentrated diet for commercial production, they generally are raised in confinement buildings in areas that produce the foodstuffs of their primary diet. Large hog operations are common in the Corn Belt area of the Midwest, where farmers can feed hogs corn from their own operations. Similarly, fowl such as chickens and turkeys generally are raised in factory-style battery cages or confinement pens. Chickens are raised for both their eggs and their meat; turkeys traditionally have been holiday fare, but have now become more commonly used throughout the year.

Tree farm
Page 505

Aquaculture. Although most fish and other seafood have been caught in the wild, there has been some interest in the United States and Canada in aquaculture—the raising of aquatic organisms in controlled environments to be harvested commercially. In areas where rice is

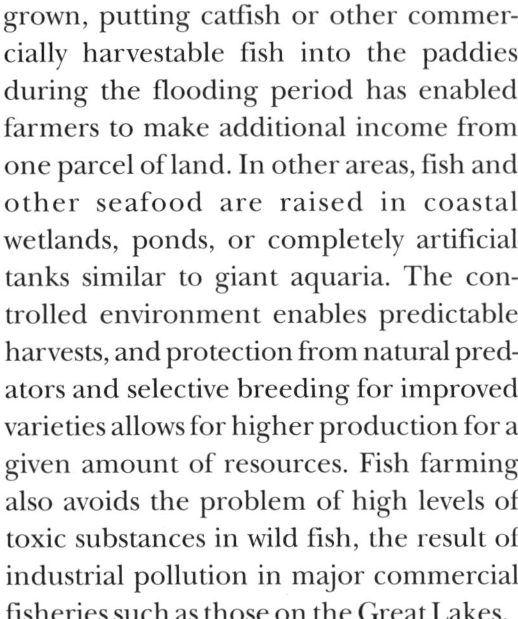

grown, putting catfish or other commercially harvestable fish into the paddies during the flooding period has enabled farmers to make additional income from one parcel of land. In other areas, fish and other seafood are raised in coastal wetlands, ponds, or completely artificial tanks similar to giant aquaria. The controlled environment enables predictable harvests, and protection from natural predators and selective breeding for improved varieties allows for higher production for a given amount of resources. Fish farming also avoids the problem of high levels of toxic substances in wild fish, the result of industrial pollution in major commercial fisheries such as those on the Great Lakes.

Fibrous Plants. In addition to food plants, the production of fibers for garments and other textiles has remained an important part of American agriculture, although such artificial fibers as nylon and polyester have taken a share of the market. Sheep produce wool as well as lamb and mutton. Cotton and flax also are important sources of natural fibers. Cotton requires a long growing season and relatively high rainfall levels; therefore, it generally is grown in an area in the southern United States often referred to as the Cotton Belt. Flax has a shorter growing season and is often planted in rotation with such small grains as wheat and oats. Flax stems are used to produce linen, and edible oils and meal are obtained from its seeds.

Trees have become a cultivated species, although their long growth cycle has limited the ability of humans to create particular varieties. During the twentieth century, concerns about the environmental damage done by the clear-cutting of virgin forests for lumber and paper encouraged many companies to reseed the cut areas with suitable tree species that could be harvested thirty or forty years later. Another form of tree farming, although on a

Land Grant Colleges

In traditional cultures, farming was taught through practical experience. However, as scientific and technological developments evolved, there was a need to apply modern techniques systematically to agriculture. In 1862 a federal law was passed establishing agricultural colleges in each state. Because the colleges would be funded by the sale of public lands, they were called "land grant colleges." Although land grant colleges were originally founded to research and to teach agriculture and agricultural engineering, many of them soon diversified. Some, such as the University of Illinois at Urbana-Champaign, became leading general universities with world-class colleges of engineering, liberal arts, and fine arts.

In addition to teaching new agricultural techniques in the classroom, the land grant colleges founded research stations to study practical aspects of farming. These university farms applied the scientific method of investigation to develop new methods, hybrids, and so on. The Morrow Plots at the University of Illinois at Urbana-Champaign are the oldest continually operated test plots in the United States, and they are of such historical importance that the undergraduate library was built underground to avoid shading them.

Land grant colleges also were mandated to teach their new methods to farmers. The Cooperative Extension Service established offices in individual counties, where local extension agents were accessible to farmers. County agents brought in speakers and other educational presentations from the parent university to educate farmers about new developments in agricultural technique. Home advisors educated farm women about more effective household techniques to improve the standard of living on American farms. To educate young people, the 4-H organization was created, emphasizing character development and practical learning with an attitude of constant improvement.

much smaller scale, is the production of small evergreens for Christmas trees.

The Business of Farming. Because of the intense specialization of modern mechanized agriculture, farming has become a business interlocked with a number of supporting businesses. Farmers have had to become entrepreneurs and look at their activities as businesses rather than as traditional occupations. Farm management—the control of capital outlay, production costs, and income—has become as vital to a farmer's economic survival as skill in growing the crops themselves. Such organizations as Farm Business/Farm Management help farmers develop the skills and thought processes needed to farm more productively and economically.

Farmers also have had to become actively involved in the marketing of their crops to ensure an adequate income. In many areas of the United States and Canada, farmers have banded together in cooperatives to gain economic leverage in buying supplies and selling their products. Some of these cooperatives have taken on some of the preliminary and intermediate steps in transforming the raw farm products into useful goods for consumers, thus increasing the prices farmers receive from buyers.

Modern farmers also are concerned with the management of the resources that support agriculture. In earlier generations, it often was assumed that natural resources were unlimited and could be used and abused without consequence. The result of this ignorance was ecological destruction such as the Dust Bowl of the 1930's, in which the topsoil over large areas of Kansas, Oklahoma, and other states dried up and blew away in the wind, ren-

The Dust Bowl conditions of the 1930's drove many midwestern farmers from their homes and gave rise to the economic and social upheavals described in John Steinbeck's novel The Grapes of Wrath *(1939).* (National Archives)

dering the land unfarmable. To prevent more such disasters and the economic dislocation they produced, various soil conservation measures were introduced through government programs that gave farmers financial aid and incentives to change their practices. The use of contour plowing and terracing on steeply sloping hillsides helped to slow the movement of water that could carry away soil, thus preventing the formation of gulleys. Reduced tillage techniques allowed more plant residue to remain on the surface of the soil, protecting it from the ravages of both wind and water.

Leigh Husband Kimmel

For Further Study

Bonnano, Alessandro. *From Columbus to Conagra: The Globalization of Agriculture and Food.* Lawrence: University Press of Kansas, 1994.

Danborn, David B. *Born in the Country: A History of Rural America.* Baltimore: Johns Hopkins University Press, 1995.

Drake, Jane, and Ann Love. *Farming.* America at Work Series. Toronto: Kids Can Press, 1998.

Ewing, Sherm, and Daniel Greer, eds. *The Ranch: A Modern History of the North American Cattle Industry.* Missoula, Mont.: Mountain Press, 1995.

Information on the World Wide Web

A good site for detailed North American agricultural information is that of the United Nations' Food and Agriculture Organization (FAO), which features a searchable database organized by individual country. (www.fao.org)

Fussell, Betty Harper. *Story of Corn.* New York: Alfred A. Knopf, 1992.

Goreham, Gary, et al, eds. *Encyclopedia of Rural America.* Santa Barbara, Calif.: ABC-Clio, 1997.

Hassanien, Neva. *Changing the Way America Farms: Knowledge and Community in the Sustainable Agriculture Movement.* Omaha: University of Nebraska Press, 1999.

The Caribbean

Agriculture has long been the chief source of livelihood in the Caribbean region. At the end of the twentieth century, it was basic to the economies of nearly every island. Two fundamentally different types of agriculture dominated: large-scale commercial, or plantation, agriculture and small-scale semisubsistence, or peasant, farming. Plantation farming provides most exports, by value, whereas peasant farming involves far more human labor.

Caribbean agriculture operates under various natural and cultural restraints. First, most of the islands have rugged terrain, restricting productive agriculture to river valleys and coastal plains. Typically, less than one-third of islands is suitable for crops. Second, the windward (northerly) portions of islands are commonly very wet, whereas their leeward (southerly) areas suffer seasonal or yearlong drought, necessitating irrigation. Third, various hazards affect agriculture, including the damaging winds of hurricanes, flooding, accelerated erosion, and landslides. In addition, some crops (notably bananas) have suffered from diseases. On the human side, most peasant farms are restricted to steep, unproductive slopes, while plantations control most of the productive lowland soils. Population pressures have led to the loss of some of the best lands, and have caused fragmentation of farmland. Farm labor shortages, climbing wages, and foreign competition have added to the burden.

Commercial Agriculture. Modern commercial plantations, born out of the colonial plantations, differ mainly in that they use hired, often part-time, labor rather than slaves. Otherwise, the plantation system has changed relatively little. Modern plantations own large tracts of land and still specialize in one crop, most commonly sugarcane, bananas, coconuts, coffee, rice, or tobacco. They use paid, often seasonal, labor. They are more mechanized and better managed than colonial plantations, although still largely owned by parties from foreign countries, including Great Britain, France, and the United States.

Sugarcane Page 506

The largest plantations are found on the largest islands, especially Hispaniola, Jamaica, and Puerto Rico. Cuba also has large-scale farming, but the operations are government-owned. Plantations always have been smaller in the Lesser Antilles, where relatively little suitable land is available.

Sugar still dominates the export economies of Cuba, the Dominican Republic, Guadeloupe, and St. Kitts. Among traditional sugar producers in the Caribbean, notably Jamaica, Puerto Rico, Trinidad, and Barbados, sugar exports are exceeded by those of other commodities. Haiti, a leading sugar producer when a French colony, now produces little. Some islands, including the Dutch Antilles, Bahamas, British Virgin Islands, Barbuda, Nevis, Anguilla, and Montserrat, have never had significant commercial sugar plantations because they lack suitable land. Overall, sugar production in the Caribbean has been on the decline since the 1960's, as a result of the variety of problems noted above.

Other commercial export crops grown in the Caribbean region include bananas, coffee, tobacco, and ganja. Bananas, introduced in the sixteenth century by Spanish missionaries, became an important export in the late nineteenth century as markets developed in Europe and America. Sweet bananas are significant exports of Guadeloupe, Martinique, Dominican Republic, Jamaica, Granada, St. Lucia, and St. Vincent. Overall production is not significant on the world scale. Coffee is raised for export mainly in Haiti, Jamaica, and the Dominican Republic. Jamaica's famous Blue Mountain coffee, grown in the Blue Mountains northeast of Kingston, is among the most prized and expensive coffees of the world. Its production and export is largely for European, Japanese, and U.S. markets.

Tobacco was important before the sugar era, and has seen a recent resurgence in the Greater Antilles, especially in Cuba, Puerto Rico, Jamaica, and the Dominican Republic, mostly for cigars. Ganja, although illegal throughout the Caribbean region, is of considerable commercial importance. It was brought to the region by East Indian indentured laborers following emancipation. Used widely for smoking and as a tea, its chief producer is Jamaica, and its main destination is the United States. Other significant export crops include cacao (for chocolate) and citrus.

PEASANT FARMING. Peasant farming in the Caribbean began after emancipation in the nineteenth century, when freed slaves sought out the only land available, in the hills and mountains. Unfortunately, this land is unsuitable for crop agriculture, suffering thin and erodible soils. Individual peasant farms average less than 5 acres (2 hectares) in area—often in disconnected plots. A variety of crops are raised, including fruits such as mangoes, plantains, akee, and breadfruit; vegetables such as yams, potatoes, and okra; sugarcane; and coffee.

Trinidadian carrying coconuts to market. (Clyde L. Rasmussen)

Peasant farms are semisubsistence, in which most food is raised for family consumption, and the rest is raised for local periodic markets or for sale to exporters, in the case of coffee. Mechanization is rarely used, whereas the hoe and machete are common-

CARIBBEAN AGRICULTURAL PRODUCTS

Commercial Export	*Subsistence Farming*
Sugarcane, bananas, coconuts, coffee, tobacco, ganga, cacao, citrus	Mangoes, plaintains, akee, breadfruit, yams, potatoes, okra, sugarcane, coffee, livestock

place. Terracing, crop rotation, and fertilization are uncommon. Many peasant farmers also raise livestock, typically scavengers such as chickens, goats, and swine. Peasant farming never developed widely in the Lesser Antilles because of the lack of land. Freed slaves here typically remained on the plantations as paid laborers.

TRENDS IN AGRICULTURE. Agriculture's share of earnings in the Caribbean region is declining. Local food production is being replaced by food imports, especially animal protein (meat, dairy, and fish), and canned prepared foods. This troubling trend creates a drain in foreign exchange and undercuts local economic production. On most islands, imported food exceeds 50 percent of consumption, but is over 80 percent in Puerto Rico, Barbados, Antigua, and Trinidad.

Overall, Caribbean agriculture was in decline in the late 1990's and the outlook for the future was grim. Various governments have addressed this problem, but little improvement has occurred. It is clear that the Caribbean islands in general have sufficient land to produce most or all of their domestic food needs.

P. Gary White

FOR FURTHER STUDY

Blouet, Brian W., and Olwyn M. Blouet. *Latin America and the Caribbean: A Systematic and Regional Survey.* 3d ed. New York: John Wiley & Sons, 1997.

Hope, K. R. *Economic Development in the Caribbean.* New York: Praeger, 1986.

London, N. A. *Principles of Caribbean Geography.* Kingston, Jamaica: Longman Caribbean, 1983.

MacPherson, John. *Caribbean Lands.* Kingston, Jamaica: Longman Caribbean, 1980.

Pastor, Robert A., ed. *Migration and Development in the Caribbean.* Boulder, Colo.: Westview, 1985.

Sealey, Neil. *Caribbean World: A Complete Geography.* New York: Cambridge University Press, 1992.

West, Robert C., and John P. Augelli. *Middle America: Its Lands and Peoples.* Englewood Cliffs, N.J.: Prentice-Hall, 1989.

PERIODIC MARKETS IN JAMAICA

Periodic markets are outdoor markets held in towns and villages throughout Jamaica and operated on a specific day of the week. At these markets fruits, vegetables, and meats are sold to supplement peasant farm income. So-called higglers, usually women, gather the produce from a number of remote peasant farms, then bring it to market by rural bus. In Jamaica, 60 percent of local food passes through periodic markets. The origin of such markets traces to the colonial plantation era when slaves were given small provision plots to grow their own food, the surplus from which they sold in local Sunday markets. In contemporary Jamaica Sundays are rarely market days because of the influence of Protestant missionaries. Periodic markets are in decline over the island due to the rise of supermarkets.

Industries

North America

North America has the most productive economy in the world. This economy is based on the extraction of natural resources, the processing of raw materials into useable goods such as cars and computers, the sale of goods and services, and the management of information. The North American economy is so complex because it depends on having different goods and services produced and consumed in many different places. The region's economy is built largely on its industrial geography.

Industrial Geography of North America: An Overview. One way to compare two countries is to compare their gross domestic products (GDPs). The GDP is the total value—usually expressed in dollars—of goods and services produced within a country during a year. The GDP does not accurately measure how productive the industry is within the country, so geographers often divide a country's GDP by its population to determine the average GDP per person. This per-capita figure is a more accurate measure because it reveals how much, on average, each person within a country produces, in other words, how technologically advanced the economy of a country is. People can produce more each year if they use advanced tools and computers in the manufacturing process. Figures for per capita GDP and GDP can reveal a great deal about the U.S., Canadian, and Mexican economies.

The United States has the largest of the three economies. In 1996 its GDP was ten times larger than that of Mexico or Canada. The Mexican economy is slightly larger than the Canadian economy, but this does not mean that the Mexican economy is more productive than Canada's. The 1996 populations for the United States, Mexico, and Canada were 266 million, 98 million, and 30 million, respectively. Canada has about the same economic output as Mexico, with only 30 percent of its population. This difference can be explained by looking at the different goods and services produced and the levels of technology used in the U.S., Canadian, and Mexican economies.

National Comparisons by Industrial Sector. Any detailed comparison of economies must differentiate among types of industries. Geographers have traditionally divided industries into four categories: primary, secondary, tertiary, and quaternary. Primary industries are those that extract natural resources and raw materials, such as mining, fisheries, forestry, or agriculture. Secondary industries process raw materials into consumer goods. Factories that manufacture such products as cars, toys, and clothing fall into this category. The tertiary or service sector is diverse, including stores that sell manufactured goods and people involved in education, finance, or clerical work. Finally, the emerging quaternary sector includes businesses involved in information analysis and high technology. For this discussion, the tertiary and quaternary sectors are combined.

With these categories in mind, one can examine the extent to which each country depends on each sector. One measure looks at the proportion each sector contributes to total GDP in each country. For example, manufacturing represents 29 percent of the Mexican GDP, 31 percent of the Canadian GDP, but only about 18 percent of the U.S. GDP. Alternatively, one can examine the proportion of the workers in each country employed in a particular sector. The United States and Canada have similar proportions of workers in each sector, but a quarter of the Mexican population are engaged in low-wage jobs extracting natural resources. Consequently, Mexico is less prosperous than the United States or Canada.

Per-capita GDP data show that Mexican workers as a whole are less productive and earn lower wages than their Canadian and U.S. counterparts. However, such data do not show how the economies of these three countries are changing, nor the regional changes occurring within the United States.

Regional Changes in an Emerging North American Economy. Historically, the United States, Canada, and Mexico have had distinct economies. Over time, however, the economies of the three countries have become more alike. Mexico is becoming a more modern country with an economy that is growing faster than that of the United States or Canada. However, as Mexico's economy becomes more like that of the United States, dramatic changes have been occurring within the economy of the United States itself.

The U.S. Department of Commerce identifies eight economic regions and tracks the total value of the goods and services produced in each region. The defined regions are the Far West, the Great Lakes, the Middle Atlantic, New England, the Plains, the Rocky Mountain, the Southeast, and the Southwest. These regions have grown at different rates since 1977. For example, the economy of the Far West region was nearly five times larger in 1998 than it had been in 1977.

In the 1990's, the fastest-growing regions were in the South and West. This was a profound change from the traditional pattern of industrial growth. The original industrial core was located in New England, the Middle Atlantic, and the Great Lakes regions of the United States and Canada. However, technological change, labor issues, and freer trade have given rise to new regions of industrial growth in North America.

Rise of the Industrial Core. Early centers of commerce developed in New England and the Great Lakes regions first because of technological limitations. Before the advent of steam-driven transportation, commercial centers were located either at natural harbors or where navigable rivers flowed into the Atlantic Ocean. This explains the location of port cities such as Montreal, Boston, and New York. Manufacturing centers grew alongside rivers, where falling water generated energy to operate textile or flour mills. Lowell, Massachusetts, and Richmond, Virginia, developed where they did for this reason. Rudimentary land transportation and natural barriers such as the Appalachian Mountains prevented significant westward expansion during this time.

Steam power and the Erie Canal, completed in 1825, revolutionized the North American economy. Barges carried timber and farm products from the Midwest

Ford Model T factory at Highland Park, Michigan, where assembly-line production began in 1913. Ford's success helped to make the Detroit region the automobile capital of North America. (Library of Congress)

along the Erie Canal to New York City. By 1850 train travel had eclipsed barge travel along the canal. The rail system expanded into the North American interior, prompting the spread of industry into Ohio, Michigan, and Illinois. Steamboats on the Ohio and Mississippi Rivers accelerated the growth of factories in St. Louis, Pittsburgh, and Cincinnati. In Canada, Montreal and Toronto grew rapidly as canals and locks enabled travel among the Great Lakes.

Mississippi River Pages 508, 573

Chicago Pages 388, 454

Comparable industrial expansion did not occur in the U.S. South. Its slave-based agrarian economy was oriented toward exporting cotton to European markets, not expanding into the U.S. interior. The Civil War also affected the regional structure of U.S. industry. As the Union troops advanced through Confederate states, much of the industrial base was destroyed. This widened the economic gap between the industrial North and agrarian South. As a result, the southern economy languished well into the twentieth century.

In the latter half of the nineteenth century, industrial cities such as Cleveland, Cincinnati, St. Louis, Detroit, and Chicago battled for control over the Midwestern economy. Chicago became the United States' Second City after New York, because the rail system, the emergence of catalogue retailers such as Sears Roebuck, and its location on Lake Michigan with canal access to the Mississippi River permitted it to process more timber, farm products, and manufactured goods than other Midwestern cities.

Despite Chicago's regional domination, other Midwestern cities emerged as important industrial centers too. The U.S. automobile industry first developed in Detroit, Michigan. It was there that Henry Ford developed assembly line mass production to build affordable cars for consumers. Steel, tire, and other factories emerged in Midwestern cities such as Pittsburgh, Cleveland, and Toledo to support the expanding automotive industry.

Canadian economic growth occurred in the shadow of Manifest Destiny—the U.S. government doctrine that it should control all land between the Atlantic and Pacific Oceans. When Canada gained its nominal independence from England in 1867, fear of U.S. domination prompted Canada to build a transcontinental railroad and to impose tariffs on U.S. imports. The Canadian Pacific Railroad was completed in 1885, connecting Ontario to British Columbia on the Pacific Ocean. The Canadian Pacific was built to project the illusion, if not the fact, that western Canada was a settled territory that should not be invaded.

To promote Canadian manufacturing, Canada imposed tariffs on U.S. products coming into Canada. These tariffs were taxes on U.S. goods, making them artificially more expensive for the Canadian consumer. Canadians might purchase inferior Canadian goods because superior U.S. imports were much more expensive. Increased demand for Canadian products spurred industrial growth in Canada. U.S. firms realized that the only way to reach Canadian consumers was to build factories in Canada. Companies such as General Motors built factories in southern Ontario because of its proximity to the U.S. industrial heartland. As a result, Canada's industrialization owes much to U.S. firms who located in Canada to avoid paying Canadian tariffs.

The economy of the industrial core was based on primary and secondary industry. Iron ore from the upper Great Lakes and coal from Appalachia were used to make steel in places such as Pittsburgh, Cleveland, and Detroit. This steel was used in automobiles, skyscrapers, and many other products. Of course, there were service sector jobs too, but the rapid industrial growth here was based on smokestack industries, extracting and processing raw materials.

The Rise of the South and the West. A clear divide once existed in the United States between the wealthy industrial North and the poorer South and West. Between the 1970's and 2000, however, the four fastest-growing regions in the United States were located in the South and West. At that same time, the traditional industrial core had the slowest-growing regional economy. Changing patterns of regional growth can be understood by looking at natural resource wealth. Texas, Louisiana, and Oklahoma have relied heavily on selling oil products to the rest of North America. Forestry has been important for economic growth in Washington, Oregon, and California, as well as in the Southeast.

However, other factors are responsible for the dramatic growth in the South and West. Expanded air and auto travel drew economic activities out of the industrial Northeast and Midwest. The groundwork for this industrial diffusion rested in a set of social policies called the New Deal, implemented in 1935. Before this time, unions could not represent workers during wage negotiations. The New Deal allowed workers to form unions without management interference. Corporate and political leaders feared that powerful unions would weaken the U.S. economy with high wage demands. As a result, a federal law was passed in 1948, allowing individual states to determine labor laws. Twenty-one states located primarily in the South gave workers the "right to work" without joining a union or paying dues. This legislation weakened unions and lowered wages in these states—a crucial fact for understanding North America's economic geography.

During the late 1960's, U.S. manufacturers had to compete against more efficient firms from West Germany and Japan. Inflation encouraged U.S. workers to strike for higher wages. U.S. companies had to find ways to cut costs in order to compete. As a result, many factories moved from union strongholds in the northern Rust Belt states to southern and western Sun Belt states where unions were weak and wages low. Other U.S. firms moved to northern Mexico, where wages were lower still.

Mexico's industrial sector has always lagged behind those of the United States and Canada. Mexico has relied on its abundant mineral resources, such as gold, silver, copper, and iron. Mexico is also the world's eighth-largest producer of petroleum products. Oil and chemical production spurred economic growth in the traditional industrial core region of central Mexico, near Mexico City, Guadalajara, and San Luis Potosi. Changes in Mexican economic policy also affected this pattern of industrial growth.

In 1965 the Mexican government created the Border Industrialization Program, which created a 12-mile-long (19 km.) strip along the Mexico-United States border. This region was intended to lure U.S. firms to Mexico with the promise of low-wage, nonunion labor. Firms could ship unfinished products to Mexico without tariffs, and final assembly could occur in Mexican factories called *maquiladoras*. The finished goods could then be shipped back to the United States. Mexico benefited from job growth in border towns such as Tijuana, Ciudad Juarez, Nuevo Laredo, and Matamoras. U.S. firms benefited from paying wages to Mexican workers that were 80 percent lower than wages paid to U.S. workers for comparable work.

While the *maquiladora* program was expanding growth in northern Mexico, changes were occurring in the United States and Canada too. Companies wanted fewer regulations, weaker unions, and the ability to conduct business across national borders. This movement culminated in free trade agreements between the United States and Canada in 1989, and the addition of Mexico to this partnership in 1994 under the North American Free Trade Agreement (NAFTA). Most corporations welcomed these developments because NAFTA removed all tariffs on goods traded among the three countries. Workers worried that as free trade made it easier for firms to move to regions with lower wages, their ability to negotiate with corporations would diminish. This concern has risen as Mexicans have become highly skilled workers, competing directly against factory workers in Canada and the United States.

Military expenditures also have affected the South and West. A disproportionate amount of military spending on bases and equipment occurred in the Sun Belt, prompting some to call this region the Gunbelt. Important technology centers began to emerge during this time. Places where radar, aviation, nuclear, and other technologies were developed during and after World War II provided the context for private sector technological research and development. Motorola, maker of cellular telephones and computer chips, is headquartered in Arizona. Dell Computers and Texas Instruments are located in Texas. Apple Computer and many other computer firms are located in the Silicon Valley of California. Microsoft and Boeing Aircraft are located in the Seattle, Washington, area. Most of the high-technology, quaternary economic growth has occurred in the South and West of the United States.

Conclusions. Dramatic changes occurred in the North American economy during the twentieth century. The traditional North American industrial core developed on the basis of primary and secondary industry. The South and West developed after World War II because of military spending, weakened labor laws that lured northern industry southward, and new technologies such as airplanes and computers. Mexico has been transformed too. New economic development in Mexico's northern border areas, spurred by NAFTA, has begun to rival the traditional industrial region of central Mexico. As a result of freer trade, economic restructuring also has occurred in Canada. New automotive factories have been built in Ontario. Resource-rich provinces such as British Columbia and Alberta have increased timber and oil exports to the United States. Freer trade has spurred changes in the industrial geography of all three countries, and change is not finished yet. As long as technology and markets continue to change, so too will the geography of North American industry.

Christopher D. Merrett

For Further Reading

Birdsall, Stephen, John Florin, and Margo Price. *Regional Landscapes of the United States and Canada, 5th Edition.* New York: John Wiley & Sons, 1999.

Bone, Robert. *The Regional Geography of Canada.* Toronto: Oxford University Press, 2000.

Borchert, John. "American Metropolitan Revolution." *Geographical Review* 57, 3 (1967): 301-332.

Cronon, William. *Nature's Metropolis: Chicago and the Great West.* New York: W. W. Norton and Company, 1991.

Garreau, Joel. *The Nine Nations of North America.* New York: Avon Books, 1981.

Goldberg, Michael and John Mercer. *The Myth of the North American City: Continentalism Challenged.* Vancouver: University of British Columbia Press, 1986.

Merrett, Christopher D. *Free Trade: Neither Free nor About Trade.* Montreal: Black Rose Books, 1996.

The Caribbean

Tourism and plantation agriculture are the main economic activities of the Caribbean region. Together they make up the service sector, which is more important to the economy than either manufacturing or mining. The service sector is the largest contributor to gross domestic product and the biggest source of jobs. The relatively low rates of unemployment in the Caribbean region are largely due to the numbers of people working in the service sector.

Tourism has become the major industry and source of revenue in Puerto Rico, the Bahamas, and the Dominican Republic. The Virgin Islands, Antigua, Guadeloupe, and Martinique also have become popular tourist destinations. Most of the tourists come from the United States, but many come from Europe and Japan. In 1996, more than 15 million tourists flocked to the Caribbean in search of sun, sand, and beautiful scenery. Individual hotels and resorts once promoted their facilities themselves, but now many governments promote the tourist attractions of their countries.

The tourism industry in the Caribbean region is dependent on the health of the wealthier economies of the world. When a recession occurs in the United States, for example, the tourist industry declines in the Caribbean. If local terrorist activities or natural disasters such as earthquakes, hurricanes, or volcanic eruptions occur in this region, the tourist industry suffers.

Tourism has some negative impacts on the Caribbean region. Local people hired for unskilled jobs in the service industry are poorly paid and often face layoffs in the summer off-season. Since jobs are usually scarce, even these jobs are better than none at all. The environmental costs are high for the region as well. The beaches and mountains are becoming polluted with the waste that tourism creates. Although tourism brings in much-needed foreign currency, most of it is used to buy the food and equipment required by the tourists. Tourism dominates the economies of the smaller Caribbean Islands while diversifying those of larger islands such as Jamaica.

Sugarcane is still the major export crop in Cuba, Barbados, the Dominican Republic, and some of the smaller islands. Bananas are the next leading agricultural export. Many Caribbean countries have preferential trade agreements, including price supports, with European Union members. This means that Caribbean bananas are given preference over cheaper Central American bananas by former European colonial powers such as France and Great Britain. Agriculture's prospects are bleak, however, as soils are becoming depleted and eroded, and world markets are increasingly competitive.

MINING. No mining or insignificant amounts of it are done on most islands in the Caribbean region, except in Cuba, Jamaica, and Trinidad. Cuba's mining industry has attracted foreign interest. In 1994 the mining authority was created. As of 1999, 15,400 square miles (40,000 sq. km.) was allocated for mining ventures. Major foreign investors included Australian (nickel), Canadian (gold, silver, and base metals), and South African (gold, copper, nickel) companies. Nickel and cobalt production rose to a record 68,000 tons in 1998. Nearly half of this output came from the Moa Bay plant, which is run as a joint venture between Cuba and Canada. Cuba has one small gold mine at Castellanos in Pinar del Rio province.

Jamaica is the world's third largest producer of bauxite, after Australia and Guinea. In 1997 bauxite production rose to its highest level since 1981, with a further increase in 1998, to 12.7 million tons.

Trinidad's economy is dominated by petroleum and petroleum products, which provide about one-fifth of government revenue. Three-quarters of oil production comes from the ocean. Trinidad has one oil refinery, located at Pointe-a-Pierre. The island also has considerable proven natural gas reserves, which are used as basic raw material for the production of petrochemicals such as methanol and ammonia, and to provide electricity for Trinidad. New plants will raise annual methanol capacity to 2.97 million tons and ammonia capacity to 3.4 million tons by 2001, making Trinidad the world's largest exporter of each.

The Caribbean region is a major refiner and shipper of oil for the United States market. Oil also is refined in Puerto Rico, Curaçao, and St. Croix. Factors that contribute to this development are close proximity to North America and the Panama Canal, deep harbors, access to Venezuelan oil, and weak environmental rules.

Manufacturing. The Caribbean region is dependent on the United States and Europe for markets, technology, investment, credit, and aid. To break this cycle of dependency, countries in the Caribbean region have tried two strategies to expand the manufacturing sector and free the region from total dependency on imported manufactured products. The first policy, import substitution, was intended to promote manufacturing for local consumption by protecting local industries with tariffs levied on similar imported goods. Import substitution was regulated by the government. This policy encouraged industrialization throughout the region between 1950 and 1975, but failed to produce the desired economic boom. It was replaced by a second development strategy—export-oriented industrialization (EOI).

Export-oriented industry—producing manufactured goods that can be sold abroad—has been a major factor in the development strategies of most Caribbean countries. Governments often offer incentives such as tax breaks and duty-free zones to attract foreign investment and manufacturing.

Most islands have established export processing zones (EPZs), located near ports or international airports. These special zones offer foreign companies ready access to cheap labor. Companies can import materials tax-free, but only if the majority of the final assembled product is reexported. As a result of EPZs, manufacturing exports from the Caribbean increased dramatically during the 1980's. For example, exports to the United States increased two and one-half times between 1983 and 1988. Many new industrial products have been assembled in the Caribbean region, from Barbadian medical products to Trinidadian electronic aircraft equipment.

The main drawback to EOI has been its instablity. Foreign companies are mobile and will quickly leave one island and set up on another when local conditions deteriorate or wage rates rise. Islands in the Caribbean have long been in competition with one another. Foreign firms have invested, moved profits, and withdrawn operations from various islands with great ease. This has been a destabilizing factor in most Caribbean economies.

Manufacturing made sizeable gains in the late twentieth century. Before 1950, most industrial production was in the hands of artisan producers. The food, drink, and clothing industries comprised small companies that supplied local markets and used local raw materials. Industrial production was more widespread than it is today, with manufacturing concentrated in the larger cities and ports where resources were more abundant.

Since the 1950's, manufacturing, mining, and the processing of food and other commodities have been used to increase employment and strengthen the local economies of the islands. Manufacturing, mining, and food processing are important contributors to the gross domestic product of the islands; however, they do not contribute more than 20 percent of the total in any island economy. Industrialization has failed to provide adequate jobs or sufficient wealth for the islands to offset the decline in agricultural production.

Haiti's small economy concentrates on light manufacturing (aided by low-wage labor), tourism, and coffee-growing. The Dominican Republic produces baseballs for the U.S. market and has sent some of the best major league baseball players to the United States as well. Puerto Rico manufactures petrochemicals, electrical equipment, food products, clothing, and textiles. *Maquiladora* export production in the Dominican Republic works much the same as it does on the United States-Mexico border and provides many unskilled, assembly-type jobs.

Carol Ann Gillespie

FOR FURTHER STUDY

Blouet, Brian W., and Olwyn M. Blouet. *Latin America and the Caribbean: A Systematic and Regional Survey.* 3d ed. New York: John Wiley & Sons, 1997.

Bolioli, Oscar L. *The Caribbean: Culture of Resistance, Spirit of Hope.* New York: The Friendship Press, 1993.

Clawson, David L. *Latin America and the Caribbean: Lands and Peoples.* New York: McGraw-Hill, 1999.

Hope, K. R. *Economic Development in the Caribbean.* New York: Praeger, 1986.

Knight, Franklin W., and Colin A. Palmer. *The Modern Caribbean.* University of North Carolina Press, 1989.

Sealey, Neil. *Caribbean World: A Complete Geography.* New York: Cambridge University Press, 1992.

_______. *Tourism in the Caribbean.* London: Hodder and Stroughton, 1982.

Engineering Projects

North America

Adapting natural landscapes through various engineering methods is a recurring theme in North American history. Ingenuity is a characteristic often used to describe both the indigenous peoples and immigrants of North America, who have been challenged by the continent's geography. Engineering ideas initially were applied to military fortifications, which were placed on geographically strategic sites such as bluffs. Then, civil engineering techniques prevailed to develop natural harbors, create transportation routes, and enact flood control measures.

Despite regional differences—such as Mexico's diverse arid and tropical areas and Canada's and the United States' contrasting mountains and prairies—North Americans shared engineering concerns about using and controlling the environment to benefit humans. In Mexico, minerals and oil were extracted. Native American tribes formed timber weirs to dam creeks. People in the United States and Canada developed methods to use water, wind, and solar resources to generate energy to process and transport raw materials. Westward migration resulted in creative engineering techniques to traverse the Rocky Mountains and benefit from topographical features. More sophisticated engineering works evolved as scientific comprehension of North American geography advanced.

Rivers
Page 511

Trade Connectors. North American demographics emphasizes settlement patterns near water, and North American rivers have both helped and hindered movement. Humans require a variety of engineered devices to use waterways efficiently as trade routes. The Mississippi River, which approximately bisects the United States, flows from Minnesota to the Gulf of Mexico. Prior to engineering intervention, it was only erratically useful for migrants and traders. The river's physical characteristics often caused delays or destroyed boats. Currents changed according to seasons, and the water flow moved sediment and debris into sandbars that obstructed travel and sometimes snagged steamboats.

During winter, northern sections of the river became ice-choked; in the spring and summer, the river often flooded because of ice melt and torrential rain. The 1811 and 1812 earthquakes at New Madrid, Missouri, altered the Mississippi River's course and created new channels adjacent to the previous riverbed. The Mississippi River's tributaries poured water and mud into the main river, and, by the 1870's, the mouth at the Gulf of Mexico was clogged with so much sand that vessels could not enter or exit the river.

Attempting to ease travel and prevent destruction caused by the river, James B. Eads studied hydrodynamic data to de-

Building the Trans-Alaska Pipeline

Stretching 1,287 miles (2,071 km.) between Prudhoe Bay and Valdez, the Trans-Alaska pipeline transports approximately 2.145 million barrels of oil daily. The bay, located where the Arctic Ocean meets the North Slope of Alaska, holds an estimated 10 billion barrels of petroleum resources. Valdez, on the Gulf of Alaska, is a major oil terminal.

Eight international oil companies formed Alyeska to build the pipeline, which crosses the Arctic Circle, 3 mountain ranges, 350 rivers, and seismically active areas. More than twenty thousand workers built the $8 billion pipeline during the 1970's. Each pipe section is approximately 48 inches (122 centimeters) in diameter and 40 feet (12 meters) long. Half of the pipeline is elevated to prevent the permafrost from melting because of the oil's frictional heat. Lifted by 78,000 supports cooled by liquid ammonia, the pipe is coated with teflon so it can move within the supports during earthquakes. Part of the pipeline is positioned underground where caribou migrate, and it is insulated with fiberglass and brine to reinforce the frozen soil supporting the pipe. Concrete weighs down sections buried underneath rivers. A pipeline bridge spans the 2,300-foot-wide (701 meters) Yukon River. Valves are located at vulnerable sites to shut off flow if the pipe ruptures. Engineers use special vehicles to fix problems inside the pipeline.

velop engineering solutions. Congress had ordered the U.S. Army Corps of Engineers to clear the river's mouth and dig a canal upstream from the sandbars. After disagreements about this procedure, Eads directed the army engineers to build jetties in the Mississippi River's mouth by using the river's currents to move and deposit sediment away from the main channel. An underwater grid of willow, rock, and silt formed the foundation of masonry built above the riverbanks to prevent tidal flooding. The jetties forced water into this narrow channel, quickening the current's flow to prevent sandbars from forming. As a result of these jetties, the river became accessible to most ships, even those with deep drafts. Such river improvements established a precedent for other Army Corps projects.

River projects Pages 508, 573

Canals, Shipyards, and Roads. The Army Corps of Engineers has erected and managed hydraulic engineering projects on the river and other waterways. The locks and dams it has built on the Mississippi River are the most significant of its projects. Built in the 1920's and 1930's, this dam system, which also spans the Illinois River, enables barge traffic to move along the rivers. Without the twenty-nine dams located between St. Louis and St. Paul, the river would not be navigable. Each dam pools the water to sufficient depths to accommodate large vessels.

Costing $110 million annually to operate, the dam system is designed to ensure that the river will behave consistently. Without the dams, the river would be unpredictable, going through cycles of flooding and drought and forming sandbars and unsafe sections. Corps engineers dredge the river to improve passage; repair the system; and stress the need for improvements, such as increasing the size of the locks, which cannot accommodate large convoys of around fifteen barges tied together; these must be split up to move through each lock. Delays as long as two hours create traffic jams on the river and affect farmers' profits. The dams also harm habitats: $20 million is spent annually to fix damages.

Before the twentieth century, canals offered travelers and traders more direct routes to desired destinations. The post-Revolutionary Patowmack Canal was built because George Washington wanted to expand trade from the Atlantic Ocean to the frontier. The narrow, twisting Potomac River often flooded in the spring and dried up in the summer, impeding navigation. In a sixteen-year period, workers dredged the river bed and blasted rock with black powder to build a diversion canal with five locks at the Great Falls, which dropped 80 feet (24 meters) in a 1-mile (1.6-kilometer) stretch. The company was bankrupted by 1828 by excessive costs, but the project was significant for inspiring further canal construction based on lock engineering.

Later canals linked major cities and included more sophisticated technology such as hydraulic locks. For example, the St. Lawrence Seaway was a joint engineering effort between Canada and the United States. The Great Lakes-St. Lawrence system relied on cooperation between Environment Canada and the United States Army Corps of Engineers, who addressed such concerns as water level fluctuations, coastal erosion, and shoreline protection and management. Those engineers used the Geographic Information System to facilitate their work.

The 363-mile-long (584 km.) Erie Canal, connecting Lake Erie to the Atlantic Ocean, is perhaps the best-known North American waterway. Canada's Rideau Canal represents how engineers adapted local conditions and materials instead of relying on European traditions. At the Hog's Back, a steep drop on the Rideau River, engineers used stone and timber to dam unpredictable flood waters in order to complete construction. After private ownership failed, the Canadian government assumed control of the Welland Canal, which circumvented Niagara Falls.

Ports and shipyards along the coasts and large inland bodies of water enhanced local economies by encouraging commerce. Engineers developed natural harbors, such as the Chesapeake, Campeche, and Hudson Bays. The Portsmouth Naval Shipyard in New Hampshire (1774) was the first established in the United States, implementing technological procedures that were later adopted at other North American ports. Businesses, manufacturers, and industries benefited, producing steamships and naval vessels and providing fuel and other necessities for crews. The Mexican ports at Ensenada and La Paz on the Baja California Peninsula export anchovies, sardines, and shrimp.

Like shipyards, airports encourage domestic and international trade. Interstates, highways, and railroads cross North America, both conforming to topographical landscapes as well as transforming areas to create direct routes between metropolitan areas. The Trans-Canada Highway, stretching 4,784 miles (7,821 km.), was the world's longest paved highway when completed in 1970. United States Interstate 35 and Mexico's Pan-American Highway are considered vital trade routes, especially after the passage of the North American Free Trade Agreement in 1994. The North American trade region is the world's largest free-trade market.

Above and Below Ground. Bridge design and materials differ according to local conditions and needs. Some bridges span narrow streams, others stretch across wide bays. Notable North American bridges include the Verrazano-Narrows (4,260 feet/1,298 meters), Mackinac Straits (3,800 feet/1,158 meters), George Washington (3,500 feet/1,067 meters), and Pont de Québec (1,800 feet/549 meters).

Welland Canal Page 509

Bridge construction long perplexed engineers, who determined how to pour concrete piers in water and balance loads. Engineers such as Eads innovated in construction methods and the use of materials such as steel to connect the eastern and western banks of the Mississippi River. Although the project was deemed technologically impossible by many engineers, Eads studied how the river's sands shifted from currents and sunk granite piers ninety feet into the riverbed to a foundation of solid bedrock. He used pressurized underwater chambers, introducing that building technology in North America.

John A. Roebling, who designed the Brooklyn Bridge, created suspension bridges that prevented the structures from being damaged by floating ice and boats. The 4,200-foot-long (1,280 meters) Golden Gate Bridge enables workers to commute from suburbs within the San Francisco Bay area. Other bridges connect countries, such as the Buffalo and Fort Erie Public Bridge between New York and Canada. Many bridges, such as the Ashtabula and Quebec Bridges, have collapsed during erection or due to stress, killing workers and motorists. By contrast, the Frankford Avenue Bridge in Philadelphia, Pennsylvania, built in 1697, was still in use in the year 2000.

Golden Gate Bridge Page 508

Engineers locate some trade connectors underground because of weather conditions or to increase usability of crowded urban areas. Subways move workers and goods beneath city streets, and tunnels transport cargo through mountains and under bays. The St. Clair River Tunnel (1891) was the first tunnel built underneath a river. Engineers mastered excavation techniques to deal with soft, moist earth and lined the tunnel with cast iron.

The Holland Tunnel, connecting New York and New Jersey (1920), was the first major underwater tunnel for automobiles. Pipelines above and below ground move petroleum and natural gas from de-

The Brooklyn Bridge. (PhotoDisc)

posits to distribution centers. By the late twentieth century, Canada was connected to the United States by several natural gas pipelines, supplying the United States with more energy than it received from Saudi Arabia, Mexico, and Venezuela combined.

Alberta, considered Canada's energy capital, was the greatest provincial producer of gas and oil. The Maritime Provinces of Newfoundland and Nova Scotia also extracted millions of barrels daily. Arctic Circle reserves, estimated to total trillions of cubic feet, remained untapped only because of Native Americans' and environmentalists' objections.

Resource Containment. Engineers design and supervise construction of dams throughout North America for flood control and hydroelectric power generation. Mexico's Chicoasen Dam (856 feet/261 meters) is the tallest North American dam, sixth in height globally. (Rogun in Tajikistan, at 1,099 feet/335 meters, is the tallest.) British Columbia's Mica Dam stands 794 feet (242 meters) high. Smaller dams only several meters tall provide local water supplies.

California's Oroville Dam (754 feet/235 meters) is the tallest U.S. earthen dam. Besides producing energy, it prevents an estimated billion dollars in flood damages annually. Quebec's La Grande Complex will consist of nine dams diverting rivers over 68,000 square miles (42,255 sq. km.) and generating 15,719 megawatts of electricity when completed. It has been delayed by Native American and environmentalist objections.

The Tennessee Valley Authority (TVA) dams economically transformed the southeastern United States during the twentieth century. Established by Congress as a New Deal agency in May, 1933, the TVA offered employment to laborers during the Depression. A series of dams were built along the Tennessee River system to generate energy and control floods. The TVA enhanced the economies of communities in the Tennessee River Valley by offering affordable and consistent renewable energy supplies. Electricity drastically changed people's lives at home and at work. To meet World War II munitions demands, the TVA built twelve hydroelectric stations and a steam plant to power war industries. By 1945 the TVA had created a 650-mile-long (1,050 km.) navigation channel that stretched along the Tennessee River's entire length. The TVA became the United States' largest public power provider.

Engineers seek to improve dam technology for efficiency and safety, as well as addressing environmental concerns. British Columbia has twenty-two hundred dams, of which 18 percent have been deemed potentially hazardous. Built in the region's mountains above populated areas, these dams, if damaged, could cause massive fatalities and extensive environmental and agricultural destruction, especially if flood waters contaminated other water sources, with costs running to millions of dollars.

Some dams are poorly placed, such as the St. Francis Dam, built on a fault at the southern end of the Los Angeles aqueduct system. Collecting water from the Sierra Nevada, the dam failed within one week after its construction concluded in 1926, killing 451 people. The South Fork Dam collapsed from the pressure of twenty million tons of water from torrential rains, killing 2,209 people in the Johnstown flood in 1889. Such disasters resulted in legislators passing laws stipulating safety standards for dams.

Reservoirs such as the Los Angeles Aqueduct are essential to provide ample clean water for urban populations, especially in arid regions. Engineers design extensive waterworks and pumping systems to de-

One of the great engineering projects of its time, Boulder Dam (later renamed Hoover Dam), was built on the Colorado River during the 1930's and created Lake Mead. (Nevada Commission on Tourism)

BUILDING THE HOOVER DAM

Built to control the Colorado River, the Hoover Dam was erected in Black Canyon during the early 1930's and demonstrates how technology can alter nature. Engineers planned to collect flood water to irrigate the Nevada and Arizona desert and create hydroelectric power for industries and homes. Funded by the federal government, the dam cost $48,890,955 and provided jobs for five thousand workers during the Great Depression. Hundreds of laborers suffered from the region's extreme heat, and 112 people died from illness and accidents while building the dam.

When it was constructed, Hoover Dam was the largest dam ever envisioned. Workers blasted river diversion tunnels in the bedrock before dredging the canyon floor and pouring 4.1 million cubic meters of concrete through a grid of blocks and pipes, which were flushed with chilled water so that the concrete cooled in two years instead of the century it would have taken to cool naturally. The billions of watts of energy produced by the 60-story-tall dam's enormous generators and turbines encouraged settlement of southwestern cities such as Las Vegas and Los Angeles. The dammed water created Lake Mead, Earth's largest artificial lake. Considered the eighth wonder of the world, Hoover Dam inspired innovative engineering construction techniques.

liver water to consumers. Most of these engineering achievements are public works projects; however, some power sources are privately owned. Solar panels and windmills exist throughout North America to collect renewable power sources.

Other engineering projects that generate and contain valuable resources include nuclear reactors, which provoke worry about potentially lethal accidents. Engineers have advanced oil drilling technology, building elaborate deep-sea drilling platforms to extract petroleum and natural gas from deposits located beneath the ocean floor. The petroleum industry expanded as engineers created refineries and other devices to store and process these natural resources. Mexico produces 950 million barrels of petroleum annually, in addition to billions of barrels extracted from land-based oil fields of the United States and Canada. The discovery of valuable minerals motivated migration within North America to remote Mexican mines, where a sixth of the world's silver is mined, to Yukon gold fields, and to coal mines in the eastern United States. Engineers erected ironworks and furnaces near these rich deposits.

Elizabeth D. Schafer

For Further Study

Berlow, Lawrence H. *The Reference Guide to Famous Engineering Landmarks of the World: Bridges, Tunnels, Dams, Roads, and Other Structures.* Phoenix, Ariz.: Oryx, 1998.

Colignon, Richard A. *Power Plays: Critical Events in the Institutionalization of the Tennessee Valley Authority.* Albany: State Universities of New York Press, 1997.

Jackson, Donald C. *Great American Bridges and Dams.* Washington, D.C.: Preservation Press, 1988.

Mead, Robert Douglas. *Journeys Down the Line: Building the Trans-Alaska Pipeline.* New York: Doubleday, 1978.

Newhouse, Elizabeth L., ed. *The Builders: Marvels of Engineering.* Washington, D.C.: National Geographic Society, 1992.

Petroski, Henry. *Invention by Design: How Engineers Get from Thought to Thing.* Cambridge, Mass.: Harvard University Press, 1996.

Reynolds, Terry S., ed. *The Engineer in America: A Historical Anthology from Technology and Culture.* Chicago: University of Chicago Press, 1991.

Shallat, Todd. *Structures in the Stream: Water, Science, and the Rise of the U.S. Army Corps of Engineers.* Austin: University of Texas Press, 1994.

Stevens, Joseph. *Hoover Dam: An American Adventure.* Norman: University of Oklahoma Press, 1988.

Transportation

North America

Transportation is movement of any kind. In a geographical context, the word refers to the movement of people, ideas, and goods among towns, cities, and regions. Transportation is the foundation by which people and commodities move for exploration, economics, and communication. Transportation allows for areas to specialize. For example, California grows citrus fruit and the Midwest grows corn. Transportation enables each area to develop, exchange, and sell products that best suit its particular physical geography.

Animals. Historically, animals have been used as a form of transportation. Many people traveled on horseback and moved goods by horse and buggy or horse-drawn carriages. Today, animals are still used in some regions of North America. In parts of Pennsylvania, Michigan, New York, and Ontario, religious groups such as the Amish and Mennonites, who do not use electricity or gasoline-powered engines, transport themselves and their goods by horse and buggy. In the Great Plains and prairies, ranchers travel great distances on horseback to watch and herd their livestock. Although the horse is the animal most commonly used for transportation, other animals also provide means

The Amish people, of a highly conservative Protestant sect, live in small communities centered in Pennsylvania, where they shun modern conveniences, such as electricity, telephones, and cars. (Pennsylvania Dutch Visitors Bureau)

of movement. In northern Canada and Alaska, dog sleds are used during the winter months for transportation across the ice and snow. The animal-powered transportation is often slow, and thus more modern transportation methods are much more common.

Water Transportation. Boats have been used for exploration, transportation of commodities, and passenger travel. With the European discovery of North America in the fifteenth and sixteenth centuries, explorers relied almost entirely on boat travel. The coastline of North America and its major rivers were accurately mapped hundreds of years before the interior lands was mapped. Most of the people who first settled and lived in the New World lived along the coast or near rivers. French settlers, in particular, explored and traveled great distances by boat, eventually settling much of the St. Lawrence River Valley, along the coast of the Great Lakes, and down the banks of the Mississippi River all the way to the Gulf of Mexico.

Mississippi River Page 573

Because early European settlements in North America were colonies of European countries, transportation of goods from the eastern seaboard to Europe was important. The Hudson Bay and St. Lawrence River Valley housed major transportation ports where boats were loaded with exports destined for Europe. Canadian coastal waters provided many commodities that were in high demand in Europe. Whale products provided millions of tons of oil, while fish provided a good source of protein. Inland, settlers gathered furs, trees, and agricultural products that were sent back to Europe.

Welland Canal Page 509

In the eighteenth and nineteenth centuries, many canals were built to transport goods in areas that did not have navigable rivers. Boats and barges were used to transport materials. Many canals linked major waterways; for example, the Erie Canal linked the Atlantic Ocean with the Great Lakes, and the Panama Canal linked the Atlantic Ocean with the Pacific Ocean.

Large boats or freight ships still transport heavy goods long distances and overseas. Many large ports are located along the Atlantic and Pacific coasts of North America. In the late 1950's the St. Lawrence Seaway was improved and many sections were dredged. This enabled large seagoing vessels to transport goods from the Great Lakes to anywhere else in the world. Many of North America's manufactured goods were made in the Midwest; thus the Great Lakes and St. Lawrence Seaway became important assets in North America's economy. In 1999 Los Angeles was North America's largest port, with more than seventeen million tons of goods being shipped every year. New York is the

Road sign warning motorists to watch for slow-moving Amish carriages. (PhotoDisc)

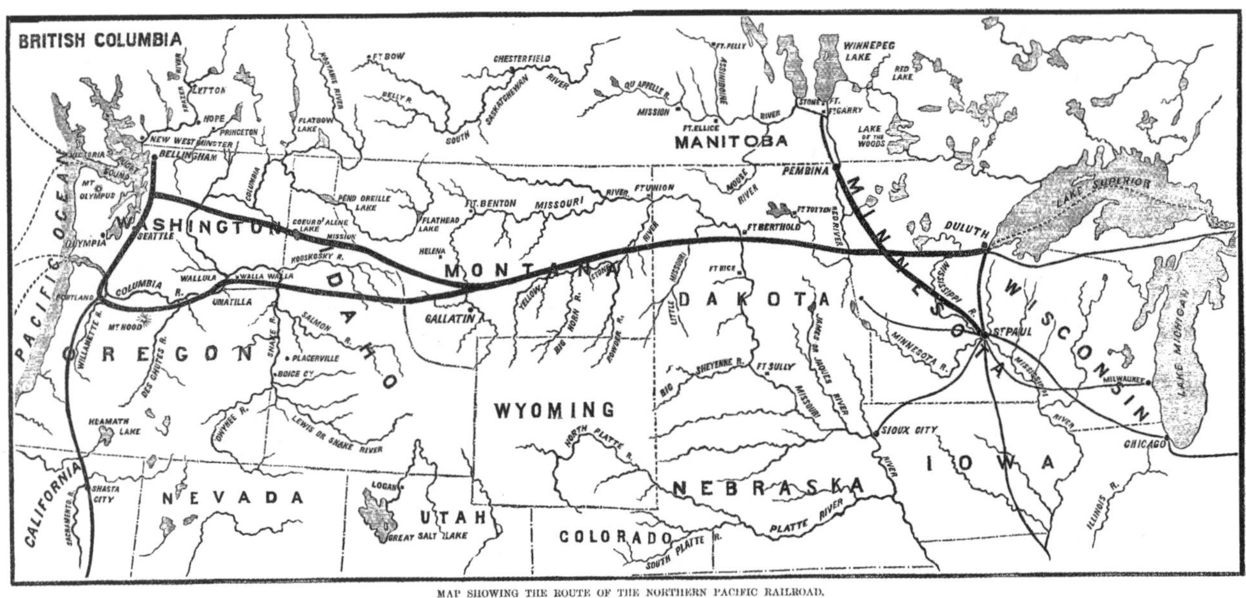

Contemporary map showing the expansion of the Northern Pacific Railroad in the late nineteenth century. (Corbis)

second-largest port, and the largest on the East Coast, shipping nearly ten million tons of goods each year.

Ships also carry passengers. Cruise boats transport millions of North Americans every year. Popular destinations for both Canadian and U.S. passengers include the Caribbean islands and the coast of British Columbia and Alaska. In some areas, ferries provide a convenient form of transportation for people. Washington, British Columbia, and Alaska have a series of coastal ferry routes that enable people to travel from one place to another. In northern Quebec and Nunavut, ferryboats in the summer months allow people to travel from one island to another.

Railroads. The development of the railroad in the mid-nineteenth century drastically changed transportation patterns throughout North America. Between 1850 and 1920, hundreds of thousands of miles of rail track were laid down in North America. The railroads improved upon what the canals had tried to do: They connected natural resources with manufacturing plants, and final products with the marketplace and consumers. Most rail lines traveled in an east-west direction, eventually connecting the Atlantic and Pacific Oceans.

The United States, Canada, and Mexico are all vast countries, largely unsettled in the mid-nineteenth century, and railroads provided them much faster means of transportation than ever before. Towns began to be settled all along the railroad tracks, developing a larger population in the western states and provinces. As more people moved to and settled the American West, more natural resources were discovered, which brought more prospectors, manufacturing plants, and eventually more settlers.

The invention of the refrigerated boxcar enabled perishable agricultural products to be transported from prime agricultural areas to the Eastern seaboard, where most of the population lived. Refrigerated boxcars also enabled cattle to graze on the Great Plains and prairies, and for meat to be sent back to the majority of the population without spoiling.

The railroad affected the geography of

North America in other ways. For the first time, people could travel the vast continent relatively quickly. Towns that in the past had been secluded and remote could now get news and information more quickly. People started to demand standardized items, so that if something they had purchased in Boston broke while they were in North Dakota, they could find similar parts with which it could be fixed.

The spread of railways throughout the United States helped force the national standardization of time zones. Clocks in various cities were also synchronized within the four time zones used today—eastern, central, mountain, and Pacific—so that trains could run on schedules that everyone could use. Many people began to travel, and national parks were established in both the United States and Canada to protect and preserve unique geographic wonders.

The proliferation of railway lines throughout the eastern and southern United States by the mid-nineteenth century played a major role in the Civil War. The speed and ease with which trains moved troops and equipment helped make the Civil War what many have called the first modern mechanized war. Indeed, such was the importance of the railways that trains and tracks themselves became targets of military assaults.

Railways also played a major role in Mexico's early twentieth century revolution. Both rebels and government troops used them to move across great distances, thereby spreading the fighting through a large part of the country.

Decline of the Railroads. In the face of new competition from automobiles, trucks, and airplanes, the twentieth century saw a decrease in the total mileage of railroad tracks throughout the United States and Canada. In some instances, these old, deserted lines have been changed into rails-to-trails. These are long pathways that provide a means of recreational transportation where people can hike or ride bikes or horses.

The rail lines still in use at the end of the century continued to carry goods and people from one place to another. These lines have heavy traffic loads and usually transport bulky commodities such as minerals and grains. The U.S. government supports long-distance rail through Amtrak; in Canada, it is supported through Canada Via Rail. Both companies provide long-distance service for passengers; however, it is much slower, and no cheaper, than other forms of transportation. In the 1990's rail travel in the United States and Canada accounted for less than 6 percent of personal transportation. Short-distance rail lines, however, remain popular in some densely populated areas. New York, Boston, Baltimore, Chicago, San Francisco, and Washington, D.C., have busy commuter rail lines that transport people to and from work.

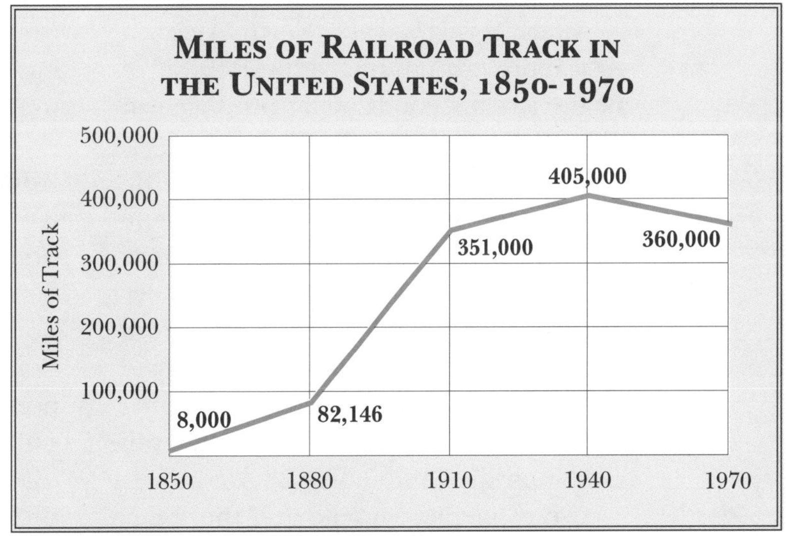

Source: U.S. Census Bureau Statistics.

Automobiles. In the twentieth century, transportation patterns in North America were affected profoundly by the automobile and the trucking industry. Because of these new modes of transport, people and goods were no longer tied to the routes dictated by the railroad, but could travel whenever and wherever they wanted. Almost all the U.S. states and Canadian provinces have well-developed, extensive road systems that allow people and goods to be transported quickly, easily, and relatively cheaply. Canadians and Americans place a strong importance on their automobiles and their mobility. Close to one-fifth of their income is spent on their vehicles. Mexico also has an extensive network of roads, but they are neither as large nor as well maintained as those of their more prosperous northern neighbors.

Henry Ford developed the Model T and the idea of the assembly line, which quickly made the automobile accessible to the majority of the population, not just the wealthy. In less than two decades, the United States became a motorized country. By the Great Depression of the 1930's, the automobile industry was the largest consumer of raw materials and oil in the United States.

After World War II, North America grew more prosperous, with two-thirds of all the world's goods being produced in the area from western Pennsylvania to St. Louis and north into Ontario around the Great Lakes. As North Americans became much wealthier, they bought ever more cars. Between 1950 and 1990, the number of cars in the United States increased from 40 million to about 123 million. By the late 1990's, roughly 85 percent of all personal transportation in the United States utilized individual automobiles.

Use of the automobile and the transportation of people and goods in the United States were enhanced by the development of the national Interstate Highway System. The idea was developed in the 1930's, but construction did not began in 1950's. A federal gasoline tax provided 90 percent of the funds for the highways, and each state had to provide the remaining 10 percent of the cost. In the following decades, tens of thousands of miles were constructed.

The Interstate Highway System is relatively evenly distributed geographically. Roads were not concentrated where the population lived or the manufacturing plants existed; the goal was to make the highway a national transportation system. The Interstate Highway System accounts for only a small fraction of the total number of road miles in the United States, but it carries nearly one-fifth of all the vehicles. This makes it a major contributor to the nation's strong economy, and to the growing vehicle tourism industry.

Two other highway systems are noteworthy in North America. First is the Alcan, or Alaskan-Canadian Highway. It was built during World War II when the United States was concerned that the Japanese might invade Alaska. The second is the Trans-Canada Highway, which was completed in 1962. It links St. Johns, Newfoundland, to Victoria, British Columbia, cutting across lower Canada and connecting Canada's major cities.

Trucking. Trucks also have benefited from the extensive road systems. In cities, trucks have dominated freight transportation since the 1920's. Trucks enable manufacturers and retailers new geographic options for setting up shop. In the past, with horse-drawn carriages, rail depots, or ship ports, transporting goods away from a central destination was expensive. Many manufacturers and retailers tried to locate themselves close to the downtown to minimize those transportation costs. Trucks al-

Built during World War II, when the United States was concerned that the Japanese might invade Alaska, the Alcan Highway remains the primary overland link between Alaska and the Continental states. (AP/Wide World Photos)

lowed people to move to the suburbs where more open space and cheaper land were available.

Automobiles and trucks have contributed to a large change in residential and commuting patterns. In the past, most people lived downtown, near their work. Today, many people live in suburbs and commute downtown or to another suburban area to work.

Airplanes. Airplanes became a common form of transportation for both goods and passengers in the second half of the twentieth century. Both Canada and the United States have large cities spaced far apart. Airline transport moves people and goods much more quickly than any other form of transportation. The United States and Canada only make up about 5 percent of the world's population, but they create nearly 45 percent of the world's air traffic. Airline passenger travel increased dramatically after 1978, when the United States government deregulated the airlines. In 1990, over 466 million passengers traveled by airplane.

Airline traffic is concentrated in the largest airports, or hubs. The largest U.S. airports are located in Chicago, Dallas-Fort Worth, Atlanta, Los Angeles, and San Francisco; however, there are more than 1,000 airports in North America. In places like Alaska, the Yukon, Alberta, and Montana, where little towns are spaced far away from larger cities, many individuals own private airplanes and travel regularly into larger towns to purchase needed goods.

The relative reduction of airline prices has changed the way many businesses operate. The movement of their goods and employees is much faster, allowing large businesses to manage smaller businesses from a distance. Businesses realized that they did not need to keep large inventories on hand, but instead could fly supplies in quickly when they were needed. This concept of just-in-time delivery has been profitable for many companies.

Pipelines. An important form of transportation of goods is often ignored because it is out of sight and usually buried under the ground: the transportation of crude oil, oil products, and natural gas via pipelines. Most underground pipelines are located at the source of the oil and gas in the south central United States, in places like Texas and Louisiana, and travel underground to the Northeast, where most of the consumers are located. The exception to this is in Alaska, where the pipeline is above the surface and travels from Prudhoe Bay southward to the seaport of Valdez.

Alison Philpotts

FOR FURTHER STUDY

Coates, Peter A. *The Trans-Alaska Pipeline Controversy: Technology, Conservation, and the Frontier.* Bethlehem, Pa.: Lehigh University Press, 1991.

Daniels, Rudolph. *Trains Across the Continent: North American Railroad History.* Bloomington: Indiana University Press, 2000.

Edwards, John D., Jr, ed. *Transportation Planning Handbook.* 2d ed. Washington, D.C.: Institute of Traffic Engineers, 1999.

Itzkoff, Donald M. *Off the Track: The Decline of the Intercity Passenger Train in the United States.* Westport, Conn.: Greenwood Press, 1985.

Kane, Robert M. *Air Transportation.* 13th ed. Dubuque, Iowa: Kendall/Hunt, 1999.

Pindell, Terry. *Making Tracks: An American Rail Odyssey.* New York: Grove Weidenfeld, 1990.

Rae, John B. *The American Automobile Industry.* Boston: Twayne, 1984.

Richter, William L. *The ABC-Clio Companion to Transportation in America.* Santa Barbara, Calif.: ABC-Clio, 1995.

White, Lawrence J. *The Automobile Industry Since 1945.* Cambridge, Mass.: Harvard University Press, 1971.

THE CARIBBEAN

Through most of the history of the Caribbean region, its islands have been linked more closely with the outside world than with each other. Although this changed somewhat in the late twentieth century, as air transportation began moving tourists among the islands, other kinds of transportation links among the Caribbean Islands remain weak. This is especially true for inter-island sea transportation, the mode by which most goods move to and from the region. The improvement of inter-island connections is the greatest transportation problem facing the region.

Caribbean transportation systems vary greatly among the many different countries. In Puerto Rico, the Bahamas, and the Virgin Islands, highly efficient, modern transport networks move people and goods. These countries are also well integrated into the international transportation systems that are the foundation on which the early twenty-first century global economy rests. Transportation costs also tend to be relatively low. Several other countries in the Caribbean region—

including Haiti, Cuba, and the Dominican Republic—have poorly developed transportation systems and a transportation infrastructure that is inadequate to accommodate the needs of the people. Delays in the transfer of both people and goods are common. Transfer costs tend to be relatively high in countries with poor transportation systems.

International and Inter-Island Links. Since World War II, many Caribbean islands have been integrated into international transport systems. As the Caribbean emerged as a major tourist destination, especially for North Americans and Europeans, an improved transportation infrastructure was essential to accommodate the millions of tourists who visited it annually. Many islands are served by airlines from North and South America, Europe, and Asia. New and improved airports and other transportation infrastructure were built on most of the islands, and port and harbor facilities were expanded to accommodate the increasing number of cruise ships that called at Caribbean ports. There also have been efforts to expand inter-island air transportation, primarily to serve tourist demands.

Government efforts to promote economic development and raise the living standards of Caribbean residents also have resulted in improved transport networks. In several countries, foreign aid was instrumental in improving transportation infrastructure. Programs such as the Caribbean Basin Initiative, which have resulted in the creation of new and expanded industries in several Caribbean countries, also led to enhanced transportation infrastructure.

Local Transportation Services. Most island residents are more dependent on bus transportation than are North Americans. On most islands where private motor vehicles are scarce, well-developed urban and intercity bus systems move people quickly and efficiently. Bus service in rural areas, however, usually has been inferior to urban and intercity transit. Nevertheless, in terms of cost and reliability, public transportation in many Caribbean countries is superior to that in much of North America.

On most Caribbean islands, an extensive, well-maintained road network enables trucks, buses, and private vehicles to service even the most remote rural areas. Since rail transport is little used in the region, most goods are moved by trucks. Local companies provide low-cost, efficient service to most island communities. A few countries, notably Haiti, the Dominican Republic, and Cuba, have inadequate road systems. In these countries, poor roads often hinder the movement of produce from rural areas to markets. Some remote villages may not be accessible by

Buses play a much greater role in Caribbean transportation than they do in Canada and the United States. (Ciro Colho/mercurypress.com)

road, especially during periods of heavy rainfall. As a result, perishable produce can deteriorate before it reaches urban centers, where it is in demand. Poor roads are often the single greatest obstacle to rural economic development in these less-developed countries.

Although not typical of inadequate transport systems in the region, Haiti's internal transport system exhibits many problems of poor countries with scarce resources. Many of Haiti's roads are impassable during the frequent torrential rains. On many major roads, bridges have not been constructed, forcing vehicles frequently to ford streams. Many small interior towns and villages can be reached only by foot, often over rugged terrain. Such inadequate transportation systems contribute to widespread poverty.

Sea Transportation. At the close of the twentieth century, the Caribbean region was almost exclusively dependent on sea transport for the movement of goods. Air cargo transport had increased somewhat in importance, but remained insignificant compared to ocean transportation.

There was little intraregional traffic, which reflected the scarcity of trade among Caribbean countries. The interchange of goods was largely between individual Caribbean countries and their trade partners in North America, Europe, and Asia. The major ports in the region were served by a diverse array of ships including bulk carriers (specialized commodity carriers such as banana and oil ships), container cargo vessels, general cargo vessels, and roll-on/roll-off ships (vessels to transport vehicles). These large vessels provided service on a regular schedule, but this service often was limited to the major ports of the region, which had modern port facilities.

Many islands in the region's less-developed countries had inadequate sea transport service. The volume of cargo passing through ports in the less-developed countries was often insufficient to warrant frequent service by ship lines. These islands often lacked efficient port facilities. Moreover, large ships tended to bypass smaller ports in order to reduce port charges. Providing sea transport to less developed Caribbean countries remained a major transportation problem at the beginning of the twenty-first century.

Rail Service. In most Caribbean countries, rail systems have not been well developed. On many of the small islands, rail lines were never constructed. During the nineteenth century, rail lines were built to serve the mines and sugarcane plantations in several of the larger island countries, including Cuba, Puerto Rico, Jamaica, Haiti, and the Dominican Republic. In some countries, these lines remained important at the close of the twentieth century. The Dominican Republic is typical of these countries. There, trains moved half of the sugarcane from the fields to the mills, and state-operated rail lines served the salt and bauxite mines.

Robert R. McKay

For Further Study

Hope, K. R. *Economic Development in the Caribbean.* New York: Praeger, 1986.

Magnusson, Michael. *Latin Glory: Airlines of Latin America.* Oscela, Wisc.: Motorbooks International, 1995.

Sealey, Neil. *Caribbean World: A Complete Geography.* New York: Cambridge University Press, 1992.

______. *Tourism in the Caribbean.* London: Hodder and Stroughton, 1982.

Trade

North America

Canada, the United States of America, and Mexico make up the political and economic entities of the North American continent. European explorers and colonists opened up the continent to world trade in the fifteenth and sixteenth centuries.

Canada, the largest of the three North American countries, with an area of 3.8 million square miles (9.85 million sq. km.), has the smallest population—approximately 30 million inhabitants in the year 2000. The first major wave of European settlers in Canada came from France. Great Britain defeated France in the Seven Years' War—known as the French and Indian War in North America—and took over control of Canada in 1763. Substantial immigration from the British Isles followed. The province of Quebec has remained largely French in its culture and population. In the twentieth century, English was the predominant language in all of the provinces except Quebec, although both languages are recognized as official for the country.

The United States, although slightly smaller in area than Canada, possesses a broader spectrum of natural resources and a more temperate climate. Accordingly, it has attracted more immigrants from a greater number of foreign countries than has its northern neighbor. In the 1990's, approximately 10 percent of its population was of African ancestry, and an additional 10 percent were of Latin extraction—mostly immigrants from Mexico, but including people from virtually every country in Central and South America. During the twentieth century, the Asian minority in the United States increased perceptibly, with a substantial influx of Koreans and Vietnamese as a result of conflicts in both countries in the latter half of that century. The U.S. population exceeded 250 million in the year 2000, in an area in excess of 3.5 million square miles (9 million sq. km.).

Mexico's population has continued to grow more rapidly than those of its northern neighbors. At the end of the twentieth century, it had more than 100 million inhabitants, in an area in excess of 761,000 square miles (2 million sq. km.).

Trade and Products: Mexico. For the better part of the twentieth century, oil was Mexico's major natural resource and its primary export. Oil production in Mexico is a government monopoly. Petroleos Mexicanos, commonly referred to as PEMEX, handles the exploration, production, and distribution of petroleum products throughout the country, as well as sales to foreign customers.

Tourism is Mexico's second major industry. However, the tourist industry has been plagued by reports of civil unrest in many parts of the country. Foreign visitors at times have been the victims of holdups and physical attacks, sometimes at the hands of police officials.

Mexico produces a variety of agricultural products, many for export, such as corn, cotton, fruits, wheat, beans, coffee, tomatoes, and rice. Various metals are mined as well, including silver, copper, gold, lead, and zinc.

Mexico's major trading partners are the United States, Japan, and Western European countries. In terms of manufacturing and commercial agriculture, Mexico has a critical competitive advantage: Its labor costs are lower than those generally found in the United States, Canada, and Western Europe. Mexico also favors expanding the North American Free Trade Agreement (NAFTA) to its neighbors to the south, the small Central American republics.

Canada. Canada's principal products are grains, lumber, and oil. Its major exports are wood pulp, newsprint, crude petroleum, chemicals, machinery, natural gas, aluminum, and assorted wood products. Canada's principal industrial products are transportation equipment, petroleum, and chemicals. Because of the weather conditions in the country's north, most of the country's economic activity is found in a belt along its border with the United States. Canada benefits from a highly educated, well-trained work force.

In the southern provinces bordering on the United States, there is a substantial industrial complex, producing automobiles, trucks, aircraft, and ships. The United States, Japan, the United Kingdom, the Commonwealth of Independent States (which includes Russia and several of its former satellites), Germany, Mexico, South Korea, and Taiwan are its major trading partners.

United States. The United States is the world's largest producer of manufactured goods. Having a wide variety of natural resources, it rarely depends on raw materials from the rest of the world in its manufacturing sector, except in the production of petroleum, where its domestic output does not meet its industrial needs. Japan, one of the country's major trading partners, consistently ships more to the United States than it receives from it in terms of exports. This unfavorable balance of trade results in Japan holding great amounts of U.S. debt, in the form of stocks and bonds. For example, U.S. roads are full of Japanese automobiles, both manufactured in Japan and built in U.S. factories owned by the Japanese. Few American-built cars are found on Japanese roads, for Japan seeks to restrict imports, especially those that compete with Japanese domestic products. Canada, Japan, and Western Europe have been the country's major traditional trading partners, but the NAFTA agreement has moved Mexico up among the leaders in exporting to the United States.

Trade among the three North American countries was hampered for many decades by government regulation. Duties of various types were imposed by the respective governments for two purposes: Those duties, or tariffs, produced revenue for the governments of the countries that imposed them, and taxing imports on incoming goods provided an economic shelter for domestic producers by making imports less competitive with local products.

Such barriers slowed the movement of goods across borders, even though a market for them existed domestically. For example, a Mexican citizen might want to own a U.S. car rather than one made in Mexico, but if the duty on U.S. cars was inordinately high, the Mexican customer might buy a Mexican-produced automobile even though its quality did not match that of the foreign import. Similar protective tariff restrictions also existed as a result of Canadian and U.S. duties on foreign imports. Tariffs acted as a brake on the passage of goods among the three countries. Government officials, as well as local producers, determined that those restrictions impeded the sale of both agricultural produce and manufactured products across national borders.

COMPETITION FROM THE EUROPEAN UNION. Countries seeking to trade with one another in Western Europe faced similar restrictions. In 1991, in order to expand trade possibilities, they established the European Union, designed to encourage the flow of trade among its members. In 1999 the organization adopted a new European common currency, called the euro. European Union currency and coinage are being designed and will replace the old national currencies in January, 2002. The greatly reduced tariff regulations, together with more open markets and a common currency, have already resulted in lower prices to consumers on a wide variety of goods, as well as a lowering of bank interest and taxes.

NORTH AMERICAN FREE TRADE AGREEMENT. In 1990 the governments of the three North American countries, recognizing the need for a trade reform program, began to plan a comprehensive free trade agreement for their own continent. At stake could be the development of a market for 370 million people and, ultimately, $6.5 trillion of production.

Realizing the challenge that the European Union represented to outsiders and the limitations that the Japanese imposed on their trading partners in regard to incoming goods, this new alliance of North American countries promised expanded trade horizons within the continent itself. On December 17, 1992, after two and one-half years of research, the leaders of the United States, Canada, and Mexico signed the North American Free Trade Agreement. All indications were that trade among the three countries would ultimately take precedence over trade with countries outside North America.

Although the three partners initially encountered some problems in implementing the agreement, it has been an effective method of increasing trade among them. The figures over the first few years since the treaty was signed are impressive. The agreement stimulated the construction of many new factories and encouraged the formation of business partnerships across the national borders of all three countries. Average tariff rates among the three countries have dropped

DOLLARIZATION FOR A COMMON CURRENCY?

The designation of the euro as the European Union's common currency gave rise to speculation as to whether the North American Free Trade Agreement (NAFTA) partners—Canada, United States, and Mexico—might adopt the U.S. dollar as the common currency for all three countries. Some political figures and business interests have argued for this idea, asserting that a common NAFTA currency would aid the countries involved to realize more effectively the economic returns of the agreement.

Proponents of "dollarization" point to the U.S. dollar as the more stable monetary unit, with global acceptance in economies throughout the world. Moreover, the dollar is not subject to either sudden devaluation or wildly fluctuating exchange rates. Even El Salvador, in Central America, and Argentina, at the opposite end of the hemisphere, have considered the dollarization of their monetary systems. A precedent for the use and acceptance of the U.S. dollar already exists in the Republic of Panama, which has used U.S. currency and coinage since the country's inception in 1903. Nevertheless, many nationalists strongly oppose the adoption of the dollar as the official medium of exchange in lieu of their own domestic currencies.

to only 2 percent on goods shipped.

Some segments in the industries of all three participants had initial reservations about the pact. Labor in the United States, for example, feared the loss of jobs to Mexico's lower wage scales. Actually, more jobs have been created in the United States since the treaty's signing than have been lost. It is estimated that 700,000 jobs in the United States are supported by exports to Mexico.

Northern Mexico has become an economic extension of the United States, with hundreds of new jobs resulting from the creation of new plants. This economic phenomenon has permitted the development of a whole new pool of Mexican wage earners who are in the market for consumer goods from the United States for the first time. The job market in northern Mexico has attracted workers from all over the country, since the local labor supply has tightened up as a result of the demand created by the establishment of new factories in the area. Every satisfied worker established in a job in a Mexican factory is one fewer potential illegal entrant into the United States.

Initial Results. A 1997 report on NAFTA's progress indicated positive results. Total North American trade increased from $293 billion in 1993 to $420 billion in 1996, a gain of 43 percent during NAFTA's first three years. Economic relations between Mexico and the United States, often seriously strained in the past, had improved greatly. Mexico recovered more quickly from its 1994-1995 recession, as compared to previous economic crises, because of the country's increased exports to its North American trading partners. Accompanying the increased economic activity has been a liberalization of Mexico's political structure.

The NAFTA Commission. This commission is the central oversight body on implementation of the trade agreement's regulations. It is chaired jointly by the U.S. Trade Representative, the Canadian Minister for International Trade, and the Mexican Secretary of Commerce and Industrial Development. Under its auspices, working groups and advisory bodies consider ways to implement the treaty's conditions and to examine unresolved issues. Review panels exist to analyze disputes on the alleged dumping of goods or the adoption of new regulations that would restrict the movement of trade. The process of consultation, evaluation, and dispute settlement are open to the public.

Problems Affecting Future NAFTA Trade. Implementation of the agreement has not been without its difficulties. The expansion of factory facilities in northern Mexico has had serious repercussions with reference to the standards of living in that area. Increased demand on local water resources, as a result of the influx of waves of new workers, has caused northern Mexico's water table to drop. Many of the new workers' communities that have sprung up since the upswing in trade among the three countries are without running water or electricity. Adequate new housing construction lags. The demand for heating fuel has strained the region's capability to deliver resources.

The movement of contraband goods, already endemic in the border area, has increased as legitimate trade has grown. The substantial increase in the number of incoming trucks has led to their use as conveyances for illicit cargos, primarily illegal drugs, but also illegal aliens. To preclude the entry of illegal cargo, each truck entering the United States from Mexico would have to be carefully searched. Such close supervision has not been the practice at the border.

U.S. truckers have objected to the substantial increase in the number of Mexican trucks traveling U.S. highways since the inauguration of the agreement. They complain that foreign truckers operate with inferior and dangerous equipment not up to American safety standards. The prevalence of marginal tires and equipment on Mexican vehicles is cited as an example of this problem.

Grain farmers in Canada and the northern United States have feuded over the passage of certain types of grain, such as bulgur wheat, from north to south. Each side accuses the other of seeking to block sales of the other's products. Mexico has also been accused by American growers of dumping agricultural produce such as melons and tomatoes on U.S. markets. The commission must find a solution to such disagreements, where both countries are competing to market similar or identical products.

Mexico is concerned with its increasing dependence on the United States to absorb its exports. By 1998, 85 percent of Mexico's foreign trade ended up being with their neighbor to the north. In addition, the *maquiladoras,* or assembly firms, along the U.S. border provided jobs for more than a million Mexican workers in 1999. In order to provide their producers with a broader market and to reduce their dependence on the United States, the Mexican government is negotiating trade agreements involving a reduction in tariffs with the fifteen-nation European Union.

Nevertheless, based on the results through 2000, NAFTA appeared to be in the process of continuous expansion. Future successes will be determined by a continuing upswing in employment figures as well as the ability of NAFTA's own governing bodies to maintain a level playing field for the producers of the three countries. The possibility exists that if the organization continues to progress, it could be extended to the countries of both Central and South America, making the agreement a hemisphere-wide one. The continued globalization of economic activity dictates the development of more such agreements throughout the world in the future.

NAFTA and the Environment. When U.S. president Bill Clinton campaigned for congressional support for NAFTA, he indicated that a key concept in the treaty's content would be the improvement of environmental conditions along U.S. borders. By 2000 this goal had met only modest success. While many of the factories erected by large multinational corporations on the Mexican side of the border have adopted strict regulations concerning environmental protection, many smaller, more marginal firms have failed to do so. Enforcement of regulations to preserve the environment has been haphazard. Local authorities on the Mexican side of the border claim that the money and manpower necessary to implement the laws have not been made available. The waterways between Mexico and the United States still contain a high degree of pollution, from both industrial and human waste. The governments of both countries must take a more active role in enforcing environmental controls if the situation is to improve.

Popular Opposition to Trading Patterns. Strong protests against existing trade treaties and the further domination of the world's economy by a few of the richest countries materialized during a meeting of the World Trade Organization in Seattle, Washington, during November and December of 1999. Representatives of a wide variety of dissident groups launched public demonstrations against meetings of industrial and political leaders who, the protesters argued, were concentrating more economic power in the hands of the wealthiest segment of society at the expense of the impoverished majority in the poorer countries of the world. The dissidents argued for a more equitable distribution of global resources as well as assistance to the economies of the developing countries.

Groups of demonstrators locked arms to block access to the Seattle convention center, impeding the arrival of the organization's delegates. Rioting resulted in the destruction of automobiles and the breaking into and looting of stores in the vicinity of the center. Protesters included labor union members, environmentalists, and representatives of Third World countries, among others. In the year 2000 the members of NAFTA had reason to anticipate continued pressure from environmentalists who opposed implementation of the agreement.

Carl Henry Marcoux

For Further Study

Bertrab, Hermann von. *Negotiating NAFTA: A Mexican Envoy's Account.* Foreword by Sidney Weintraub. Westport, Conn.: Praeger, 1997.

Grinspun, Ricardo, and Maxwell A. Cameron, eds. *The Political Economy of North American Free Trade.* New York: St. Martin's Press, 1993.

Moller, Rosa María. *The Effects of the North American Free Trade Agreement on State Policies.* Sacramento: California Research Bureau, California State Library: 1995.

National Commission for Employment Policy (U.S.). *The Employment Effects of the North American Free Trade Agreement: Recommendations and Background Studies,* Washington, D.C.: National Commission for Employment Policy, 1992.

The Caribbean

Caribbean economies are small, dependent, and linked in many ways to the economies of the industrialized countries that trade with them. During the 1960's, Caribbean sugar and banana exports commanded high prices in the world markets. In the 1970's, world oil prices soared to unheard-of heights and caused deep recessions in most industrialized nations. These recessions in the 1970's and 1980's led to a decrease in demand and falling prices for the Caribbean's chief exports—sugar, bananas, coffee, citrus, bauxite, and aluminum. As a result, the volume of trade between the Caribbean and the industrialized nations dropped. At the same time the Caribbean region's exports dropped, their imports increased, causing a trade deficit.

Most Caribbean countries import manufactured goods and most of their food and energy supplies. Trinidad, Barbados, and Puerto Rico, for example, import more than three-quarters of their food needs. International prices and terms of trade are determined by nations outside the region. Transnational corporations provide the marketing and refining of raw materials. The manufactured goods imported into the Caribbean region are relatively expensive compared to the prices of sugar, bananas, and bauxite on the world market.

The United States is the Caribbean region's most significant trade partner. For example, nearly 50 percent of Barbados's exports and imports involves the United States. Similarly, 64 percent of the Dominican Republic's exports goes to the United States, and 35 percent of imports is from there. Two-thirds of Haiti's imports comes from the United States, and 85 percent of Haiti's exports is destined for the United States. Canada, and the European Union (EU), and other Latin American countries are also trade partners. The Caribbean islands of Guadeloupe and Martinique are departments of France and, therefore, part of the European Union.

The United States is not a trading partner with Cuba. After the Bay of Pigs (1961) and Cuban missile crisis (1962), the United States placed an economic embargo on Cuba and prohibited U.S. citizens from traveling to the island. Cuba instituted special trade agreements with the Soviet Union and exported sugar, tobacco, and minerals to them in exchange for petroleum, wheat, fertilizer, and equipment. After the fall of the Soviet Union, Cuba encouraged foreign investment and trade with Canada, Spain, and France, and with other Latin American countries. However, Cuba's trade relationship with the United States remained uncertain at the start of the twenty-first century. In 1996 Cuban jets shot down two planes flown by a Miami-based Cuban exile group. In response, the United States enacted the Helms-Burton Act. This act penalizes companies that do business with Cuba, strengthening the trade embargo against Cuba.

Many Caribbean nations have preferential trade agreements with European Union members. Without these guaranteed markets, many Caribbean countries could not compete internationally. Because of their colonial history of plantation economies, plantation agricultural crops such as sugar and bananas are among their leading exports. Sugar is the leading export in the Dominican Republic, Cuba, St. Kitts, and Guadeloupe.

High production costs and low world market prices have made sugar's future prospects as an export unfavorable. Bananas are another important export for many Caribbean islands. Guadeloupe, Martinique, the Windward Islands, and Jamaica export bananas to the European Union, where the old colonial powers give the crop preference over cheaper bananas from Central America. In France, bananas are purchased from Martinique and Guadeloupe. Great Britain buys bananas from its former colonies, Jamaica and the British Windward Islands.

Martinique Page 570

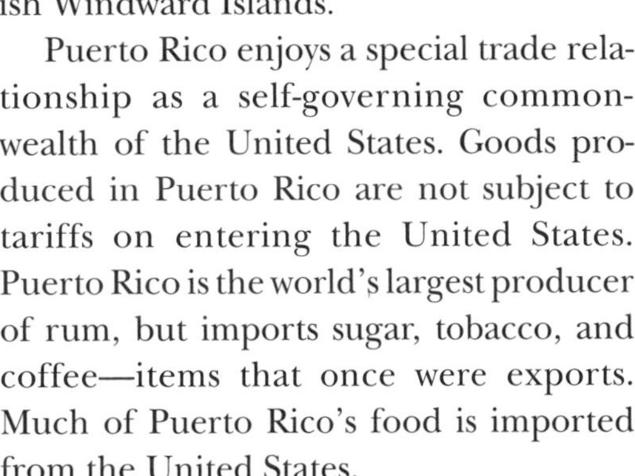

Puerto Rico enjoys a special trade relationship as a self-governing commonwealth of the United States. Goods produced in Puerto Rico are not subject to tariffs on entering the United States. Puerto Rico is the world's largest producer of rum, but imports sugar, tobacco, and coffee—items that once were exports. Much of Puerto Rico's food is imported from the United States.

Not all trade in the Caribbean region is legal. Marijuana, called ganja in the Caribbean, was introduced by Hindu East Indians in the nineteenth century and used in religious rituals. Most ganja is grown by small farmers in Jamaica. Jamaica is a significant supplier of marijuana to the United States. The Caribbean region serves as a channel through which South American drugs such as cocaine pass. The Bahamas is a distribution center for illegal drugs headed for U.S. markets.

Caribbean Community and Common Market (CARICOM). This association of Caribbean islands was formed in 1973, in an effort to create a common market and wield more influence in world markets. CARICOM was made up of thirteen former British colonies: Antigua-Barbuda, the Bahamas, Barbados, Belize, Dominica, Guyana, Jamaica, Grenada, St. Kitts-Nevis, St. Vincent and the Grenadines, Montserrat, St. Lucia, and Trinidad and Tobago. In 1995 Suriname became the first non-British island to become part of CARICOM. Haiti and the Dominican Republic have observer status. Positive changes have developed in the Caribbean region because of the existence of CARICOM. Its members achieved economic integration when the Caribbean Food Corporation was formed. This initiative was created to improve the marketing of local foods.

The West Indies Shipping Corporation, also created as an outgrowth of CARICOM, coordinates the transportation of West Indian goods. CARICOM has failed to narrow the economic gap between the "haves" and the "have-nots" in the Caribbean region, however. Jamaica and Trinidad, two of CARICOM's bigger members, gain the most benefits from the organization. Islands that are closer together seem to trade more within CARICOM than islands separated by large expanses of ocean. The economic integration that the Caribbean region seeks is impeded by water, distance, and the relatively small size of its market.

Caribbean Basin Initiative (CBI). This initiative, which went into effect in 1984, was created by the United States to promote economic growth and trade in the Caribbean region while safeguarding U.S. political and economic interests in the region. Cuba and Grenada were not included in CBI for political reasons. The plan's benefits were to include low-interest loans, duty-free exports to the United States, tax exemptions for business conventions held in the Caribbean region, and simplified investment and tax treaty negotiations.

The Dominican Republic and Jamaica have been the leading beneficiaries of CBI, with most investment in the region going to garment assembly plants. The Caribbean Basin Initiative has had little positive impact on the region. Funds made available by the CBI have been minimal, and the U.S. market has permitted entry on a duty-free basis to only 7 percent of the Caribbean region's exports. The main recipients of CBI investment are U.S. corporations that have plants in the Caribbean and thereby have access to cheap labor.

Carol Ann Gillespie

For Further Study

Blouet, Brian W., and Olwyn M. Blouet. *Latin America and the Caribbean: A Systematic and Regional Survey.* 3d ed. New York: John Wiley & Sons, 1997.

Bolioli, Oscar L. *The Caribbean: Culture of Resistance, Spirit of Hope.* New York: Friendship Press, 1993.

Clawson, David L. *Latin America and the Caribbean: Lands and Peoples.* Dubuque, Iowa: Wm. C. Brown, 1997.

Knight, Franklin W., and Cohn A. Palmer. *The Modern Caribbean.* Chapel Hill: University of North Carolina Press, 1989.

Communications

North America

Since the American Revolution, North America has played a critical role in the development and deployment of innovative communications systems and technology throughout the world. When Europeans began to colonize the New World, messages traveled only as fast as humans could move on horseback or aboard ships. At the beginning of the twenty-first century, messages are delivered worldwide at the speed of light.

Print Communication. The first book printed in North America was made in Mexico in 1539. The first printing press in Great Britain's North American colonies was established in 1638 at Harvard College. Presses such as the Harvard press produced religious materials as well as governmental and educational pamphlets and books.

The first newspaper in North America was published by Benjamin Harris in 1690. The tradition of newspapers as a form of mass communication has continued into the twenty-first century. In the year 2000, 300 daily newspapers were being published in Mexico, 110 in Canada, and more than 1,500 in the United States.

Daily newspapers in the United States reach approximately sixty million readers. Although the number of individual newspapers in the United States was declining by the end of the twentieth century, newspapers still produced the largest amount of gross advertising revenue of any form of mass media. In the wake of technological advances, newspapers have changed their focus from pure news reporting to in-depth reporting, analysis, and interpretation of news. They also are providing online versions of their product, thus ensuring their continued importance in shaping the public's understanding of the world around them.

In 1741 Andrew Bradford published the first magazine in the American colonies, beginning a tradition of providing a compilation of essays and articles for readers. Sales remained low throughout the eighteenth century, because of low levels of literacy and slow postal systems. By the end of the American Civil War in 1865, compulsory education had helped to increase the literacy rate in the United States and railroads had improved the mail system. As a result, the U.S. magazine became a staple of popular culture.

The late nineteenth century saw the introduction of such mass-circulation magazines as *Ladies' Home Journal* and *Cosmopolitan.* By the beginning of the twentieth century, political and social reformers were using magazines as a means of communicating their ideas about social change. Magazine journalists used their forum to expose corruption and scandal in U.S. society. This new approach to journalism was called "muckraking."

In the years that followed, the magazine continued to develop as a form of mass communication. Ranging from comic books to trade newsletters, the magazine has become a critical means of reaching segmented audiences. As the population grew, more and more titles dealt with specialized interests, covering such narrowly focused special-interest categories as erotica, sports, fitness, lifestyles, regional or ethnic issues, and age-related topics. During the 1990's, one magazine alone, *Modern Maturity*, reached more than 22.5 million households.

POSTAL SYSTEMS. In early colonial times, the delivery of mail was entirely dependent upon travelers who were willing to carry correspondence. In 1691 the British monarchy established the groundwork for a North American postal system. Benjamin Franklin was appointed joint postmaster general for the Crown in 1753, and immediately began to improve postal service.

As technology advanced, so did the mails. Moving from foot to horseback, stagecoach, steamboat, rail, automobile, and airplane, postal systems were able to distribute mail more quickly and efficiently. The success of mail service in North America has allowed business and personal communication to be transacted economically across long distances. By 1998 the United States Postal Service estimated that it was delivering 107 billion pieces of first-class mail each year to 130 million delivery points. The U.S. Postal Service handles an estimated 41 percent of the world's total mail volume. Japan is a distant second, with 6 percent.

Canada has the second-largest postal system in North America. The Canadian government provides mail service to some 18,200 post offices through the Canada Post Corporation's retail outlets. During fiscal year 1995-1996, Canada Post processed more than 11.8 billion pieces of mail. Around the same period, Mexico's Servicio Postal Mexicano (Sepomex) was undergoing a steady series of upgrades to keep pace with its northern neighbors.

TELEGRAPHY AND TELEPHONY. In 1844 Samuel F. B. Morse designed a means of sending sound waves over wires. By 1861 a transcontinental line was completed, linking the east and west coasts. The telegraph was limited in that it could only transmit in coded signals, the dots and dashes of Morse code.

Italian inventor Antonio Meucci developed a transducer that allowed voices to be transmitted over telegraph wires. In 1876 Alexander Graham Bell developed a workable system for actually implementing Meucci's ideas, which became the telephone. By 1877 the first permanent outdoor telephone wires had been strung. As early as 1882, Bell's telephone provider, American Bell, was taking in more than $1 million per year in revenue.

The next logical step was to find a means of transmitting signals through the air. The first step in that direction came in 1901, when Guglielmo Marconi successfully transmitted Morse code signals across the Atlantic. In 1906 Lee De Forest perfected the Audion tube, which enabled radio receivers to pick up complex sounds such as voices and music. De Forest's creation led to radio telephones and paved the way for long-distance service. On January 25, 1915, the first transcontinental telephone service was established between New York City and San Francisco. By 1927 the first transcontinental line had been established between New York and London. This was quickly followed by the establishment of service to other countries.

The next big evolutionary development for telephone service and all communications came on July 1, 1948, when the Bell System unveiled the transistor, which allowed for the amplification of the signal. This amplification allowed a new form of transmission of telephone messages: microwave. On August 17, 1951, Bell Laboratories opened the first transcontinental microwave system. Comprising 107 relay stations spaced about 30 miles (48 km.) apart, the microwave system spanned the United States.

Satellite Systems. In 1945 Arthur C. Clarke proposed that artificial satellites containing radio repeaters be placed in geostationary orbit around the earth's equator. In December, 1958, the U.S. satellite *SCORE* was the first to relay a human voice from space back to the earth, sending President Dwight D. Eisenhower's Christmas message to earthbound receivers. By 1965 the commercial communication satellite *Intelsat 1* (also known as "early bird") was successfully placed into orbit. Intelsat provided 240 high-quality relays for television signals and allowed the exchange of programs between Western Europe and North America.

In 1983 the first cellular phone network was made available in the United States. Cellular technology combines microwave and satellite technology to allow mobile, wireless telephones. By 1985 the cellular network was extended to cellular phones in cars. As of 1996, the United States had more than 32.5 million mobile phone users.

The addition of fiber-optic cables that allow digital information to be sent as pulses of light has allowed the telephone to move data worldwide at the speed of light. The United States has developed a complex telephony network. A combination of fiber-optic cable, microwave relay stations, satellites, and traditional and coaxial cable provides telephone service to nearly everyone in the United States. The current network of geostationary communication satellites handles approximately 75 percent of international telephone calls, as well as television signals, data transmissions, electronic mail, and facsimiles.

By way of comparison, Canada estimated a total of 17.9 million telephones within its borders in 1996. Some one hundred companies combined to provide service to nearly 99 percent of all Canadian households. Canada's telephony network uses a satellite system to provide nearly total nationwide access. The Canadian network features the world's longest microwave relay system, which extends for 3,980 miles (6,400 km.).

Despite the launch of the two Solidaridad satellites in 1993 and 1994, Mexico has less thorough coverage, with fewer than 12 million telephones in a country of over ninety million people. The Mexican telephone network was privatized in 1990, and, while Teléfonos de México (Telmex) has seen strong growth as a result of competition in the telecommunications market, as of 1999 it was estimated that there were fewer than eighteen lines for every hundred Mexicans.

Radio. In 1912 the U.S. Congress ordered the Department of Commerce to begin issuing licenses for commercial radio operators. This was done in an effort to keep public signals from interfering with government transmissions. In 1920 the first commercial station, KDKA in Pittsburgh, Pennsylvania, went on the air. In 1927 Congress established the Federal Radio Commission (which later became the Federal Communications Commission—FCC) to regulate the airwaves in the interests of the public. By the 1930's, radio was firmly established as a part of U.S. popular culture. The advent of radio revolutionized the reporting of news, because coverage of events was much more rapid than was possible with newspapers. Live coverage of events in the 1940's, especially the work of World War II correspondents, allowed listeners to vicariously experience events that would have seemed more remote when reported only through newspapers.

Prior to World War II, frequency modulation (FM) was introduced. FM operates on a higher frequency than amplitude modulation (AM), and it sends its signals in a straight line, whereas AM bounces its signal off the ionosphere. As a result, FM produces a higher-quality broadcast signal. By the 1990's, FM had overtaken AM as the most popular radio format. By 1990 there were 4,792 AM stations and 5,678 FM stations, which could reach 95 percent of U.S. homes. At that time, U.S. commercial radio stations generated more than $8 billion dollars in advertising revenue.

Radio is a massive medium, providing North Americans with entertainment and information. Despite the vast size of the audience and the prevalence of nationally syndicated programming, radio remains a primarily local medium in that the information and entertainment that each station provides is carefully tailored to serve a local population. After having survived competition from television, radio is integrating its services into emerging Internet technologies, thus extending an individual station's reach beyond the limits of its transmitter, enabling local stations to reach an international audience.

In the United States in 1994, the FCC had licensed more than ten thousand commercial radio stations, and it was estimated that there were 2,122 radio receivers for every 1,000 people in the United States. U.S. radio also broadcasts to foreign countries under the auspices of the Voice of America. It was estimated that in 1996, Voice of America had more than 126 million listeners.

Canada had 841 radio stations in 1996 and 968 radio rebroadcasters. It was estimated that there were 919 radio receivers for every 1,000 Canadians. Mexico, meanwhile, had 1,500 broadcast stations licensed by the Dirección General de Concessiones y Permisos de Telecommunicaciónes, most of which broadcast the National Hour program. It was estimated that there were 227 radio receivers for every 1,000 Mexicans.

TELEVISION. In 1928 General Electric began experimenting with broadcasting television signals. The National Broadcasting Corporation (NBC) began experimental telecasting in 1930; by 1939, the NBC station in New York was broadcasting a regular schedule of programs. Television remained a toy for the wealthy until 1948, when both NBC and the Columbia Broadcasting System (CBS) turned their full attention to developing television as a medium of mass communication. By 1952 there were more than 17 million television receivers in the United States.

By 2000 it was estimated that television sets were in use in more than 97 percent of U.S. households. One reason for this expansion of coverage was the development of cable television. Cable, first known as Community Antenna Television (CATV), originated in 1949, originally a means to bring television service to remote geographical areas of the United States that otherwise faced inadequate reception of television signals. By the 1970's, specialty programming was created just for cable systems. This programming included channels devoted to 24-hour news coverage (CNN), sports reporting (ESPN), and music videos (MTV).

Cable's influence expanded, thanks to satellite-based distribution of programming. These systems allow individuals to use a satellite receiving dish as small as 12 inches (30 centimeters) across as a means of receiving television and radio signals directly from geostationary orbiting satellites. Subscribers can receive more than one hundred channels of programming.

The Canadian Broadcasting Corporation (CBC), which is financed by the Canadian government but allowed to operate independently, operates national television and radio networks. CBC and the privately owned Canadian Television Network (CTV) serve 99 percent of the Canadian population. Approximately 75 percent of Canadian households subscribe to cable TV systems.

Mexico's television services have been privatized. Most services are provided by Televisión Azteca and Azteca Televisa. It is estimated that there were only slightly more than twelve million television sets in Mexico.

Television remains the mass medium of choice in North America, serving as mass entertainer, mass persuader, mass informer, and mass educator. As the cost of satellite delivery systems for individual homes continues to fall, and as Internet technologies emerge, enabling the use of the Internet as a delivery system for television, people will have more options from which to choose television programming. As options increase, new market and social forces will emerge to shape the form of television in the twenty-first century.

THE INTERNET. With the development of computing networks, a revolutionary communications system has arisen that is uniting all existing forms of communication and molding them into a powerful new means of distributing information. Much of the development of these networks occurred in North America.

In 1957 the U.S. Department of Defense shepherded the design and planning of a network of computers linked by telephone lines. The network, ARPANET, had its first node attached at the University of California, Los Angeles (UCLA), on September 2, 1969. ARPANET usage continued to grow at a steady rate until 1974, when the first public network, Telenet, was made available.

In 1984 Canada began a one-year push to link all Canadian universities to the growing network. By 1986 the first Freenet, encouraging public use of network services, went on line. At the same time the National Science Foundation created NSFNET, which increased connection speed and provided the opportunity for most U.S. universities to connect to it.

The year 1990 saw two milestones in the development of the Internet: ARPANET went off-line, and the first commercial dial-up access service, The World, made the net available to home computers through telephone lines. In 1991 Tim Berners-Lee developed the World Wide Web. The World Wide Web remained a domain primarily for physicists until the Mosaic browser was released in 1993. As a result of Mosaic, the Web's traffic grew several thousand-fold over the next year. By 1995 Compuserve, America Online, and Prodigy began to offer dial-up access nationwide. In June, 1995, an estimated twenty-three thousand Web sites were available on the World Wide Web. By December of 1999, that number had grown to nearly ten million.

THE CANADIAN RADIO-TELEVISION AND TELECOMMUNICATIONS COMMISSION

The Canadian Radio-Television and Telecommunications Commission (CRTC) is the governmental agency that regulates all electronic communication systems in Canada. The CRTC is a licensing agency for radio and television stations, but its focus is to ensure that a certain percentage of programs aired in Canada have Canadian content. These content quotas are aimed at maintaining Canadian cultural identity despite the overwhelming influence of U.S. programming. The CRTC also encourages production of Canadian radio and television programs.

THE EVOLUTION OF E-MAIL

One of the most popular features of networking is electronic mail (e-mail). E-mail enables users to send messages to other network users through the lines that make up the Internet. The first messages that most would recognize as e-mail were made possible in 1972, when Ray Tomlinson modified an e-mail program for use on ARPANET. Tomlinson chose the @ (at) sign, which has come to symbolize electronic mail. By 1973 e-mail comprised 75 percent of all traffic on ARPANET; by mid-1999 almost 200 million people worldwide used e-mail and the Internet.

The World Wide Web, or Web, was introduced in Mexico near the end of 1993. By the end of the 1990's, the number of Web servers had grown at an average of five to six new servers per month. In 1994 the National Council for Science and Technology financed a national Internet backbone with the cooperation of MEXNET (a network composed of Mexican universities). The result of this effort was the National Technological Network, which has helped Mexicans become a part of the Internet despite the comparatively high costs of telecommunications access in Mexico.

Numbers alone do not account for the impact of the Internet as a communications system. The Internet takes the old model of central distribution of information from a broadcast network or a printing press and turns it on its head. Thanks to the Internet, individuals now can broadcast their individual world views and observations around the world. The Internet allows formerly marginalized communities to have a voice in the reporting and interpretation of news. Although traditional mass media entities rushed to provide an Internet presence, those old voices no longer monopolize North American communication systems.

B. Keith Murphy

FOR FURTHER STUDY

Gross, Lynne Schafer. *Telecommunications: An Introduction to Electronic Media.* Madison, Wis.: Brown & Benchmark, 1995.

Hafner, Katie. *Where Wizards Stay Up Late: The Origins of the Internet.* New York: Touchstone, 1998.

Tedford, Thomas L. *Freedom of Speech in the United States.* New York: McGraw-Hill, 1993.

Wilson, Stan Le Roy. *Mass Media/Mass Culture.* New York: McGraw-Hill, 1994.

THE CARIBBEAN

The twenty-nine island countries of the Caribbean enjoy the same types of communications systems the rest of the world has. Radio communication is the choice of most of island residents and has been the main source of communications for decades. Television is gaining acceptance, and has been increasingly available since the early 1990's.

Print communications are also important to the Caribbean people, with most of the newspapers published in either Spanish or English. New technologies were just starting to be used widely in the region in the late 1990's, but their use was growing rapidly. Global fiber-optic technology is advancing into the region; when completed, it will be among the most modern in the world.

Radio. In the late 1990's, the Caribbean region had 573 radio stations, including 10 shortwave radio facilities. Cuba had the most radio stations with 156, the Dominican Republic was second with 126, and Puerto Rico was third with 113. Amplitude modulation (AM) stations were the greatest in number in the islands. The number of frequency modulation (FM) stations was growing and expected to continue to expand for the foreseeable future. Five Caribbean nations do not have any FM stations, but were in the process of adding this form of communication. The shortwave radio band does not play as important a role in the communications process as it once did. Of the ten stations being operated in the late 1990's, some are expected to be phased out.

Television. Television plays an important part in Caribbean society. Many people in the region get entertainment, news, and information about world affairs from television. There are 148 television stations in the Caribbean, plus nine repeater stations that take the transmitted signal and rebroadcast it. Cuba leads the region in numbers, with fifty-eight television stations; the Dominican Republic has twenty-five stations; Puerto Rico has eighteen stations plus three that are assigned to the U.S. Armed Forces Radio and Television Service.

New technologies for television viewing are also growing in importance on the islands, including cable television, satellite receivers, microwave, and fiber-optics communications.

Telephones. Telephone systems in the Caribbean range from primitive to quite advanced. Cuba has the largest population in the region, but its telephone system is considered to be among the world's least developed, and it has not been advancing. The Puerto Rican system is considered to be one of the most advanced anywhere. It is modern and is integrated with that of the U.S. high-capacity submarine cable and Intelsat with high-speed data capacity. Most of the region uses the

Radio Stations in the Caribbean Region

Country	*AM*	*FM*	*Shortwave*
Cuba	150	5	1
Dominican Republic	120	0	6
Puerto Rico	50	63	0
Haiti	33	0	2
Netherlands Antilles	9	4	0
Anguilla, B.W.I.	5	6	1
Montserrat	8	4	0
U.S. Virgin Islands	4	8	0
Trinidad	1	10	0
Aruba	4	6	0
Guadeloupe	2	8	0

A Caribbean Anomaly

Located just off the north coast of Venezuela and west of the Netherlands Antilles, the island of Aruba, a mecca for tourists, had much better developed communications systems in 1999 than did most other areas of the region. The island had about 33,000 telephones—nearly one for each two islanders. Moreover, the telephone system worked exceptionally well, particularly for international calls.

digital telephone system, and most countries have some sort of cellular telephone operation.

Most islands rely on satellite earth stations and microwave relay stations to communicate around the world. Many of the older, well-established telephone systems still use coaxial submarine cable systems to communicate to Europe and the United States. Several nations in the extreme south of the Caribbean region still use radiotelephone links to communicate with each other. There are approximately 3.2 million telephones in the Caribbean region.

Newspapers. The newspaper was the first communications outlet for the people of the Caribbean. In the late 1990's, 107 newspapers were being published in the islands. The capital of Cuba, Havana, has the highest-circulation newspaper, with more than 600,000 readers; a total of seventeen newspapers were being published in Cuba. San Juan, Puerto Rico, had two daily newspapers with a total circulation of almost 500,000, and the Sunday newspaper in Kingston, Jamaica, had a circulation of 100,000.

The region's newspaper industry is not as strong as it was before television arrived, but newspapers are considered by many people to be the most reliable source of information for world news. Most of the newspapers in the region are published in Spanish, with English being the second most used language. In all the Caribbean nations, free press is considered the key to a free democracy. However, not all of the region's countries enjoy a true free press.

Internet. The Internet is a growing business in the Caribbean region, with countries there taking a leadership role in its development. The growth of the Internet is especially significant in the more advanced nations, but it still lags in the poorer countries, where no real growth is expected for several years.

Mexico is working with some of the Spanish-speaking nations in the Caribbean, assisting in the development of the Web and in support areas, such as e-commerce and program development. The English-speaking nations have support from England and Europe, and have been leaders in Internet improvement.

Earl P. Andresen

For Further Study

Blouet, Brian W., and Olwyn M. Blouet. *Latin America and the Caribbean: A Systematic and Regional Survey.* 3d ed. New York: John Wiley & Sons, 1997.

Sealey, Neil. *Caribbean World: A Complete Geography.* New York: Cambridge University Press, 1992.

South America, Central America, and the Caribbean. London: Europa Publications, 1999.

Information on the World Wide Web

A good starting place for Internet research on communications systems in the Caribbean region is the CIA World Fact Book 2000. (www.cia.gov/cia/publications/factbook)

Summer ice floes in Canada's Hudson Bay, which is actually an inland sea. (R. Kent Rasmussen)

Nevada's largest city and one of the fastest-growing major cities in the United States, Las Vegas has built its economy on legal gambling and entertainment. (PhotoDisc)

The largest of the volcanic Windward Islands, Martinique is still a colonial possession of France. (Clyde L. Rasmussen)

An active volcano in Hawaii National Park, Mauna Loa has erupted an average of once every three to four years since 1830. The volcano is 13,680 feet (4,170 meters) high and is the largest mountain in the world in cubic content. (Corbis)

One of the chief scenic attractions of Mexico's capital city is the floating gardens of Xochimilco, a town located about twelve miles (twenty km.) southeast of Mexico City. The gardens began with the early Aztecs, who grew flowers and produce on rafts floating in shallow water. (Corbis)

Miami, Florida. (PhotoDisc)

Minneapolis, the largest city in Minnesota, is separated from its sister city, St. Paul, by the Mississippi River. (PhotoDisc)

The Mississippi River, the greatest river of North America, begins in Minnesota and flows about 2,350 miles (3,781 km.) to the Gulf of Mexico. (PhotoDisc)

Montreal is the largest city in Quebec, Canada, and the second-largest in Canada. It is located at the confluence of the Ottawa and St. Lawrence Rivers. (Corbis)

Covered bridge in Hartland, New Brunswick. (Digital Stock)

Boardwalk at Atlantic City, whose casinos and other attractions have long made the city the most popular tourist destination in New Jersey. (PhotoDisc)

New York City's Manhattan Island in the late nineteenth century. (Corbis)

Modern Manhattan and New York Harbor from the air. (PhotoDisc)

Horseshoe Falls, part of Niagara Falls, where rainbows are virtually perpetual during sunlight hours. (PhotoDisc)

Sea stack formations along Oregon's Cannon Beach on the Pacific Coast. (PhotoDisc)

Palenque. Mayan temple ruins in Mexico's Chiapas state, where dense topical forests were cut down to give visitors access. (Corbis)

Philadelphia, the largest city in Pennsylvania, stands on the west bank of the Delaware River, which separates Pennsylvania from New Jersey. (PhotoDisc)

Pittsburgh, the second-largest city in Pennsylvania, is located where the Allegheny and Monongahela Rivers meet to form the Ohio River. (PhotoDisc)

The second-highest mountain in Mexico, Popocatepetl rises to at height of 17,887 feet (5,465 meters). It was regarded as a dormant volcano popular until late 1994, when it began belching clouds of smoke and ash. In December, 2000, it began to erupt. (Corbis)

Portland, Oregon's largest city, is on the Columbia River, which forms the state's border with Washington. (PhotoDisc)

A Mexican resort town on the Pacific coast, Puerto Vallarta rings the largest natural bay in Mexico and the third largest in the world. (Clyde L. Rasmussen)

Salt Lake City is the capital and largest city of Utah. Although it is the world headquarters of the Church of Jesus Christ of Latter-day Saints within a state whose residents are about 70 percent church members, its own population is nearly half nonmembers. (PhotoDisc)

San Diego, California's oldest and second-largest city. (PhotoDisc)

Seattle, the largest city and chief port of Washington. (Corbis)

Located near the mouth of the Fraser River, Vancouver is the largest city in British Columbia and third-largest in Canada. Built in the 1870's as a sawmill town, it has become a major shipping port and the industrial, financial, and commercial center of the province. (Corbis)

Inner harbor of Victoria, the capital city of British Columbia. Located at the southern tip of Vancouver Island on Canada's West Coast, it is the western terminus of the Trans-Canada Highway, which spans the country. (Corbis)

Cruise ships at St. Thomas in the U.S. Virgin Islands. (PhotoDisc)

Virginia. Jamestown, where the first British settlers in North America landed, has a historical park containing replicas of the early immigrants' ship. (PhotoDisc)

West Virginia is a largely mountainous state with many scenes similar to this.

Yosemite Falls, the highest waterfall in the valley of Yosemite National Park. (Corbis)

The Yosemite Valley provides some of the most spectacular scenery in the world, including this view of the granite mountain called Half Dome. (PhotoDisc)

Gazetteer

Places whose names are printed in SMALL CAPS *are subjects of their own entries in this gazetteer.*

Acapulco. Old Spanish colonial port on Mexico's Pacific coast. For centuries, Acapulco was the eastern end of the Philippines-Mexico trade route. In the 1950's, a highway linking MEXICO CITY and Acapulco was built. In the 1960's, high-rise hotels were built and motion picture celebrities boosted tourism. Death-defying cliff divers of La Quebrada provide a spectacular tourist attraction as they climb barefoot to a sixty-foot-high cliff to dive into the surf.

Aguascalientes. Smallest Mexican state; capital city has the same name. Only 860,000 people live in this state, with more than half residing in its capital city. Situated on the edge of the high plain (*altiplano*) in a transition zone between the arid north and the more temperate regions of central Mexico, Aguascalientes is named for its hot springs. The economy is strong and growing steadily, with manufacturing and assembly plants providing many jobs.

Alabama. Became twenty-second state on December 14, 1819. Located in U.S. South. Total area is 52,423 square miles (135,776 sq. km.), with 1998 population of 4.4 million. Named after tribe of the Creek confederacy. First permanent European settlement was in 1702. Alabama Territory was created in 1817. In 1846 Montgomery (1998 population, 197,014) was made the capital; also was capital of Confederate States of America in 1861. Largest city is Birmingham (1998 population, 252,997).

Alaska. Became forty-ninth state on January 3, 1959. Located in far northwest NORTH AMERICA. The largest U.S. state in size at 656,424 square miles (1,700,140 sq. km.), its 1998 population was 614,010. Name may come from Aleut word meaning "mainland." Purchased from Russia for $7.2 million in 1867. Capital is Juneau (1998 population, 30,191) and largest city is Anchorage (1998 population, 254,982).

Acapulco Pages 380, 511

Alaska Highway. Cross-country artery linking ALASKA and Alaska Highway with the rest of the United States. Formerly known as the ALCAN HIGHWAY, it is 1,523 miles (2,45 km.) long and runs through the YUKON connecting DAWSON CREEK, BRITISH COLUMBIA, with Fairbanks, Alaska. U.S. Army engineers constructed it during World War II at a cost of $135 million to provide an overland military supply route to Alaska.

Anchorage Page 512

Alberta. Most western of Canada's three PRAIRIE PROVINCES. Bounded by BRITISH COLUMBIA on the west, SASKATCHEWAN on the east, the NORTHWEST TERRITORIES on the north, and MONTANA in the south. In 1999 three million people lived here in an area of 255,285 square miles (661,954 sq. km.), close to the size of TEXAS. The majority of people live in EDMONTON and CALGARY. Alberta's resources include oil and gas, ranching in the foothills, and farming. Ethnic groups include Germans, Ukrainians, and Scandinavians.

Albuquerque. Largest city in NEW MEXICO. Located on the RIO GRANDE at 4,945 feet (1,507 meters) elevation, with 1998 population of 419,311. Founded in 1806 and named for Duke of Albuquerque, the Spanish viceroy of NEW SPAIN.

Alcan Highway. See ALASKA HIGHWAY.

American Falls. See NIAGARA FALLS.

Americas. Collective term for the lands of the WESTERN HEMISPHERE, including NORTH AMERICA, Central America, South America, and the islands of the CARIBBEAN.

Anegada. One of the British VIRGIN ISLANDS in the CARIBBEAN SEA. Located about 14 miles (22.5 km.) north of VIRGIN GORDA. Unlike the other islands in this chain, which are hilly and volcanic, Anegada is a flat coral and limestone atoll. It is 9 miles (14 km.) long and 2 miles (3 km.) wide, with a population of 150. Snorkeling and scuba diving in the beautiful reefs attract many tourists.

Anguilla. Most northerly of the LEEWARD ISLANDS. Located between the CARIBBEAN SEA and the Atlantic Ocean. It stretches from northeast to southwest about 16 miles (26 km.) and is only 3 miles (5 km.) across at its widest point. The dry, limestone island has no streams or rivers, only saline ponds used for salt production. Named Anguille ("eel") by the French, it has been a British colony since 1650, with a brief period of independence in the 1960's.

Antigua. Largest, most developed of the British LEEWARD ISLANDS (108 square miles/280 sq. km.). Includes the island of BARBUDA. Made of limestone coral and covered in dry, grassy flatlands. Sugarcane plantations were the mainstay of the economy two centuries ago, but it is now a popular tourist haven. The population of sixty-five thousand is almost entirely of African origin. The capital—St. John's—is a busy harbor town.

Appalachian Mountains. Mountain system of eastern North America stretching from southern Canada to ALABAMA. It is an eroded, fold-and-thrust belt, 250-300 million years old. Highest peak is Mount Mitchell, NORTH CAROLINA, at 6,684 feet (2,037 meters).

Arctic map Page 381

Arctic Territories. Often referred to as the NORTHWEST TERRITORIES. A region in northern Canada which encompasses the territorial administrative regions of Baffin, Keewatin, Kitikmeot, Fort Smith, and Inuvik. The territories have an area of 1,322,910 square miles (3,426,320 sq. km.). They reach into the Arctic Circle and include thousands of islands, the largest of which are Victoria Island in the west and BAFFIN ISLAND in the east. More than one-half the region's roughly 58,000 people (1991) are Inuits (Eskimos) and Native Americans. Heavy federal funding provides services.

Arizona. Became forty-eighth state on February 14, 1912. Located in the U.S. Southwest. Total area of 114,006 square miles (295,276 sq. km.) with 1998 population of 4.7 million. The name is thought to come from the Pima word for "place of the small spring." Explored by Spanish conquistador Francisco Vásquez de Coronado in 1540. The first permanent European settlement was at Tubac in 1752. North of Gila River became part of United States when the Treaty of Guadalupe Hidalgo was signed in 1848 at the end of the Mexican War. In 1850 it was organized as Territory of New Mexico. In 1853 the United States purchased the remainder of the present-day state south of Gila River via the Gadsden Purchase. In 1863 the Arizona Territory was created. Capital and largest city is PHOENIX (1998 population, 1.2 million).

Arkansas. Became twenty-fifth state on June 15, 1836. Located in south central area of the United States. Total area of 53,182 square miles (137,742 sq. km.) with 1998 population of 2.5 million. Named after the local Arkansa people. Explored by Hernando de Soto in 1541 and added to the United States in 1803 as part of the Louisiana Purchase. Little Rock is the capital and largest city (1998 population, 175,303).

Aruba. Low, barren, arid island located off the Venezuelan coast, outside the hurricane belt. It is 19.5 miles (31.5 km.) long and 6 miles (9.5 km.) across at its widest point, with an area of 75 square miles (193 sq. km.). Once a member of the Netherlands Antilles, it became independent in 1996. It is popular with tourists because it does not levy sales tax or customs duties and it has a pleasant, sunny climate. The capital is Oranjestad—a charming Dutch colonial town.

Atlanta. Capital and largest city of Georgia. Located at 1,050 feet (320 meters) elevation, with a 1998 population of 403,819. Founded in 1837 as Terminus and renamed Atlanta (derived from the Western and Atlantic Railroad) in 1845; became state capital in 1877. Burned during the Civil War, in November, 1864, by federal troops during Sherman's March to the Sea. Site of 1996 Summer Olympic Games.

Baffin Island. Largest island in Canada. Located between Greenland and the Canadian mainland in the Canadian Arctic. Iqaluit, the capital of Nunavut, is located on the southeastern part of the island. Named after William Baffin, the English navigator who discovered it in 1616. The island is 195,928 square miles (507,451 sq. km.) in area, larger than the state of California.

Bahamas. Independent commonwealth occupying an archipelago of low coral islands located in the Atlantic Ocean 50 miles (80 km.) off the eastern coast of Florida and southward along the Cuban coast. Capital is Nassau. Comprises nearly seven hundred islands and cays (small islands) and almost twenty-four hundred low, barren rock formations. Only twenty-nine of these islands are inhabited, with New Providence and Grand Bahama having four-fifths of the population. The total area is 5,380 square miles (13,934 sq. km.). Christopher Columbus made his first landfall on Hispaniola in 1492. Independent since 1973. Tourism and banking are the main commercial activities. Illegal drug smuggling also plays a role in the economy. In contrast to other Caribbean islands, plantation agriculture was never an important activity because of the poor soils.

Baja California Page 515

Baja California. Mexican peninsula, 800 miles (1,300 km.) long. Thin and mountainous with dry, sandy shores, spectacular desert scenery, and varied wildlife. The name means "Lower California."

Baja California Sur. State in northwestern Mexico that occupies the southern half of Baja California peninsula. Volcanoes dominate the central and eastern parts of its 28,369 square miles (73,475 sq. km.) of territory. Some cotton is grown. Industry has been confined to the processing of cotton byproducts, fish-packing plants, and saltworks. Its population was 279,299 in the late 1980's.

Baltimore Page 512

Baltimore. Largest city in Maryland. Located on Chesapeake Bay at 20 feet (6 meters) altitude, with a 1998 population of 645,593. Founded in 1729 and named for the barons Baltimore, the British founders of the Maryland Colony. During the War of 1812, the British bombardment of Fort McHenry inspired Francis Scott Key to write "The Star-Spangled Banner."

Bahamas Page 389

Banff Page 513

Banff National Park. First national park in Canada; founded in 1885. It is a world-class destination for thousands of tourists each summer. The city of Banff, located in the center of the park, had a population of 5,688 in 1991.

Barbados. Caribbean island located 100 miles (160 km.) east of the arc of the Lesser Antilles; capital is Bridgetown. A coral island, it is actually part of the South American continental shelf. It was colonized by the English in the 1620's. It has one of highest population densities in the world (1,548 per square mile). Sugar and rum exports provided early prosperity; tourism has become a major source of employment.

Barbuda. Small Caribbean island linked to Antigua since it gained its independence from Great Britain in 1981. Its population of twelve hundred has refused to be affiliated with Antigua culturally or politically.

Bays. See under individual names.

Belle Isle, Strait of. See Newfoundland.

Bequia. One of the Grenadine Islands in the Caribbean Sea; located 8.5 miles (13.7 km.) south of St. Vincent. The population depends on fishing, whaling, shipbuilding, and tourism for revenue.

Bering Strait map Page 445

Bering Strait. Sea channel connecting the Arctic Ocean and the Bering Sea and separating North America from Asia by a distance of slightly more than 50 miles (80 km.). During the Ice Age, it is believed, the sea level dropped enough to expose a land bridge—now known as Beringia—over which the first humans to enter the Western Hemisphere came from Asia.

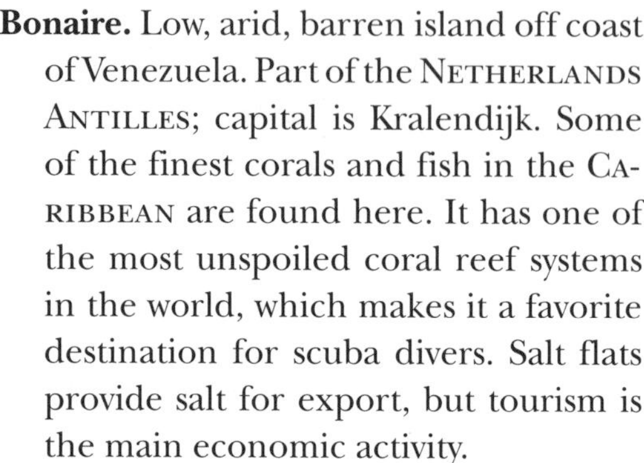

Bonaire. Low, arid, barren island off coast of Venezuela. Part of the Netherlands Antilles; capital is Kralendijk. Some of the finest corals and fish in the Caribbean are found here. It has one of the most unspoiled coral reef systems in the world, which makes it a favorite destination for scuba divers. Salt flats provide salt for export, but tourism is the main economic activity.

Bonaventure Island. See Gaspe.

Boston. Capital and largest city of Massachusetts. Located at the mouth of the Charles River on Boston Bay at 21 feet (6 meters) elevation, with a 1998 population of 555,447. Named for Boston, England. First permanent settlement by Europeans was in 1630. Site of the Boston Massacre of 1770 and the Boston Tea Party of 1773. Home of Old North Church, Beacon Hill, Paul Revere House, and Bunker Hill—site of first major engagement of the American Revolution on June 17, 1775.

British Columbia. Most western of Canadian provinces. Bounded by the Pacific Ocean on the west, Alaska and the Yukon Territory on the north, Alberta on the east, and the U.S. states of Washington and Idaho on the south. In 1999, 4.03 million people lived here, the majority in the Fraser Valley in its

Boston, Massachusetts. (Corbis)

southern part. Logging is a major business. The 366,255 square miles (949,700 sq. km.) of land is equal to the combined size of California, Oregon, and Washington.

British Leeward Islands. See Leeward Islands.

British Virgin Islands. See Virgin Islands, British

Buffalo. Second largest city in New York. Located on the eastern end of Lake Erie at the mouths of the Niagara and Buffalo Rivers at 585 feet (178 meters) elevation, with a 1998 population of 300,717. Settled in 1790 by the Dutch.

Cabo San Lucas. Mexican resort city located at the southern tip of Baja California, where the Gulf of California meets the Pacific Ocean. Its jagged, rocky beach is accessible only by boat. At this southernmost tip of the peninsula, called Finisterra (Land's End), granite batholiths (rock formations) mark the end of a spine of rock that stretches south from Alaska's Aleutian Islands. This is one of the world's best game-fishing locations and the only Mexican city to have a marine preserve within its city limits.

Caicos. British crown colony comprising several small, low-lying coral islands 22 miles (35.5 km.) west of Grand Turk Island in the Atlantic Ocean. The only inhabited islands are South, East, North, Middle, and West Caicos and Providenciales; Pine Cay and Parrot Cay are the only inhabited cays. The name "Caicos" is derived from the Spanish word meaning "string of islands." Salt and cotton were early sources of revenue but have been displaced by banking and insurance.

Calgary. Second largest city in Alberta, Canada. Located along the Bow River in the southern part of the province, it has been a major city in the oil industry. In 1998 the population was 907,100. Calgary hosted the 1988 Winter Olympics and is home of the Calgary Stampede Rodeo.

California Page 514

California. Became thirty-first state on September 9, 1850. Located in the United States' Far West on the Pacific Coast. The third largest state in area, it covers 163,707 square miles (424,002 sq. km.); with 1998 population of 32.6 million, it is the largest state in terms of population. Name comes from a Spanish novel with a fictional island paradise named "California." In 1542 Spanish explorer Juan Rodriguez Cabrillo claimed the territory for Spain. English explorer Sir Francis Drake visited later in the sixteenth century. In the mid-eighteenth century, Russian traders settled California's northern coast. To prevent Russian claims, the Spanish settled in 1769. Between 1769 and 1823, Franciscan missionaries built twenty-one missions along the coast. California became a territory of the Republic of Mexico in 1825, but in 1848 was ceded to the United States by the Treaty of Guadalupe Hidalgo. In 1848 settlers discovered gold in northern California, sparking the greatest gold rush in U.S. history. Sacramento (1998 population, 404,168) is the state capital; Los Angeles (1998 population, 3.6 million) is the largest city.

Cabo San Lucas Page 513

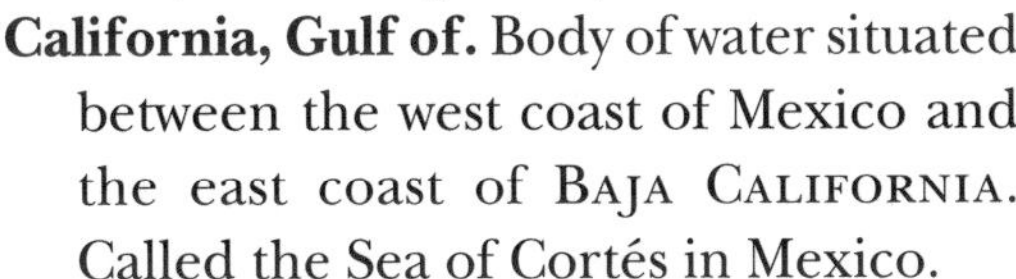

California, Gulf of. Body of water situated between the west coast of Mexico and the east coast of Baja California. Called the Sea of Cortés in Mexico.

Gulf of California Page 515

Campeche. Mexican state on the southwest coast of the Yucatán Peninsula; capital city has the same name. The state covers 19,672 square miles (50,952 sq. km.) and has a population of more than 600,000. It is arid in the north, but just a few kilometers south of the border with the state of Yucatán,

Calgary Page 514

Cancún resorts. (PhotoDisc)

lush tropical rain forests receive as much as 60 inches (1,500 millimeters) of rainfall each year. Maya archaeological sites draw tourists, and offshore oil, a thriving agricultural sector, and a commercial fishing industry have boosted Campeche's economy.

Campeche, Bay of. Body of water between the east coast of Mexico and the west coast of Mexico's Yucatán Peninsula.

Canadian Falls. See Niagara Falls.

Canadian Shield. Immense block of ancient bedrock that spans roughly half of Canada. Found from Labrador in the east to the Beaufort Sea in northwestern Canada. Most of Quebec and Ontario, parts of the Prairie Provinces, and the Arctic Territories are included in this area. It is the result of thousands of years of continental glaciation across the continent. Boreal forest, irregular drainage patterns, and thousands of lakes characterize the region, as the glaciers scoured all land under it to the level of the bedrock. Striations and glacial erratics (scratch marks on the bedrock and huge boulders) seen across the Canadian Shield are evidence of the power of glaciation. The region is rich in mineral deposits, which has brought mining to many areas. Settlement overall is sparse.

Cape Canaveral Page 515

Cancún. Mexican island on the eastern, Caribbean, side of the Yucatán Peninsula; a city of th4e same name is located on the mainland. Powdered limestone sand beaches and comfortable temperatures make this a popular Mexican resort. Inhabited by 450,000 residents, Cancún's main source of revenue is tourism.

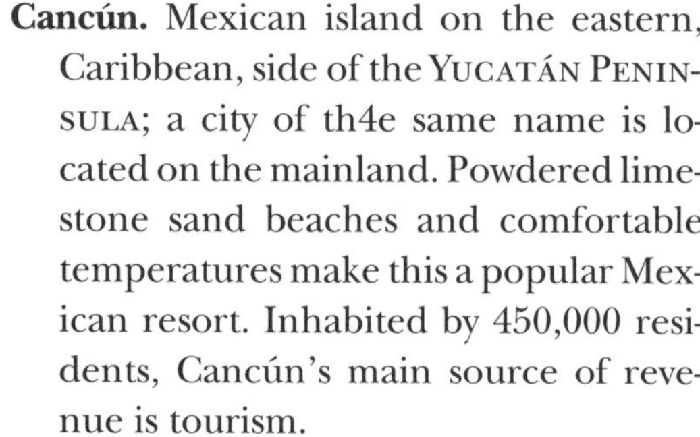

Cape Breton Island. Northeastern portion of Nova Scotia, Canada. The 2-mile-wide (3 km.) Strait of Canso separates it from the rest of the province and the Canadian mainland. The island is 110 miles (175 km.) long and up to 75 miles (120 km.) wide and has an area of 3,981 square miles (10,311 sq. km.). Economic activities include coal mining, lumbering, fishing, and summer tourism. Its population was 120,098 in 1991.

Cape Canaveral. Cape in eastern Florida. The cape area and part of nearby Merritt Island house the John F. Kennedy Space Center, operated by the National Aeronautics and Space Administration. From 1963 to 1973, the cape was known as Cape Kennedy in honor of President John F. Kennedy.

Cape Farewell. Southernmost point of Greenland. Located at 59°46′ north latitude, 550 miles (885 km.) south of the Arctic Circle. It was an important geographic point of reference for early explorers.

Cape Morris Jesup. Northernmost tip of Greenland. At 83°39′ north latitude—460 miles (740 km.) from the North Pole—it was long thought to be the northernmost piece of land on Earth; however, Oodaaq Island now holds this honor.

Cape Spear. Most easterly point in North America. Located at 47.32 degrees north latitude, longitude 52.32 degrees west, on the island of Newfoundland, Canada, 20 miles (32 km.) from St. John's. Cape Spear, and the province of Newfoundland, are closer to Ireland than to Winnipeg, Manitoba, in the middle of Canada.

Caribbean Sea. Portion of the western Atlantic Ocean bounded by Central and South America to the west and south, and the islands of the Antilles chain on the north and east. Its islands, including Puerto Rico, the Cayman Islands, and the Virgin Islands, are popular tourist sites.

Cascade Range. Mountain range in northwestern United States (California, Oregon, and Washington) and adjacent Canada. Approximately 700 miles (1,130 km.) long. Its highest point is Mount Rainier at 14,410 feet (4,392 meters) in Washington. Mount St. Helens, which erupted in 1980 and 1982, is also part of this range.

Cayman Brac. One of the Cayman Islands. Located 89 miles (143 km.) northeast of Grand Cayman. "Braca" is the Gaelic word for "bluff," and this island's most distinctive feature is a rugged limestone cliff that runs down the center of the island. Cayman Brac is 12 miles (19 km.) long; it has a population of twelve hundred and low crime rates.

Cayman Islands. British colony in the Caribbean Sea. Consists of Grand Cayman, Cayman Brac, and Little Cayman islands. Columbus passed the islands in 1503 and, noting that the waters were full of turtles, named them Las Tortugas (later changed to Cayman). The Caymans were uninhabited until the late seventeenth century, when England took over from Spain under the Treaty of Madrid. Caves and coves served as hideaways for pirates, such as Blackbeard and Sir Henry Morgan, who plundered Spain's rich treasure ships. A low crime rate and economic and political stability have made these islands pleasant and prosperous. The Cayman Islands are one of the largest offshore financial centers in the world.

Charleston. Second largest city in South Carolina. Located between the mouths of the Ashley and Cooper Rivers at 9 feet (3 meters) elevation, with a 1998 population of 87,044. Founded in 1670 as Charles Town in honor of Charles II, king of England; incorporated in 1783 with its present name. State capital until 1790. The U.S. Civil War began with the firing on Fort Sumter in 1861, after the South Carolina Ordinance of Secession was passed in Charleston in 1860.

Caribbean Page 382

Cascade Range Page 516

Charlotte. Largest city in North Carolina. Located at 720 feet (219 meters) elevation, with a 1998 population of 504,637. Settled around 1750. Named for Charlotte Sophia of Mecklenburg-Strelitz, wife of King George III of Great Britain.

Charlottetown. Capital of Prince Edward Island, Canada, located nearly in the center of the island. The site of Canadian confederation, which established the country of Canada in 1867 when the provinces of Nova Scotia, New Brunswick, Prince Edward Island, Ontario, and Quebec were joined together to form the country. Total population was 31,400 in 1998.

Chesapeake Bay. Inlet of the Atlantic Ocean separating Delmarva Peninsula from the mainlands of Virginia and Maryland. Primary feeder is the Delaware River. The Chesapeake Bay Bridge-Tunnel, completed in 1964, crosses the bay at its opening. An important part of the Intracoastal Waterway, with many major ports.

Chiapas. State in southern Mexico; capital is Tuxtla Gutierrez. Home to many of Mexico's indigenous communities, who still retain their traditional languages, customs, and dress. Maya ruins in Palenque, the old city of San Cristóbal de las Casas, and numerous Maya villages make Chiapas rich in Mexican culture.

Maya ruins Page 577

Chicago Pages 388, 454, 507

Chicago. Largest city in Illinois and third largest in the United States. Located at the southern end of Lake Michigan at 595 feet (181 meters) elevation, with a 1998 population of 2.8 million. After 130 years of exploration in the area, Fort Dearborn was built in 1803. The Potawatomi called the area "Checagou," after a wild onion that grew in the area. Destroyed in 1871 by a great fire. The cultural, transportation, and economic capital of the Midwest and central United States.

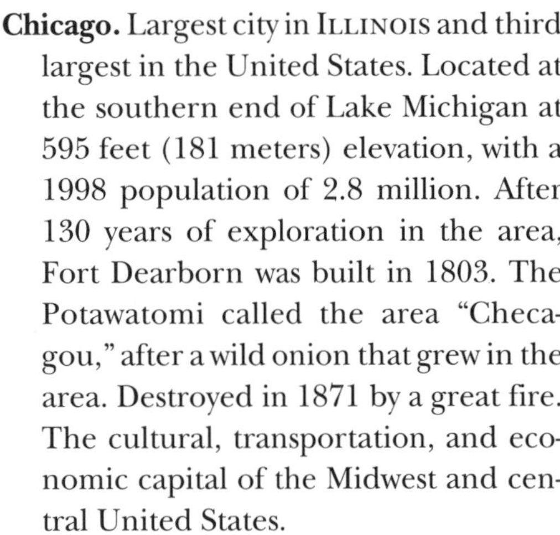

Chichén Itzá Pages 379, 510

Chichén Itzá. One of the finest Maya archaeological sites in the northern part of the Yucatán Peninsula of Mexico. The site occupies 4 square miles (10.5 sq. km.) and consists of the northern (new) zone, which shows distinct Toltec influence, and the southern (old) zone, which is mostly Puuc architecture.

Chihuahua. Largest and one of the richest states in Mexico; state capital has the same name. Wealth comes from mining, timber, cattle raising, *maquiladoras* (U.S. assembly plants), and tourism. Terrain varies greatly from the towering Sierra Madre Occidental in the southwest to the desert scrublands and salt lakes of the Chihuahuan Desert—North America's largest desert—in the northeast. In between lie grassy basins called *llanos* and wooded rolling hills.

Chihuahuan Desert. The largest of the North American deserts; centered between the Sierra Madre Occidental and Sierra Madre Oriental. The Chihuahuan is a high desert. Many of its peaks rise to 5,000 feet (1,500 meters), and its basins are around 2,300 feet (700 meters) above sea level. Three-fourths of the desert lies in Mexico, the rest in New Mexico and Texas.

Christianshåb. See Qasigiannguit.

Churchill. Northernmost seaport in Canada, located in the northeastern corner of Manitoba. Settlement began with the building of Fort Churchill in 1688. Early settlers to the Canadian Prairies, such as the Scandinavians and Germans, entered the country through this area, led by Lord Selkirk, who founded the Selkirk Settlement in southern Manitoba in 1815. A major grain-exporting port during the summer months, Churchill has the advantage of a short sea route to Europe. The population was estimated at 1,143 in 1991.

Cincinnati. Third largest city in Ohio. Located on the Ohio River at 550 feet (168 meters) elevation, with a 1998 population of 336,400. First settled in 1788. In 1789 Fort Washington was built by the U.S. Army; in 1790, the village was renamed Cincinnati in honor of the Society of Cincinnati, an organization of officers of the American Revolution.

Ciudad Juárez. See Juárez.

Cleveland. Second largest city in Ohio. Located at the mouth of the Cuyahoga River on Lake Erie at 660 feet (210 meters) elevation, with a 1998 population of 495,817. Surveyed in 1796 by Moses Cleaveland.

Coahuila. Northeastern Mexican state, located along the United States-Mexico border; capital is Saltillo. Coahuila is less busy than other border crossings, but excellent highways make it a popular crossing area for visitors from the north. Cattle ranching is a major economic activity here, and olives, cotton, and other farm products are cultivated year-round.

Cincinnati, Ohio. (Corbis)

Colima. City and capital of the state of Colima in west central Mexico, standing on the Colima River in the Sierra Madre foothills, 1,667 feet (508 meters) above sea level. It was founded in 1522. Industries center upon the processing of local agricultural products including cotton, rice, and corn. There is also salt refining, alcohol distilling, and the manufacture of shoes and leather goods. Its population was 86,044 in 1980.

Colorado. Became thirty-eighth state on August 1, 1876. Located at the convergence of the Rocky Mountains and the Great Plains. Total area of 104,100 square miles (269,619 sq. km.) with 1998 population of 3.9 million. Name comes from Spanish word for "red color." It was purchased by the United States from France in 1803 as part of Louisiana Purchase. The first permanent European settlement was in 1858, after gold was discovered. The Colorado Territory was established in 1861. Denver (1998 population, 499,055) is the capital and largest city.

Colorado River. Longest river west of the Rocky Mountains—1,450 miles (2,334 km.). It begins in Colorado and flows through Utah and Arizona before forming borders between Arizona and Nevada and Arizona and California. It then crosses into Mexico (Baja California Norte) and empties into the Gulf of California (Sea of Cortés). It carved the Grand Canyon in Arizona and was dammed by Hoover Dam and other dams. First explored by Spaniard Hernando de Alarcón in 1540; explored more thoroughly by American explorer John Wesley Powell in 1869.

Columbia River. Flows from Canada into Washington State. After confluence with the Snake River, it turns west to form the border between Oregon and Washington to the Pacific Ocean. Length is about 1,245 miles (2,005 km.). The Grand Coulee Dam in Washington is one of its large power projects. In 1811 David Thompson, a Canadian explorer, followed the river from source to mouth.

Columbia River Pages 388, 579

Colorado River Page 517

Columbus. Capital and largest city of Ohio. Located at the junction of the Scioto and Olentangy Rivers at 780 feet (238 meters) elevation, with a 1998 population of 670,234. First settled in 1797. In 1812 state legislature chose the central location for state capital. Named in honor of Christopher Columbus.

Connecticut. Fifth of the original thirteen U.S. states; ratified the Constitution on January 9, 1788. Located in New England. Total area of 5,544 square miles (14,359 sq. km.), with a 1998 population of 3.3 million. First European settlement in 1634. Name is thought to come from native term meaning "beside the long tidal river." Capital is Hartford (1998 population, 131,523); largest city is Bridgeport (1998 population, 137,425).

Copper Canyon. See SIERRA TARAHUMARA.

Cordillera Central. Mountain range in the western part of the DOMINICAN REPUBLIC. The core of its highlands rises just west of SANTO DOMINGO, the national capital, and extends northwestward to the border with HAITI. The structurally complex range has a crestline between 5,000 and 8,000 feet (1,500-2,400 meters) high, with several isolated higher peaks.

Cozumel. Mexican island situated off the east coast of the YUCATÁN PENINSULA. It was an important center for the Mayan cult of Ixchel, goddess of fertility and childbirth. The Maya called the island Cuzamil, "place of the swallows." Cozumel has become a popular tourist resort, with one of the world's best diving locations. It is 9 miles (14 km.) wide by 31 miles (50 km.) long.

Crater Lake. National park established in 1902 in the CASCADE RANGE in OREGON. The second deepest lake in North America, it is in the crater of a prehistoric volcano, Mount Mazama. Wizard Island, in the lake, is the top of the now-extinct volcano. Lake has an area of 20 square miles (52 sq. km.); park has an area of 286 square miles (742 sq. km.).

Cuba. Largest of the Caribbean islands in the GREATER ANTILLES; capital is HAVANA. Located 90 miles (144 km.) south of FLORIDA. Much of this fertile island is devoted to sugarcane, the most important crop. Cuba is ringed with 4,000 miles (6,400 km.) of sandy beaches, coral cays, islands, and large, secluded bays. The population of 11,100,000 is mainly Hispanic and Spanish-speaking, with a sizable African minority. Its three mountain ranges are the Sierra de los Organos, whose red earth is covered with tobacco plants; the Sierra de Escambray, halfway along the island; and the Sierra Maestra, in the eastern part of the island. In 1959 a communist government under Fidel Castro came into power and eliminated much of the island's poverty, hunger, disease, and illiteracy, all of which plague much of Latin America. At the end of the twentieth century, U.S. citizens were still forbidden by their government to visit the country, except for research or scientific purposes.

Cuernavaca. Capital of the Mexican state of MORELOS. Located south of MEXICO CITY, it is is a popular weekend retreat for Mexico City's residents. It is called the "City of Eternal Spring." Its mild climate encourages luxurious growth of flowers and trees. Hernán Cortés introduced sugarcane cultivation to the area, and Caribbean slaves were brought in to work in the cane fields. Filled with luxury villas, this city has seen an influx of wealthy foreigners and industrial capital. It hosts several Spanish-language schools and many foreign exchange students.

Curaçao. Largest of the NETHERLANDS ANTILLES in the CARIBBEAN SEA. Capital is Willemstad. Located 35 miles (56 km.) north of Venezuela and 42 miles (68 km.) east of Aruba. It is a coral island 38 miles (61 km.) long. The Dutch came to the island in 1634 via the Netherlands West India Company. Curaçao has the most Dutch influence of these islands. It sits below the hurricane zone, and trade winds cool the tropical temperatures. Rocky stretches of washed-up coral have broken down into smooth white or pink sandy beaches. Slave trading once was the major source of wealth. More recently, the economic base has changed from oil refining to tourism. The population is derived from more than fifty nationalities of Latin, African, and European stock.

Dallas. Third largest city in Texas. Located on Trinity River in north Texas at 435 feet (133 meters) altitude, with 1998 population of 1.1 million. Dallas was settled in 1841 by the French.

Dawson. Former capital of the Yukon Territory, Canada. Located at the confluence of the Yukon and Klondike Rivers. After gold was discovered in Bonanza Creek in 1896, Dawson's population soared to more than twenty thousand in two years. Dawson is also famous for sending the Dawson City Nuggets to Ottawa to play for hockey's Stanley Cup in 1905—a twenty-three-day journey by dogsled, boat, and train—although they did not win. The population of the city was 896 in 1991.

Dawson Creek. City in northeastern British Columbia, Canada, where the Alaska Highway begins. Completed in 1942, the highway spans 1,523 miles (2,450 km.) and is the only overland connection to Alaska. Had a population of 11,125 in 1996.

Death Valley. Located in southern California, extending into southeastern Nevada. Established as national monument in 1933; designated a national park in 1994. The largest park in the United States, with an area of 8,554 square miles (13,765 sq. km.) of desert. Contains the lowest surface point in the Western Hemisphere—282 feet (86 meters) below sea level. In 1913 a temperature of 134 degrees Fahrenheit (57 degrees Celsius) was recorded, the highest ever in the United States.

Delaware. First of the original thirteen U.S. states; ratified Constitution on December 7, 1787. Located in Northeast. Total area is 2,489 square miles (6,447 sq. km.), with a 1998 population of 743,603. First European settlement in 1638. Name comes from the name of Thomas West, Third Baron De la Warr, the first colonial governor of Virginia. Capital is Dover (1998 population, 30,369); largest city is Wilmington (1998 population, 71,678).

Denver Page 518

Denver. Capital and largest city of Colorado. Located on the South Platte River at 5,280 feet (1,609 meters) altitude. Its 1998 population was just under 500,000. Settled by gold prospectors in 1858, it became the territorial capital in 1867.

Detroit. Largest city in Michigan. Located on the Detroit River at 585 feet (178 meters) elevation, with a 1998 population of 970,196. Established in 1701; was the state capital from 1837 to 1847. World's leading automobile manufacturing center. Name is Anglicized version of French word for "strait," which comes from its location along the strait of the Detroit River between Lakes Erie and Huron.

District of Columbia. See Washington, D.C.

Death Valley Page 517

Dominica. Caribbean island wedged between two rich French islands, Guadeloupe to the north and Martinique to the south. An independent common-

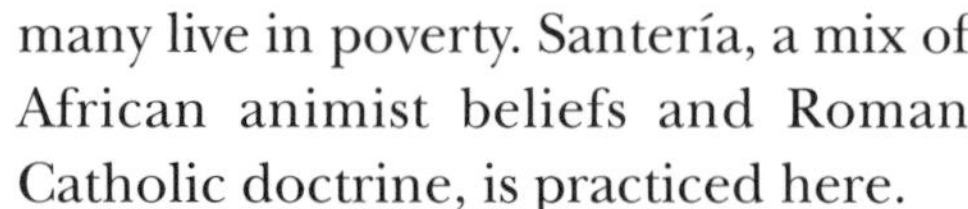

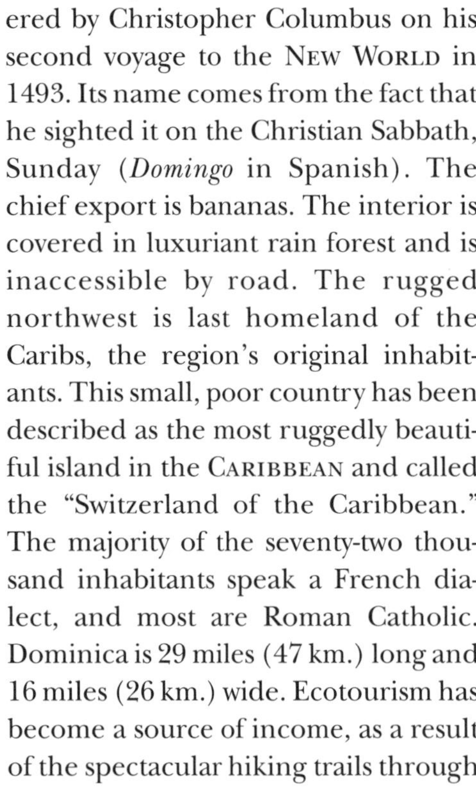
wealth; capital is Roseau. It was discovered by Christopher Columbus on his second voyage to the New World in 1493. Its name comes from the fact that he sighted it on the Christian Sabbath, Sunday (*Domingo* in Spanish). The chief export is bananas. The interior is covered in luxuriant rain forest and is inaccessible by road. The rugged northwest is last homeland of the Caribs, the region's original inhabitants. This small, poor country has been described as the most ruggedly beautiful island in the Caribbean and called the "Switzerland of the Caribbean." The majority of the seventy-two thousand inhabitants speak a French dialect, and most are Roman Catholic. Dominica is 29 miles (47 km.) long and 16 miles (26 km.) wide. Ecotourism has become a source of income, as a result of the spectacular hiking trails through the dense rain forests.

Edmonton Page 446

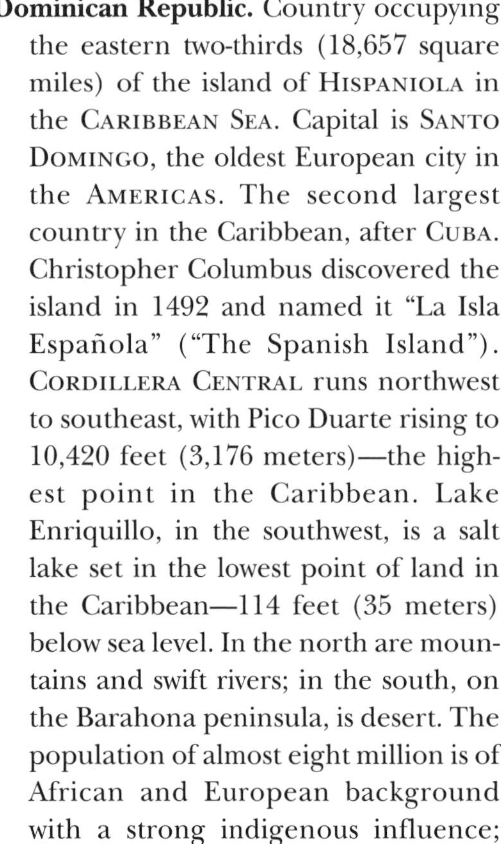
Dominican Republic. Country occupying the eastern two-thirds (18,657 square miles) of the island of Hispaniola in the Caribbean Sea. Capital is Santo Domingo, the oldest European city in the Americas. The second largest country in the Caribbean, after Cuba. Christopher Columbus discovered the island in 1492 and named it "La Isla Española" ("The Spanish Island"). Cordillera Central runs northwest to southeast, with Pico Duarte rising to 10,420 feet (3,176 meters)—the highest point in the Caribbean. Lake Enriquillo, in the southwest, is a salt lake set in the lowest point of land in the Caribbean—114 feet (35 meters) below sea level. In the north are mountains and swift rivers; in the south, on the Barahona peninsula, is desert. The population of almost eight million is of African and European background with a strong indigenous influence; many live in poverty. Santería, a mix of African animist beliefs and Roman Catholic doctrine, is practiced here.

Durango. Mexican city 195 miles (314 km.) northeast of Mazatlán. Located on a flat plateau in the center of a rich mining area, it is encircled by heavy industrial plants. Most of the wealth comes from iron ore deposits in the nearby hills. Many Western films have been filmed here.

Dutch Antilles. See Netherlands Antilles.

Edmonton. Provincial capital and largest city in Alberta. Located on the North Saskatchewan River, it is the most northern large city in Canada, with a population of 917,500 (1998). It is a major transportation center and serves areas to the north, including the Northwest Territories. The West Edmonton Mall was the largest shopping mall in the world in the late 1990's.

Ellesmere Island. Large island in the Arctic Ocean and the most northern landholding of Canada. Located northwest of Greenland near the North Pole in Nunavut. Mountainous and mostly ice-covered, it has only a few small settlements. The best-known is Alert, a weather station and military outpost at the northern tip of the island that is the northernmost community in North America. The English navigator William Baffin discovered the island in 1616.

English Harbour. Small town on the southern shore of the Caribbean island of Antigua. It was an important stop-off point for English warships in the Caribbean; they were refitted here rather than returning to England.

Erie, Lake. See Great Lakes.

Everglades National Park. The largest subtropical wilderness area in the United States, with more than 1.4 million acres. Located in FLORIDA; established in 1947. It has suffered tremendous environmental destruction from urbanization, agriculture, introduction of exotic vegetation, and the channelization of the Kissimmee River.

Federal District (Mexico). District in central Mexico. It is the seat of the national government and is similar in function to the DISTRICT OF COLUMBIA in the United States. It includes a large portion of the MEXICO CITY metropolitan area. The district averages more than 8,000 feet (2,400 meters) in elevation and occupies the southeastern corner of the Valley of Mexico. Its area is 571 square miles (1,479 sq. km.). Its population was 8,489,007 in 1995.

Finisterra. See CABO SAN LUCAS.

Florida. Became twenty-seventh state on March 3, 1845. Located in the U.S. South. Total area is 65,756 square miles (170,308 sq. km.) with a 1998 population of 14.9 million. Spanish explorer Juan Ponce de León was the first European to visit it, in 1513; name comes from "flowers," which is part of the Spanish name for Easter (the time of his arrival). Settled by Spanish in 1565; ceded to United States in 1819. Tallahassee (1998 population, 136,628) is capital; Jacksonville is largest city (1998 population, 693,630).

Fraser River. River running through BRITISH COLUMBIA, Canada. Named after the explorer Simon Fraser, who canoed down through the ROCKY MOUNTAINS to the coast. It is important both for transporting goods and to the salmon fishing industry. Begins in the north central part of the province and reaches more than 850 miles (1,360 km.) inland.

Fredericton. Provincial capital of NEW BRUNSWICK, Canada. Located along the St. John River. Founded by British Loyalists who settled 70 miles upriver from ST. JOHN in 1783, it had a population of 46,466 in 1991.

French Antilles. Two Caribbean islands, MARTINIQUE and GUADELOUPE, and Guadeloupe's five dependencies. They are French overseas departments and maintain little contact with the other islands. The inhabitants are French citizens, distinctively French in culture, language, and tradition. Because of their integration with France, the inhabitants have one of the highest standards of living in the developing world. They receive many social welfare benefits, such as health care, social security payments, and unemployment benefits. The administrative region of Guadeloupe is an archipelago, consisting of the tiny islands of Marie-Galante, Les Saintes, La Désirade, and SAINT-BARTHÉLEMY, and the northern part of ST. MARTIN.

Florida
Page 518

French West Indies. See FRENCH ANTILLES.

Fundy, Bay of. Arm of the Atlantic Ocean between the Canadian provinces of NOVA SCOTIA on the east and NEW BRUNSWICK on the west. Located eastward of MAINE, near 45 degrees north latitude, longitude 66 degrees west. Has the largest tides in the world, with 53 feet (16 meters) recorded at the MINAS BASIN, one of the farthest reaches of the bay. The high tidal range causes streams to reverse direction in flow, best exemplified by the REVERSING FALLS in ST. JOHN, New Brunswick. During low tides, water flows through rapids into the Bay of FUNDY, but at high tides, some rapids carry water upstream. Navigation by boats is difficult and can be achieved only by carefully timing the sailing times.

Gaspe. Scenic peninsula in southeastern QUEBEC, Canada. An extension of the

Appalachian Mountain chain, with many small fishing villages along the shores. Major attractions include Percé Rock, a tiny island at the eastern tip of the peninsula, named for a large sea arch visible from the mainland. Nearby Bonaventure Island has the largest breeding colony of gannets and other seabirds along the east coast of North America. Located at approximately 48 degrees north latitude, longitude 65 degrees west.

Grand Canyon Page 519

Georgia. Fourth of original thirteen U.S. states; ratified Constitution on January 2, 1788. Located in the U.S. South. Total area is 59,441 square miles (153,952 sq. km.), with a 1998 population of 7.6 million. Hernando de Soto was the first European to visit the area, in 1540. Spanish controlled it for more than a hundred years, until ousted by British. Founded as a colony in 1733 by a group led by British philanthropist James Oglethorpe; named for King George II. Atlanta is capital and largest city (1998 population, 403,819).

Godthåb. See Nuuk.

The Grand Canyon. (PhotoDisc)

Godthåbsfjord. Second largest fjord complex in the world. Located on the southwest coast of Greenland at 64°30′ north latitude, longitude 51°23′ west. The early Viking western settlement of Vesterbygden, settled just before the twelfth century, was centered here. The Viking settlement had about ninety farms but disappeared by the fourteenth century for unknown reasons.

Grand Canyon. Established as a U.S. national monument in 1908 and national park in 1918. Covers 1,904 square miles (4,931 sq. km.) in Arizona. Contains the Grand Canyon of the Colorado River, a gorge 1 mile (1.6 km.) deep, 18 miles (29 km.) wide, and 200 miles (322 km.) long on the Colorado Plateau in northern Arizona.

Grand Cayman. One of the Cayman Islands; capital is Georgetown. Banking and scuba diving are the main businesses. It has no sales tax and the merchandise for sale is duty-free.

Great Basin. Desert region in the western United States. It has a total area of 210,000 square miles (543,900 sq. km.), comprising most of Nevada and parts of Utah, California, Idaho, Wyoming, and Oregon. John C. Frémont explored and named the area in 1843-1845.

Great Bear Lake. The ninth largest lake in the world and the largest lake entirely within Canadian territory. Located in the Northwest Territories, one of its many inlets extends north of the Arctic Circle. The lake flows into the Mackenzie River. Europeans working for the Hudson's Bay Company discovered it about 1800. It covers 12,000 square miles (31,200 sq. km.).

Great Lakes. Five large freshwater lakes between north central United States and south central Canada formed by glaciation during Pleistocene epoch. From largest to smallest, they are Superior (the world's largest freshwater lake), Huron, Michigan (the only one completely within the United States), Erie, and Ontario. Primary outlet is the St. Lawrence River to the east. System forms backbone of one of world's busiest waterways.

Great Plains. Vast high-plateau grassland of central North America stretching from Texas northward into the Prairie Provinces of Canada. The principal commercial activities in this region are ranching and wheat farming.

Great Salt Lake. Largest body of water between the Great Lakes and the Pacific Ocean. Located in northern Utah, near Salt Lake City, in the Great Basin. It is the largest salt lake in the Western Hemisphere and is eight times as salty as ocean water. It changes size drastically based upon precipitation. Although several rivers feed the lake, there is no natural outlet. Remnant of Lake Bonneville, an ancient, large freshwater lake.

Great Slave Lake. The eleventh largest lake in the world and the second largest lake within Canadian territory. Located in the southern part of the Northwest Territories, its waters flow to the Mackenzie River and the Arctic Ocean. The city of Yellowknife is located on its shore. The lake was discovered by Samuel Hearne in 1771 and named after the Slave Indians of the area. It covers 11,031 square miles (28,570 sq. km.).

Great Smoky Mountains National Park. U.S. national park authorized in 1926 and established in 1930. Located in Southeast, in western North Carolina and eastern Tennessee. The Great Smoky Mountains extend the entire length of the park. Home to some of highest peaks of eastern North America. Clingmans Dome, at 6,643 feet (2,025 meters), located in Tennessee, is the park's highest peak. Name comes from the smoky blue haze emitted by the lush vegetation of area.

Lake Michigan Page 388

Greater Antilles. The four largest islands of the Antilles: Cuba, Hispaniola (Dominican Republic and Haiti), Jamaica, and Puerto Rico. The islands constitute almost 90 percent of the total land area of the entire West Indies.

Arctic map Page 381

Greenland. World's largest island, extending from Cape Morris Jesup in the north to Cape Farewell in the south, with an area of 839,000 square miles (2.18 million sq. km.). A self-governing administrative division of Denmark, Greenland is politically part of Europe but geographically part of North America, with an Arctic-type climate. Approximately 84 percent of the island is covered with the Greenland Ice Cap. Small tracts of open land along the southern and central western coasts have sparse arctic vegetation and are home to about 59,000 people, who are mostly Inuits. Capital is Nuuk. Other settlements include Maniitsoq, Narsaq, Qaanaaq, Qaqortoq, and Qasigiannguit.

Greenland Ice Cap. Approximately 84 percent of Greenland is covered with a massive ice cap that has a maximum thickness of between 10,500 and 11,150 feet (3,200-3,400 meters) and contains one-eighth of the total global ice mass (about 2.5 million cubic km.). Should the ice cap melt, the global sea level would increase 19-23 feet (6-7 meters). Shaped like an irregular, double-headed dome, the cap covers the whole of the interior of Greenland, acting as a

Guanajuato City, Mexico. (Corbis)

barrier to east-west travel. It is so heavy that it has pushed the surface of land below it below sea level.

Grenada. Most southerly in the chain of WINDWARD ISLANDS in the eastern CARIBBEAN SEA. Located approximately 12 degrees north of the equator, it is 21 miles (34 km.) long and 12 miles (19 km.) wide. Its capital, St. George's, is one of the most charming capital cities in the Caribbean. A mild climate and fertile soil have made it a major exporter of nutmeg, cinnamon, cocoa, cloves, pimento, and bay leaves. Historically, conflict and violence have marred the tranquility of this island; U.S. intervention in 1983 stabilized the situation after a violent military coup.

Grenadine Islands. See ST. VINCENT AND THE GRENADINES

Guadalajara. Capital of the Mexican state of JALISCO. Founded in 1548, it began as a supply point for the northern mining camps of Mexico after silver was discovered in ZACATECAS in 1546. An industrial boom in the late twentieth century transformed it into a major metropolitan area, second only to MEXICO CITY.

Guadeloupe. Caribbean island in the FRENCH ANTILLES, which is an overseas department of France. Shaped like a butterfly, it consists of two islets of very different landscapes, joined by a small land bridge. The "left wing"—Basse-Terre (Low Land)—is wild, mountainous, and rain-forested. The "right wing"—Grande-Terre—is a flatter, coral-based outcropping from a much older volcanic chain. Most of the beaches and tourist resorts are located on Grande-Terre. Northeast trade winds moderate the temperature. The forty-one thousand residents are mostly of African descent or mixed heritage. Sugar has remained a main source of revenue. The island covers 629 square miles (1,629 sq. km.).

Guanajuato. Mexican state in the *bajio,* or heartland of Mexico. Located at an altitude of 5,500-7,000 feet (1,675-2,135 meters), the state's fertile plains and valleys are full of productive farms. Rich in colonial architecture and history, Guanajuato once supplied one quarter of NEW SPAIN's silver output. Its capital is a beautiful colonial city of the same name.

Guerrero. Mexican state bordered on the south and west by the Pacific Ocean; capital is Chilpancingo. Steep, rugged mountains called the SIERRA MADRE DEL SUR fall dramatically into the sea. Mixed forests of red cedar, torch pines, and holm oaks cover the high mountains. Tropical forests of fig and copal mahogany take over at lower elevations. Mangroves, grasses, and reeds provide rich habitat for tropical birds near river mouths and lagoons. ACAPULCO, Ixtapa, and Zihuatanejo are popular tourist resorts on Guerrero's coast.

Gulfs. See under individual names.

Haiti. Country occupying the western third (10,715 square miles) of the island of HISPANIOLA; capital is PORT-AU-PRINCE. Consists of two mountainous peninsulas that enclose the Gulf of Gonaïve, as well as the two inhabited islands of Gonâve in the gulf and Tortuga off the north coast. Two-thirds of Haiti is mountainous. Highest peak is the Pico de la Selle (8,795 feet) in the southeast. Deforestation and soil erosion are serious problems. Originally discovered by the Spanish, Haiti was ceded in 1697 to the French, who named it St. Domingue. Haiti has a history of turmoil and political instability. At the end of the twentieth century, it was the poorest country in the WESTERN HEMISPHERE, and its population of nearly six million residents had the highest infant mortality rate, lowest life expectancy, and one of the highest illiteracy rates (60 percent) in the CARIBBEAN region. Voodoo, a mixture of African animist beliefs and Roman Catholic doctrine, is widely practiced there.

Halifax. Capital of NOVA SCOTIA, Canada, located on the shores of a natural sheltered harbor. Major seaport and commercial center and the eastern terminus of Canada's two national railway lines. Founded in 1749 by the British, many of its residents are of English, Irish, or Scottish background. Its population was 348,000 in 1998.

Hamilton. Industrial city in ONTARIO, Canada. Located at the western end of Lake Ontario, with a population of 658,600 in 1998. Home to many large steel mills and refineries, it is often compared to PITTSBURGH in the United States. Its settlement began with the arrival of United Empire Loyalists, following the American Revolution in 1778. Named for George Hamilton, who laid out the original town in 1813.

Havana. City and capital of the Republic of CUBA and of the province of Havana, with which it is coterminous. Havana is Cuba's industrial, importing, and distributing center. Dominant industries include food processing (mostly sugar), shipbuilding, fishing, and automotive production. The city covers an area of 281 square miles (727 sq. km.). Its population of 2,077,938 in the early 1990's represented nearly a fifth of Cuba's entire population.

Hawaii. Became fiftieth state on August 21, 1959. Located in the Pacific Ocean, southwest of the mainland United States. It has a total area of 10,932 square miles (28,314 sq. km.) with 1998 population of 1.2 million. The name may be derived from the native word for "homeland." Hawaii comprises eight primary islands and numerous islets, reefs, and shoals. In 1778 British explorer Captain James Cook sailed to the islands and named them Sandwich Islands in honor of his patron, the Earl of Sandwich. They became a U.S. territory in 1898. Honolulu (1998 population, 395,789) is the capital and largest city.

Hawaii Page 571

Hermasillo. Capital of the Mexican state of SONORA. This rapidly growing city in northern Mexico is situated in the middle of a rich agricultural area, where the summer temperatures can reach 111 degrees Fahrenheit (44 degrees Celsius).

Hidalgo. Mexican state located northeast of MEXICO CITY; capital is Pachuca. It contains El Chico National Park—the premier rock climbing area in Mexico. It was named to honor independence hero Miguel Hidalgo y Costilla.

Hispaniola. Large island in the Greater Antilles in the Caribbean Sea. Christopher Columbus landed here in 1492, and it was the initial focus of Spanish settlement in the New World. Divided into the Spanish-speaking Dominican Republic and French-speaking Haiti. The border between the two countries is closed.

Hoover Dam. One of highest dams in the world. Located on the Colorado River between Arizona and Nevada. Constructed 1931-1936 to create Lake Mead, one of world's largest artificial lakes. Originally named Boulder Dam, it was renamed in 1947 to honor President Herbert Hoover.

Horseshoe Falls. See Niagara Falls.

Houston Page 519

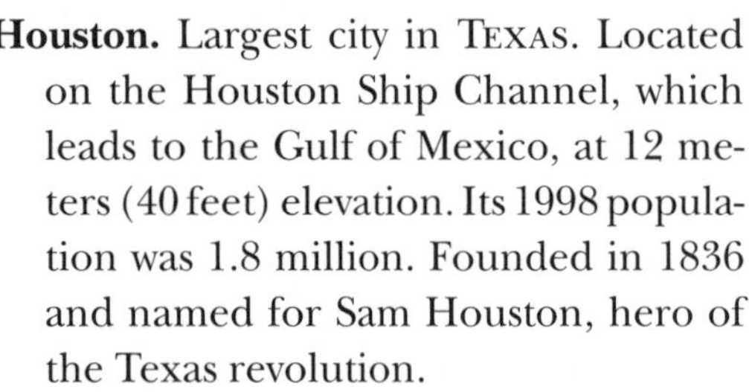

Houston. Largest city in Texas. Located on the Houston Ship Channel, which leads to the Gulf of Mexico, at 12 meters (40 feet) elevation. Its 1998 population was 1.8 million. Founded in 1836 and named for Sam Houston, hero of the Texas revolution.

Hudson Bay Page 569

Hudson Bay. One of the largest ocean inlets in the world, located in east central Canada. Bounded by Nunavut in the north and west, Manitoba and Ontario in the south, and Quebec in the east, and connected to the Atlantic and Arctic Oceans. Discovered by explorer Henry Hudson in 1610. It covers an area of about 317,500 square miles (823,280 sq. km.).

Hudson River. Important commercial waterway originating in eastern New York and flowing into Upper New York Bay at New York City. The first European to explore it was Giovanni da Verrazzano, in 1524. Also explored in 1609 by English navigator Henry Hudson, for whom it is named. Connected to Lake Erie by the Erie Canal in 1825.

Huntsville. City in Alabama that is home to the U.S. Army Missile Command at Redstone Arsenal and to the George C. Marshall Space Flight Center, where the Saturn rocket, which took humans to the Moon, was developed. First settled in 1805. Its 1998 population was 175,979.

Huron, Lake. See Great Lakes.

Idaho. Became forty-third state on July 3, 1890. Located in the Northwest of the United States. Its total area is 83,574 square miles (216,457 sq. km.) with 1998 population of 1.2 million. Its coined name is generally accepted to mean "gem of the mountains." Visited by Meriwether Lewis and William Clark in 1805. First permanent European settlement was in 1842. Boise (1998 population, 157,452) is the capital and largest city.

Illinois. Became twenty-first state on December 3, 1818. Located in U.S. Midwest. Total area is 57,918 square miles (150,008 sq. km.), with a 1998 population of 12 million. Named for the Illinois, or Illini, a confederation of Native Americans who inhabited the region at time of French exploration. Explored by the French in the late seventeenth century; first settlement in 1720. Ceded to the British in 1763 at end of French and Indian War, then ceded to the United States in 1783. Part of Northwest Territory 1787-1800; Illinois Territory was created in 1809. Springfield (1998 population, 117,098) is capital; Chicago (1998 population, 2.8 million) is largest city.

Ilulissat Icefjord (Jakobshavn Glacier). Most productive glacier in the world. Extending from the Greenland Ice Cap, it moves into the sea with an average speed of 65-100 feet (20-30 meters) per day, which amounts to 4-7 miles (7-11 km.) per year. It produces 20 million tons of ice daily, discharging it into the sea as icebergs. Located at 69°10′ north latitude, longitude 49°55′ west.

Imperial Valley. Located in southern California along the U.S. border with Mexico. One of the richest agricultural districts in the world, it relies heavily on irrigation. It is a major producer of lettuce, cotton, and other crops.

Indiana. Became nineteenth state on December 11, 1816. Located in U.S. Midwest. Total area is 36,420 square miles (94,328 sq. km.), with a 1998 population of 5.9 million. Name means "land of the Indians." French explorer René-Robert Cavelier, sieur de La Salle, explored Indiana in 1679, and the French controlled the area until the end of the French and Indian War (1754-1763), after which the British assumed control until 1783. Part of Northwest Territory 1787-1800; Indiana Territory was created in 1800. Capital and largest city is Indianapolis (1998 population, 741,304).

Indianapolis. Largest city and capital of Indiana. Located on the White River at 710 feet (216 meters) elevation, with a 1998 population of 741,304. Settled in 1820; became capital in 1824. Home of the Indianapolis Motor Speedway, site of annual Indianapolis 500 automobile race.

Iowa. Became twenty-ninth state on December 28, 1846. Located in the Midwest of the United States. Total area of 56,276 square miles (145,755 square miles) with 1998 population of 2.8 million. Named for the Iowa people. First explored by the French in the early seventeenth century, the first permanent European settlement was in 1788. Became part of the United States in 1803 via the Louisiana Purchase. Des Moines (1998 population, 191,293) is the capital and largest city.

Iqaluit. Capital of Nunavut, Canada, located on the southeastern shore of Baffin Island. Established as a trading post in 1914, it became an air base during World War II. It had an estimated population of 4,220 in 1998.

Isla Mujeres. Small, finger-shaped Mexican island 8 miles (13 km.) east of Cancún off the Yucatán Peninsula's Caribbean shore. Tourism provides jobs and revenue. The name means "Island of Women."

Isla Tiburon. Continental island, left behind as the San Andreas Fault separated Baja California from the rest of Mexico. It is 29 miles (37 km.) long and 15 miles (24 km.) wide. Its desert landscape is similar to that of Mexico's Sonoran coast. It is designated as a special biosphere reserve protecting bighorn sheep and many other Sonoran Desert species extinct or nearly extinct on the mainland. The name means "Shark Island," for the huge schools of hammerhead sharks that used to congregate in nearby waters.

Isthmuses. See under individual names

Jakobshavn Glacier. See Ilulissat Icefjord

Jalisco. State on Mexico's Pacific coast; capital is Guadalajara, Mexico's second largest city. Puerto Vallarta, a popular resort town, is located on Jalisco's coast. Jalisco's residents, nicknamed *tapatios*, have popularized mariachi music, the Mexican hat dance, the *charrareria* (Mexican-style rodeo), and tequila—a fiery liquor.

Jamaica. Third largest island in the Caribbean Sea (after Cuba and Hispaniola), covering 4,244 square miles (10,992 sq. km.). The capital is Kingston, the largest English-speaking city south of Miami, Florida. It has a huge natural harbor on its southern shore. It gained independence from Great Britain in 1962. but remains a member of the British Commonwealth.

Once the leading sugar and slave center in the region, it is now one of the world's leading producers of bauxite. Four-fifths of the island is mountainous; the heavily forested Blue Mountains in the interior grow some of the finest coffees in the world. It is the cultural leader of the Caribbean and has one of the largest tourist industries in the region.

Jost Van Dyke. One of the British VIRGIN ISLANDS in the CARIBBEAN SEA. Situated northwest of TORTOLA; named for an early Dutch settler. It is mountainous with lush vegetation. The island is 4 miles (6.5 km.) long, with a population of 140.

Juárez. Mexican city across the border from El Paso, TEXAS. Named Paso del Norte in 1659, it was renamed in 1888 in honor of Mexican President Benito Juárez. Located 3,760 feet (1,128 meters) above sea level on the RIO GRANDE, at the edge of the CHIHUAHUAN DESERT. *Maquiladora*-based manufacturing has changed the size and feel of this border town of more than one million inhabitants.

Julianehåb. See QAQORTOQ.

Kansas City, Missouri. (Corbis)

Kansas. Became thirty-fourth state on January 29, 1861. Located in the Midwest of the United States. Total area of 82,277 square miles (213,097 sq. km.) with 1998 population of 2.6 million. The name is Sioux for "south wind people." In 1541 Spanish explorer Francisco Vásquez de Coronado visited the area. Claimed by France in 1682 and became part of the United States in 1803 via the Louisiana Purchase. Topeka (1998 population, 118,977) is the capital and Wichita (1998 population, 329,211) is the largest city.

Kansas City, Kansas. Located at confluence of Kansas and Missouri Rivers at 750 feet (229 meters) elevation. The second largest city in the state (1998 population, 139,685), it is adjacent to KANSAS CITY, MISSOURI.

Kansas City, Missouri. Largest city in Missouri (1998 population, 441,574). It is located at the confluence of Kansas and Missouri Rivers at 750 feet (229 meters) elevation. Located adjacent to KANSAS CITY, KANSAS.

Kentucky. Became fifteenth state on June 1, 1792. Located in the eastern United States between the South and the GREAT LAKES regions. Total area is 40,111 square miles (104,665 sq. km.) with 1998 population of 3.9 million. Name comes from Cherokee word thought to mean "meadow." Daniel Boone was one of the first to explore it, coming through the Cumberland Gap of the APPALACHIAN Mountains in 1769. First permanent European settlement in 1774. Although a slave state, it remained neutral during Civil War. Capital is Frankfort (1998 population, 26,418); largest city is Louisville (255,045).

Kingston. Capital and chief port city of Jamaica on the southeastern coast of the island. Kingston was founded in 1692 after an earthquake destroyed Port Royal, which was located at the mouth of the harbor. Its population was 103,771 in 1991.

La Malinche. Mexico's fifth-highest mountain at 14,637 feet (4,462 meters). Located in Tlaxcala state.

Labrador. Part of Canada located north of Newfoundland, bounded by the Strait of Belle Isle and Quebec on the south, Quebec on the west, and the Atlantic Ocean on the east.

Lakes. See under individual names.

L'Anse aux Meadows. Canadian national historic site located on the northeastern shore on the island of Newfoundland near the Strait of Belle Isle. Remains of Viking houses dated to about 1000 c.e. were discovered here in 1963 by Norwegian archaeologist Helge Ingstad. Discovery of the site confirms the presence of the Norse Vikings well before the arrival of Columbus in 1492.

Las Vegas. Largest city in Nevada (1998 population, 404,288). Located in southern Nevada near the Colorado River, Hoover Dam, and Arizona, at 2,030 feet (619 meters) elevation. The name is Spanish for "the meadows." It was a stop on the Old Spanish Trail between Santa Fe, New Mexico, and Southern California. One of the fastest-growing cities in the United States in the last quarter of the twentieth century.

Leeward Islands. Six small, resource-poor Caribbean islands lying in two lines. In the west, Montserrat, Nevis, and St. Kitts are rain-forested peaks of a fairly young volcano chain (about 15 million years old). To the east lie much older, flat, limestone island peaks—Antigua, Barbuda, and Anguilla. Originally agricultural colonies that produced sugarcane, cotton, and coconuts, their chief economic activities are now tourism and manufacturing.

Lesser Antilles. Archipelago of small, volcanically formed islands in the Caribbean Sea, grouped into the Leeward Islands and the Windward Islands. Trade winds from the east keep temperatures in this tropical region comfortable. Rich volcanic soils make agriculture productive. Sugar, bananas, and tourism are the leading industries.

Little Cayman. The smallest of three islands in the British colony of the Cayman Islands. Little Cayman lies 5 miles (8 km.) west of Cayman Brac. It is 10 miles (16 km.) long, has a maximum width of 2 miles (3 km.), and has a total area of 10 square miles (26 sq. km.).

Logan, Mount. Highest mountain peak in Canada. Located in the St. Elias Mountains of southwestern Yukon Territory at 60.54 degrees north latitude, longitude 140.33 degrees west. It is 19,524 feet (5,951 meters) high, second in North America only to Mount McKinley of nearby Alaska.

Las Vegas Page 569

Los Alamos National Laboratory. Located in Los Alamos, in the central part of New Mexico. The U.S. government used the site for nuclear weapons research; the first atomic bomb and hydrogen bomb were developed here.

Los Angeles Pages 453, 520

Los Angeles. Largest city in California, and second largest in the United States (1998 population, 3.6 million). Located in Southern California at 340 feet (104 meters) elevation. The name is Spanish for "the angels." Settled in 1781 by the Spanish and served as the colonial capital.

Louisbourg. Canadian town on the northeastern shore of Nova Scotia on Cape Breton Island. Founded in 1713 as a fishing and shipbuilding center, it later was fortified by the French. The French and English fought many battles for control of this major fort, which was destroyed by the English in 1760. The fort is being restored and is a major tourist attraction. A total of 1,261 people lived here in 1991.

Louisiana. Became eighteenth state on April 30, 1812. Located in the south central area of the United States. Total area of 51,843 square miles (134,274 sq. km.) with 1998 population of 4.4 million. The French explorer René-Robert Cavelier, sieur de La Salle, claimed the entire Mississippi drainage area, including Missouri Valley, for France in 1682, naming it Louisiane for King Louis XIV. NEW ORLEANS was established in 1718. In 1762 transferred to Spain; returned to France in 1800. France sold Louisiana to the United States in the Louisiana Purchase of 1803. The capital is Baton Rouge (1998 population, 211,551); New Orleans (1998 population, 465,538) is the largest city.

Lunenburg. Small, historic fishing village on the southeastern shore of NOVA SCOTIA, south of HALIFAX. Home of the famous Bluenose schooner, pictured on the obverse of the Canadian dime. The first German immigrants to Canada settled here in the early 1750's. The population was 2,781 in 1991.

Mackenzie River. Longest river in Canada (1,025 miles; 1,649 km.), flowing north-northwest from the GREAT SLAVE LAKE in NORTHWEST TERRITORIES to the Arctic Ocean. Including all headwaters, which begin in BRITISH COLUMBIA and drain into the Great Slave Lake, the entire river system runs 2,635 miles (4,239 km.). It is a major transportation route from the south to the Arctic Ocean until the river freezes over. Barges travel along the river during the short summer seasons. Named after Alexander MacKenzie, who discovered and explored the river from Lake Athabasca in northern ALBERTA to its delta in 1789.

McKinley, Mount. Highest peak in North America at 20,320 feet (6,194 meters). Located in the ALASKA Range in Denali National Park, which was established in 1917.

Maine. Became twenty-third U.S. state on March 15, 1820. Located in New England. Total area is 35,387 square miles (91,652 sq. km.), with a 1998 population of 1.2 million. Name comes from ancient French province. First explored in 1520's with first European settlement in 1624. Annexed by MASSACHUSETTS in 1652. Augusta is capital (1998 population, 19,978); Portland is the largest city (1998 population 62,786).

Malinche. See LA MALINCHE.

Mammoth Cave National Park. Largest known cave system in the world, with 348 miles (560 km.) of charted passages. Result of erosion (and deposition) of limestone. Park, established in 1941, covers 82 square miles (212 sq. km.) in KENTUCKY.

Maniitsoq (SUKKERTOPPEN). City in GREENLAND. Located at 65 minutes north latitude, longitude 52°40′ west, it has a population of four thousand. The earliest settlements were of the Saqqaq culture, which date back approximately four thousand years, followed by Eskimo and Norse settlements. Danish colonizers founded a trading post in 1755 with the name Sukkertoppen (Sugar Loaf). This area contains some of the oldest bedrock in the world, dating back 3.5 billion years. Greenlandic for "the Uneven."

Manitoba. Most eastern of Canada's three PRAIRIE PROVINCES. Bounded by SASKATCHEWAN on the west, ONTARIO on the east, Nunavut and Hudson Bay on the north, and North Dakota and Minnesota on the south. In 1999, 1.14 million people lived on 251,000 square miles (650,840 sq. km.), equal in size to North Dakota, South Dakota, and Nebraska together. The majority of the population is concentrated in the city of Winnipeg. The southern part of the province has rich farmland; the central part is made up of many lakes—the most notable being Lake Winnipeg and Lake Manitoba. The northern part has much boreal forest.

Maritime Provinces. Collective term for the Canadian provinces of Newfoundland, New Brunswick, Nova Scotia, and Prince Edward Island. During the French period of rule during the 1600's, much of the region was known as Arcadia, which was ceded to the British by the Treaty of Utrecht in 1713.

Martinique. Largest of the volcanic Windward Islands in the Caribbean Sea. Settled by French in the 1630's, by the eighteenth century, it was one of the richest sugar islands in the Caribbean. Its highest peak, Mount Pelée, erupted in 1902, killing 30,333 people and destroying the town of St. Pierre.

Maryland. Seventh of thirteen original U.S. states; ratified Constitution on April 28, 1788. Located along mid-Atlantic Coast. Total area is 12,407 square miles (32,134 sq. km.), with a 1998 population of 5.1 million. Named for Queen Henrietta Maria, wife of King Charles I of England. First permanent European settlement in 1634. Capital is Annapolis (1998 population, 33,585); Baltimore is largest city (1998 population, 645,593).

Massachusetts. Sixth of the original thirteen U.S. states; ratified Constitution on February 6, 1788. Located in New England. Total area is 10,555 square miles (27,337 sq. km.), with a 1998 population of 6.1 million. Name comes from native word for "large hill place." First European settlement was in 1620, by Pilgrims arriving on the *Mayflower.* Was a leader in movement for independence from Great Britain, and many early and important battles of American Revolution were fought there. Boston is capital and largest city (1998 population, 555,447).

Cape Cod Page 516

Matamoros. One of Mexico's fastest-growing industrial cities. Located on United States– Mexican border not far from the Gulf of Mexico near the mouth of the Rio Grande. Matamoras prospered during the U.S. Civil War by supplying Confederate troops in Texas

Martinique Page 570

Replica of the Mayflower *at Plymouth, Massachusetts.* (PhotoDisc)

through the port of Bagdad, enabling them to avoid the Union blockade of the Texas Gulf Coast. It is one of four Mexican cities to have its name preceded by the letter *H*—a designation meaning "Heroic, Loyal, and Unconquered." By the late 1990's, it hosted more than eighty *maquiladoras.*

Mazatlán. Mexico's most northern major resort, situated on the central Pacific coast just south of the Tropic of Cancer in the state of Sinaloa. It is only two centuries old, young compared to many Mexican cities. It has a mild tropical climate, half a million residents, and more than one million visitors yearly.

Memphis. Largest city in Tennessee (1998 population, 603,507). Located on the Mississippi River at 275 feet (84 meters) elevation. First settled by the Chickasaw; founded as a U.S. city in 1819 by future U.S. president Andrew Jackson.

Mérida. Capital of the Mexican state of Yucatán. A significant city during Spanish colonial rule, it enjoyed an economic boom in the early twentieth century. Its wealth came from rope made of agave fiber. It has become an important manufacturing city and a university, business, and cultural center of Mexico.

Mexico City Pages 448, 571

Mesa Central. Southern portion of the central Mexican Plateau. It receives more rainfall and has more moderate temperatures than Mesa del Norte. Several of Mexico's major cities—including Mexico City, Guadalajara, and Puebla—and traditional rural areas are found here. It is the traditional center of Mexico's indigenous population and Mexico's main region of food production.

Mesa del Norte. Arid northern part of the central Mexican Plateau.

Mexican Plateau. Geologically unstable high central plateau of Mexico. Framed by two mountain ranges—the Sierra Madre Oriental on the east and the Sierra Madre Occidental on the west—it slopes northward from 7,000 to 8,000 feet (2,100 to 2,400 meters) along its southern margin to 3,000 feet (900 meters) or less along the border with Texas. Its wide plains average more than 6,000 feet (1,830 meters) above sea level. It is Mexico's largest and most populous region.

Mexico (state). State on the central Mexican Plateau almost completely surrounding the Federal District, which encompasses Mexico City. The state's area is 8,245 square miles (21,355 sq. km.). Its elevation is typically more than 10,000 (3,000 meters) above sea level. The state contains many preconquest ruins. Its capital is Toluca. It has agriculture and manufacturing, including assembly plants, aluminum processing, ironworks, and steelworks. The state has the highest population density of any Mexican state, with a total population of 9,815,795 in 1990.

Mexico City. Capital of Mexico. Located on a high plateau in the mountain-ringed Valley of Mexico in the central highlands of the country, at 7,240 feet (2,240 meters) elevation. The oldest capital of the New World and the world's most populated city, it is a hectic, overpopulated, often smog-ridden metropolis. Pollution is a major problem. It is the center of business, government, and culture in Mexico. Hernán Cortés, a Spanish conquistador, led his army into the Aztec capital of Tenochtitlán, which was situated on islands in Lake Texcoco. This later became Mexico City. Because it was built on a soft, dried-up lake bed lacking a rock base, the city is sinking at a rate of close to one inch per year. It is estimated that Mexico City sank as much as 25 feet during the twentieth century. The area is a highly volcanic region that experiences occasional devastating earthquakes. Called the Federal District, or simply "Mexico," by most Mexicans.

University of Mexico Library in Mexico City. (Corbis)

Mexico, Gulf of. Mostly enclosed arm of the western Atlantic Ocean, bounded by eastern Mexico and the U.S. states of Florida, Alabama, Mississippi, Louisiana, and Texas. The island of Cuba closes part of the gap between Mexico's Yucatán Peninsula and the southern tip of Florida that separates the gulf from the Caribbean Sea. Most ocean water enters through the Yucatán passage and exits the gulf around the tip of Florida, becoming the Florida Current.

Mexico, Valley of. High, broad basin of volcanic soil and cool temperatures located at the southern end of the Mexican Plateau, where Mexico City is situated.

Miami. Second largest city in Florida. Located at 10 feet (3 meters) elevation, with a 1998 population of 368,624. Spanish established a mission there in 1567. It has a subtropical environment and a large Cuban population.

Michigan. Became twenty-sixth state on January 26, 1837. Located in Great Lakes region of the United States. Total area is 96,810 square miles (250,466 sq. km.), with a 1998 population of 9.8 million. Named after Lake Michigan, which is said to have been derived from Algonquian term "mici gama," meaning "big water" or "great lake." French first explored in 1618; first settlement in 1668. Ceded to the British in 1763 at end of French and Indian War; ceded to United States in 1783. Part of Northwest Territory 1787-1800. Michigan Territory was established in 1805 with Detroit as capital. Lansing is capital (1998 population, 127,825); Detroit is largest city (1998 population, 970,196).

Michigan, Lake. See Great Lakes.

Miami
Page 572

Michoacan. State in central Mexico. The mountains here are the winter nesting grounds of millions of monarch butterflies migrating from Canada. Its terrain varies from coastal lowlands to high peaks, so the climate ranges from tropical to moderate. Paricutín Volcano is located here on a high plateau.

Middle Island. See Pelee Island.

Milwaukee. Largest city in Wisconsin. Located on Lake Michigan at at 635 feet (194 meters) elevation, with a 1998 population of 578,364. First settled in 1818 by French, but Germans soon came to dominate the region.

Minas Basin. See Bay of Fundy.

Minneapolis. Largest city in Minnesota.

Located on the MISSISSIPPI RIVER across from St. Paul, at 815 feet (248 meters) elevation. Its 1998 population was 351,731. The Falls of St. Anthony, located here, are the northernmost limit of navigation on the Mississippi River.

Minnesota. Became thirty-second state on May 11, 1858. Located in the Upper Midwest of the United States. Total area of 86,943 square miles (225,183 sq. km.) with 1998 population of 4.8 million. The name is from the Sioux for "cloudy water," referring to the Minnesota River. First explored by the French in the seventeenth century; surrendered to Great Britain after the French and Indian War (1754-1763). Controlled by the British from 1763 to the end of the War of 1812 (1812-1815), although Britain gave the United States the portion east of MISSISSIPPI RIVER after the American Revolution (1775-1783). The United States acquired the area of present-day Minnesota west of the Mississippi River as part of the Louisiana Purchase in 1803. St. Paul (1998 population, 257,284) is the capital; MINNEAPOLIS (1998 population, 351,731) is the largest city.

Mississippi. Became twentieth state on December 10, 1817. Located in U.S. South. Total area is 48,434 miles (125,444 sq. km.), with a 1998 population of 2.7 million. Named after the MISSISSIPPI RIVER. Spanish explorer Hernando de Soto is thought to have passed through in 1540. First European settlement was in 1699, by the French. United States took possession in 1783; in 1798, Mississippi Territory was created. In 1817 ALABAMA Territory was created from the eastern portion. Jackson is capital and largest city (1998 population, 188,419).

Mississippi River Pages 508, 573

Mississippi River. The greatest river of North America. Begins in northern MINNESOTA, flowing about 2,350 miles (3,781 km.) to the Gulf of Mexico. Name from native "great river." Possibly discovered by Hernando de Soto in 1541, explored by Jacques Marquette and Louis Jolliet in 1673. René-Robert Cavelier, sieur de La Salle, claimed it for France in 1682. Among cities on its banks are MINNEAPOLIS and St. Paul, Minnesota; ST. LOUIS, Missouri; MEMPHIS, Tennessee; and NEW ORLEANS, Louisiana.

Missouri. Became twenty-fourth state on August 10, 1821. Located in the Midwest of the United States. Total area of 69,709 square miles (180,546 sq. km.) with 1998 population of 5.4 million. The name is Algonquin for "river of big canoes." French explorer René-Robert Cavelier, sieur de La Salle, claimed the entire Mississippi drainage area, including the Missouri Valley, for France in 1682, naming it Louisiane. French settlers founded Sainte Genevieve, the first permanent European settlement, about 1750. The United States acquired it in 1803 as part of the Louisiana Purchase. The Missouri Compromise of 1820 ended the debate on statehood and admitted Missouri to the Union in 1821 as a slave state. The capital is Jefferson City (1998 population, 34,911); KANSAS CITY (1998 population, 441,574) is the largest city.

Montana. Became forty-first state on November 8, 1889. Located between the Upper Midwest and Northwest in the United States. Total area of 147,046 square miles (380,850 sq. km.) with 1998 population of 880,453. The name is Spanish for "mountainous." Claimed, but largely unexplored, by France in the eighteenth century, acquired by the United States in 1803 via the Louisiana Purchase. Montana Territory was created in 1864. Helena (1998 population, 28,306) is the capital; Billings (1998 population, 91,750) is the largest city.

Monterrey. Mexico's third largest city. Located in the foothills of the Sierra Madre Oriental 150 miles (240 km.) from the United States-Mexico border. The heart of Mexico's wealthiest state, Nuevo León, Monterrey is a bustling industrial city with some of the most striking twentieth century architecture in Mexico.

Montreal. Largest city in Quebec, Canada, and the second largest city in Canada. Located at the confluence of the Ottawa and St. Lawrence Rivers, the total population of the metropolitan area was 3.4 million in 1998. Historically, the English population of Quebec has been strongest here. One of the oldest Canadian cities, the site—occupied by a native village—was discovered by explorer Jacques Cartier in 1535. A permanent settlement was begun in 1642 on Isle de Montreal, the easily defended island site in the middle of the river.

Montserrat. Small, mountainous, volcanic island in the Caribbean Leeward Islands. Located 25 miles (40 km.) southwest of Antigua. Volcanic activity that began in 1995 devastated the southern and eastern parts of the island, including the capital, Plymouth, and caused a massive relocation of residents to the northern part of the island. Called "The Emerald Isle of the Caribbean" because Irish Catholics came here in the 1630's to escape religious persecution by English colonists on St. Kitts and Nevis.

Morelia. Capital of the Mexican state of Michoacán. This lovely colonial city is located 195 miles (315 km.) northwest of Mexico City. First inhabited by the indigenous Tarascans, the city was founded by the Spanish in 1541 and christened Valladolid. The name was changed to honor the revolutionary hero José María Morelos, who once lived there.

Montreal Page 573

Morelos. State in central Mexico that is bordered by the Federal District on the north. Its 1,911 square miles (4,950 sq. km.) territory lies on the southern slope of the central Mexican Plateau. The state is named after Jose Maria Morelos y Pavon, one of the heroes of Mexico's war for independence. Morelos was also the birthplace of Emiliano Zapata, a hero of one of the revolutionary factions of the Mexican

Montreal, Quebec. (Corbis)

Revolution of the 1910's. Morelos is one of the flourishing agricultural states of Mexico. The population, which includes a large percentage of Native Americans and mestizos, was 947,000 in 1980.

Mountains. See under individual names.

Narsaq. Town in GREENLAND. Located at 60 minutes north latitude, longitude 46°0′ west, this area has had a long history of sporadic settlement, dating back four thousand years to the Saqqaq culture. The Danish trading post of Nordpröven (the "Northern Test") was established here in 1830. The town of Narsaq has a population of eighteen hundred, with a local economy based on sheep farming and the preprocessing of fish products. Greenlandic for "the Plain."

Nashville. Capital city of TENNESSEE. Located at 450 feet (137 meters) elevation, with a 1998 population of 510,274. Founded in 1779 as Fort Nashborough; renamed in 1784 and became capital in 1843.

Nassau. Capital of the BAHAMAS. It is a port on the northeastern coast of New Providence Island and one of the world's chief pleasure resorts. It is also an international banking center. The population of New Providence Island was 172,196 in 1990.

Nayarit. Mexican state on the Pacific coast; capital is Tepic. Nayarit rises from the coast to a fertile, rich plateau of farmland. To the east and south lie high rugged mountains, deep gorges, and green valleys where sugarcane, corn, beans, chiles, bananas, and coconuts are grown. Coastal lagoons and marshes attract hundreds of species of birds. Sea turtles nest on the warm beaches and whales play in the warm waters offshore.

Nebraska. Became thirty-seventh state on March 1, 1867. Located in the Midwest of the United States. Total area of 77,358 square miles (200,357 sq. km.) with 1998 population of 1.6 million. The name is from a Native American word for "flat water," describing the Platte River. The Spanish claimed it in 1541 but did not settle there. In 1682 France claimed all territory drained by the MISSISSIPPI RIVER, including the lower MISSOURI RIVER to the Platte River. Acquired by the United States in 1803 via the Louisiana Purchase. The first permanent settlement was in 1823. By 1854 most of eastern Nebraska was ceded to the United States, and the territories of KANSAS and Nebraska were created. Lincoln (1998 population, 213,088) is the capital; Omaha (1998 population, 371,291) is the largest city.

Netherlands Antilles. Group of Dutch islands in the CARIBBEAN SEA. They lie in two groups separated by 500 miles (800 km.) of sea: The volcanic Dutch WINDWARDS—SINT MAARTEN, SABA, and ST. EUSTATIUS—are near the northern end of the LESSER ANTILLES; the Dutch Leewards—BONAIRE and CURAÇAO—are off the coast of Venezuela. ARUBA was politically part of the latter group until it became an autonomous region in 1986, but many still refer to these as the ABC islands.

Nevada. Became thirty-sixth state on October 31, 1864. Located in the GREAT BASIN of the United States. Total area of 110,567 square miles (286,369 sq. km.) with 1998 population of 1.7 million. Name is Spanish for "snow-capped." Nevada Territory was created in 1861 from part of Utah Territory. Prior to the 1859 discovery of the Comstock Lode (gold), most travel was through Nevada to CALIFORNIA. Carson City (1998 population, 49,301) is the capital; LAS VEGAS (1998 population,

404,288) is the largest city.

Nevis. Lush, fertile island in the Caribbean which, along with its sister island, St. Kitts, forms an independent nation; capital is Charlestown. Separated from St. Kitts by a narrow channel. Columbus named this island Nieves—Spanish for "snows"—because its clouded volcanic peaks reminded him of the snowcapped Pyrenees. Tourism is the main source of revenue.

New Brunswick. One of the Maritime Provinces of Canada; Fredericton is the provincial capital. Bounded on the east by Nova Scotia, on the north by the Northumberland Strait, Gulf of St. Lawrence, and Quebec, on the west by the state of Maine, and on the south by the Bay of Fundy. Originally part of Nova Scotia, it became a province with the arrival of thousands of Loyalists after the American Revolution in 1785. The only officially bilingual province in Canada. Many French Acadians live along the northern shores; persons of Irish and English background dominate elsewhere. Logging and fishing are major industries. The province covers 28,354 square miles (73,522 sq. km.), about the size of Maine, and had a population of 754,741 in 1999.

New Hampshire. Ninth of the thirteen original U.S. states; ratified Constitution on June 21, 1788. Located in New England. Total area of 9,351 square miles (24,219 sq. km.), with a 1998 population of 1.2 million. Name comes from Hampshire County, England. First explored in 1603 and settled by colonists from Massachusetts in 1620's and 1630's. First colony to declare independence from Great Britain. Concord (1998 population, 37,444) is capital; largest city is Manchester (1998 population, 102,524).

New Jersey. Third of the original thirteen U.S. states; ratified Constitution on December 18, 1787. Located in Northeast. Total area of 8,722 square miles (22,590 sq. km.) with 1988 population of 8.1 million. Named for island of Jersey in English Channel. English explorer Henry Hudson visited in 1609. First European settlement was in 1660. Trenton is capital (1998 population, 84,494); Newark is largest city (1998 population, 267,823).

Atlantic City, N.J. Page 574

New Brunswick Page 574

New Mexico. Became forty-seventh state on January 6, 1912. Located in the Southwest of the United States. Total area of 121,598 square miles (314,939 sq. km.) with 1998 population of 1.7 million. The name was applied by Spaniards in Mexico to lands north of the Rio Grande. In 1540 Francisco Vásquez de Coronado came looking for riches. After 1595, Juan de Oñate took possession of New Mexico for Spain. In 1821 Mexico won independence from Spain. The Mexican War ended in 1848 with the Treaty of Guadalupe Hidalgo, which ceded New Mexico to the United States. In 1850 the Territory of New Mexico was created. In 1853 the United States added land south of the Gila River to New Mexico via the Gadsden Purchase. The United States organized Arizona Territory in 1863 in the western part of Territory of New Mexico, giving New Mexico its present boundaries. Santa Fe (1998 population, 67,879) is the capital; Albuquerque (1998 population, 419,311) is the largest city.

New Orleans. Largest city (1998 population, 465,538) in Louisiana. Located on the Mississippi River, at 5 feet (2 meters) elevation. Much of the city is below sea level. Settled by the French in 1718 and named for Orléans, France. It was the state capital from 1812 to 1849.

New Orleans's French Quarter is noted for its distinctive architecture. (PhotoDisc)

New Spain. Colonial-era name for Mexico.

New World. Term first applied to the Western Hemisphere by early sixteenth century geographers. "New World" differentiates the Americas from the "Old World," which was seen as consisting of Europe, Africa, and Asia.

New York (State). Eleventh of the thirteen original U.S. states; ratified Constitution on July 26, 1788. Located in Northeast. Total area of 54,471 square miles (141,080 sq. km.) with 1998 population of 18.2 million—the third-largest state in population. Named for Duke of York. First European settlement was in 1614. First explored by Samuel de Champlain and Henry Hudson; claimed by the Dutch (who called it New Netherland) in 1624. In 1664 the British took control. Albany is capital (1998 population, 94,305); New York is largest city (1998 population, 7.4 million).

Niagara Falls Page 576

New York City Pages 454, 575

New York City. Largest city in the United States. Located on New York Bay on the Hudson River at 55 feet (17 meters) elevation, with a 1998 population of 7.4 million. Founded by the Dutch as New Amsterdam; renamed by the British in honor of the Duke of York. Was U.S. capital 1785-1790. Originally consisted only of Manhattan Island, but was rechartered in 1898 to include the Brooklyn, Bronx, Queens, and Staten Island boroughs.

Newfoundland. Most eastern province in Canada. A total area of 156,185 square miles (404,990 sq. km.) is broken into two sections. The island of Newfoundland is bounded on the east by the Atlantic Ocean, on the north by the Strait of Belle Isle, and on the west and south by the Gulf of St. Lawrence. The capital is St. John's. The island was named for the discovery of "newly found land" by John Cabot, an Italian explorer who sailed for the English in 1497. It became the final province of Canada in 1949, incorporating a second region—Labrador. Fishing is the main industry of the province, and rich natural resources abound in the interior of Labrador. A total of 541,164 people lived here in 1999, most having English ancestry.

Niagara Falls. One of the major natural attractions of North America. Located along the Niagara River, which flows from Lake Erie in the west to Lake Ontario in the east, forming part of the border between Canada and the United States. Two sets of waterfalls exist: Horseshoe Falls, in Ontario, Canada, reaches a width of 2,600 feet (790 meters) and a crest of 186 feet (57 meters); American Falls, in New York

State, reaches a width of 1,000 feet (300 meters) and has a crest of 193 feet (59 meters). The first European to describe the falls was Belgian friar Louis Hennepin, in 1678.

North Carolina. Twelfth of the thirteen original U.S. states; ratified Constitution on November 21, 1789. Located in the South. Total area of 53,821 square miles (139,397 sq. km.), with a 1988 population of 7.5 million. Named in honor of King Charles I and King Charles II of England. First European settlement was in 1660. Part of province of Carolina until 1691; became separate colony in 1711 and royal colony in 1729. Raleigh is capital (1998 population, 259,423); Charlotte is largest city (1998 population, 504,637).

North Dakota. Became thirty-ninth state on November 2, 1889. Located in the Upper Midwest of the United States. Total area of 70,704 square miles (183,022 sq. km.) with 1998 population of 638,244. "Dakota" is Sioux for "friend." The French first visited the area in 1738. Acquired by the United States in 1803 via the Louisiana Purchase. The first permanent European settlement was in 1812. Dakota Territory was established in 1861 and split into northern and southern in 1867. Bismarck (1998 population, 54,040) is the capital; Fargo (1998 population, 86,718) is the largest city.

Northumberland Strait. Body of water separating Prince Edward Island from northwestern Nova Scotia at the eastern tip of New Brunswick.

Northwest Territories. Second-largest territory in Canada; Yellowknife is the territorial capital. Bounded on the north by the Arctic Ocean; on the east by Nunavut; on the south by the provinces of Manitoba, Saskatchewan, and Alberta; and on the west by the Yukon Territory. The Magnetic North Pole is located here. Barren islands, a frigid Arctic climate, sea ice, and snow are common features. With 589,300 square miles (1,526,300 sq. km.), it is slightly larger than Alaska. Home to the Inuit and other native tribes, it was inhabited by a sparse population of 41,668 in 1999.

Northwest Territory. Territory created by the U.S. Congress in 1787 encompassing the region later consisting of the states of Ohio, Indiana, Illinois, Michigan, Wisconsin, and the portion of Minnesota east of the Mississippi River. Virginia, New York, Connecticut, and Massachusetts had claims to this area, which they ceded to the central government between 1780 and 1800. Land policy and territorial government were established by the Northwest Ordinances of 1785 and 1787.

Nova Scotia. One of the Maritime Provinces of Canada; the capital is Halifax. The province was settled by the French in 1604, when Samuel de Champlain founded Port Royal in the Annapolis Valley. The French were expelled in 1755 after the British overtook the region. Many of the French Acadians moved to Louisiana, establishing the Cajun population in the United States. Maintains a strong lobster and fishing industry and mining operations, and high-technology industries are developing in its large cities. It covers 21,425 square miles (55,555 sq. km.), comparable in size to the state of West Virginia, and had a population of 940,825 in 1999.

Nuevo Laredo. Mexico's quintessential border town, closely linked in culture and economics to Laredo, Texas, across the border. A relatively new city by Mexican standards, it compensates for its lack of historical sites with a well-developed downtown sector.

Nuevo León. The wealthiest state in Mexico; capital is Monterrey. It is the smallest of the five Mexican states that border the United States, sharing only a 12-mile (19-kilometer) border with Texas. It was a colonial backwater under Spanish rule, with cattle ranching as the chief occupation. Twentieth century industrialization brought prosperity to Monterrey. With a 95 percent literacy rate, Nuevo León has one of Mexico's most well-educated populations.

Nunavut. Territory in northern Canada, established in 1999 by the Canadian government. It is bounded by Baffin Strait and Greenland on the east, Hudson Bay and the provinces of Quebec and Manitoba on the south, the Northwest Territories on the west, and the Arctic Ocean on the north. The territorial capital, Iqaluit, is located in the southeastern corner of the territory, on the southern shores of Baffin Island. The largest land area in Canada, it covers 733,600 square miles (1,900,000 sq. km.), almost as large as Alaska and Texas combined. The population—27,146 in 1999—is made up largely of the native Inuit.

Nuuk (Godthåb). Administrative capital of Greenland, located on the southwest coast at the entrance to Godthåbsfjord. The cultural and educational center of Greenland, Nuuk was established in 1721 by the Danes as Godthåb, meaning "good hope." It is one of the world's smallest capital cities, having a population of thirteen thousand, twice the size of the next largest town in Greenland. It has an extensive fishing industry facilitated by an ice-free harbor. Located at 64°15′ north latitude, longitude 51°35′ west. Greenlandic for "the Headland."

Ohio River Page 578

Oak Ridge. Community in Tennessee founded in 1942 by U.S. government as part of the Manhattan Project to develop the atomic bomb. Incorporated as a city in 1959. At the end of World War II, the population was more than 75,000, but it had fallen to 27,045 in 1998. It has become a leading research center in environmental management and nuclear energy at Oak Ridge National Laboratory.

Oaxaca. Mexican state on the Pacific Coast; capital city of the same name. The well-preserved colonial city sits in a fertile valley 4,900 miles (1,500 meters) high in the mountains of the Sierra Madre del Sur. The city is a major industrial and commercial center in the south of Mexico.

Ohio. Became seventeenth state on March 1, 1803. Located in Great Lakes area of the United States. Total area of 44,828 square miles (116,105 sq. km.), with a 1998 population of 11.2 million. Name comes from Iroquois word meaning "great river" or "beautiful river." First explored by René-Robert Cavelier, sieur de La Salle, in 1669. The French controlled the area (first permanent settlement in 1788) until the French and Indian War, after which the British assumed control until 1783. Part of Northwest Territory 1787-1800. Capital and largest city is Columbus (1998 population, 670,234).

Ohio River. Formed by the confluence of the Allegheny and Monongahela Rivers in Pittsburgh, Pennsylvania. Runs about 981 miles (1,578 km.) to the Mississippi River at Cairo in southern Illinois. First explored by René-Robert Cavelier, sieur de La Salle, in 1669. Cincinnati, Ohio, and Louisville, Kentucky, are other major cities on this navigable waterway.

Oklahoma. Became forty-sixth state on November 16, 1907. Located in southwest central area of the United States. Total area of 69,903 square miles (181,049 sq. km.) with 1998 population of 3.3 million. The name is Choctaw for "red people." The Spanish were the first Europeans to visit. In 1682 the French claimed all land drained by the MISSISSIPPI RIVER (including present-day Oklahoma) and named it Louisiana. At the close of the French and Indian War, France ceded Louisiana to Spain, but regained it in 1800. Acquired by the United States in 1803 via the Louisiana Purchase. Following the War of 1812, the U.S. government negotiated removal treaties with the Choctaw, Chickasaw, Creek, Seminole, and Cherokee (known as the Five Civilized Tribes). In 1834 the Indian Territory—including present-day Oklahoma—was created west of the Mississippi River, where Wichita, Kiowa, and Comanche peoples already lived. Forced removal of Native Americans to Indian Territory took place until 1842, along what was called "The Trail of Tears." OKLAHOMA CITY (1998 population, 472,221) is the capital and largest city.

Oklahoma City. Largest city (1998 population, 472,221) of OKLAHOMA and state capital since 1910. Located on the Canadian and North Canadian Rivers at 1,195 feet (364 meters) elevation. Site of the April 19, 1995, bombing of the Alfred P. Murrah federal building, which killed 168 people.

Ontario. Third largest province in Canada. Bounded on the west by MANITOBA, on the east by QUEBEC, on the north by HUDSON BAY, and on the south by the GREAT LAKES and five states of the United States. A total land area of 412,582 square miles (1,069,825 sq. km.) makes this comparable to LOUISIANA, TEXAS, and NEW MEXICO together. The province is the most populous in Canada (11.5 million people in 1999). The provincial capital, TORONTO, represents the cultural, economic, and political heartland of the country to many residents.

Ontario, Lake. See GREAT LAKES.

Oodaaq Island. GREENLAND island that is the northernmost landmass on Earth. Located 435 miles (700 km.) from the North Pole, it is a small island of gravel about 328 feet (100 meters) across. CAPE MORRIS JESUP formerly was thought to be the the northernmost point of land.

Oregon. Became thirty-third state on February 14, 1859. Located in the Pacific Northwest of the United States. Total area of 98,386 square miles (254,820 sq. km.) with 1998 population of 3.3 million. Origin of the name is unknown. The first European visitor was U.S. Captain Robert Gray, who traded with Native Americans in 1788 and named the COLUMBIA RIVER in 1792. After the War of 1812, Oregon was returned to the United States by terms of the peace treaty; nevertheless, the British remained in control. In 1846 U.S. claims to Oregon country south of the forty-ninth parallel were recognized by treaty. Oregon Territory was created in 1848. Salem (1998 population, 126,702) is the capital; PORTLAND (1998 population, 503,891) is the largest city.

Oregan coast Page 576

Oregon Trail. Pioneer route to the Northwest from Independence, MISSOURI, to the COLUMBIA RIVER in OREGON through present-day NEBRASKA, WYOMING, and IDAHO. The trip usually lasted four to six months; many who attempted it did not finish. The first wagon train reached Oregon in 1842.

Orizaba, Mount. Mexico's highest mountain. This towering, snow-capped volcano, 18,700 feet (5,700 meters) high, is located south of Mexico City.

Ottawa. Capital city of Canada and the second largest city in the province of Ontario. In 1998 it had 1.06 million residents. Situated on the shores of the Ottawa River, which flows east to the St. Lawrence River and the Atlantic Ocean. Home to many national attractions, including the Canadian parliament buildings and the homes of the prime minister and other officials. Established and chosen in 1855 by Queen Victoria of England, after disputes about which city would become the national capital in a unified Canada.

Palenque Page 577

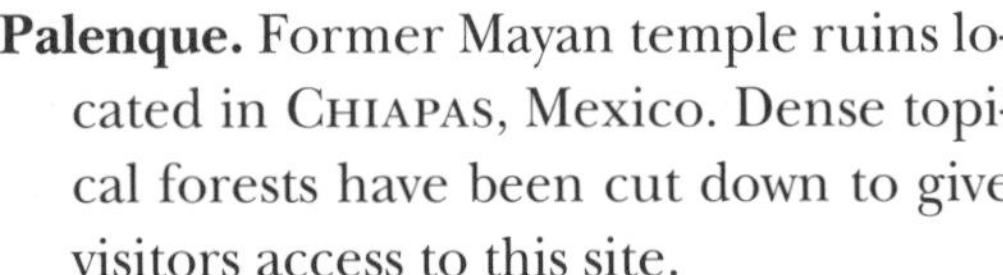

Palenque. Former Mayan temple ruins located in Chiapas, Mexico. Dense topical forests have been cut down to give visitors access to this site.

Paricutín Volcano. Volcano that erupted without warning in a Mexican farmer's cornfield in 1943. In less than a year, its cone was 1,475 feet (450 meters) high. The volcano was active for nine years, spewing ash and rocks erratically until March 6, 1952, when it ceased as suddenly as it had begun.

Pelée, Mount. Volano on Martinique whose violent eruption in 1902 destroyed the town of St. Pierre and killed 30,000 people.

Pelee Island. Island located in Lake Erie a few miles south from Point Pelee on the southern part of Ontario. The island covers 18 square miles (47 sq. km.). The southernmost point in Canada is on a rock named Middle Island, just south of Pelee Island.

Pennsylvania. Second of the original thirteen U.S. states; ratified Constitution on December 12, 1787. Located in Northeast. Total area of 46,058 square miles (119,290 sq. km.), with a 1998 population of 12 million. Settled by

Parliament buildings in Ottawa. (PhotoDisc)

Swedes in 1634. Royal charter granted to William Penn (after whom it is named) in 1681 as a haven for Society of Friends (Quakers). Most was originally part of Virginia Colony, then part of NEW YORK. Harrisburg (1998 population, 49,502) is capital; PHILADELPHIA (1998 population, 1.4 million) is largest city.

Percé Rock. See GASPE.

Peter Island. One of the British VIRGIN ISLANDS in the CARIBBEAN SEA. Located about 5 miles (8 km.) directly south across the Sir Francis Drake Channel from Road Town, TORTOLA.

Philadelphia. Largest city of PENNSYLVANIA. Located on Delaware River at 100 feet (30 meters) elevation, with a 1998 population of 1.4 million. Founded by William Penn in 1681 as Society of Friends settlement on a previous Swedish site. First and Second Continental Congresses (1774 and 1775-1776) and Constitutional Convention (1787) were held here. Was the capital of the United States from 1790 to 1800.

Phoenix. Capital, since 1889, and largest city (1998 population, 1.2 million) of ARIZONA. Located on the Salt River at 1,090 feet (332 meters) elevation. The first permanent European settlement was in 1870.

Pittsburgh. Second-largest city in PENNSYLVANIA. Located where confluence of Allegheny and Monongahela Rivers form the OHIO RIVER at 745 feet (227 meters) elevation, with a 1998 population of 340,520. Fort Duquesne was built on the site by the French around 1750; fell to the British in 1758 and renamed Fort Pitt.

Plateau of Mexico. See MEXICAN PLATEAU.

Point Pelee. Most southern point of land on the Canadian mainland. Located at 41.55 degrees north latitude, longitude 82.30 degrees west, in the northwestern end of Lake Erie, in southern ONTARIO. Point Pelee is a natural wedge-shaped sandspit jutting into the lake. It lies astride a major flyway of wild ducks, Canadian geese, swans, and other migratory birds, which find sanctuary in Point Pelee National Park.

Popocatepetl. Second-highest mountain in Mexico. Rising to 17,887 feet (5,465 meters), it forms the southeastern lip of the Valley of Mexico. It was a dormant volcano popular with climbers until December, 1994, when it began belching clouds of smoke and ash.

Pittsburgh, Pennsylvania. (Corbis)

Philadelphia Page 577

Pittsburgh Page 578

Popocatepetl Page 578

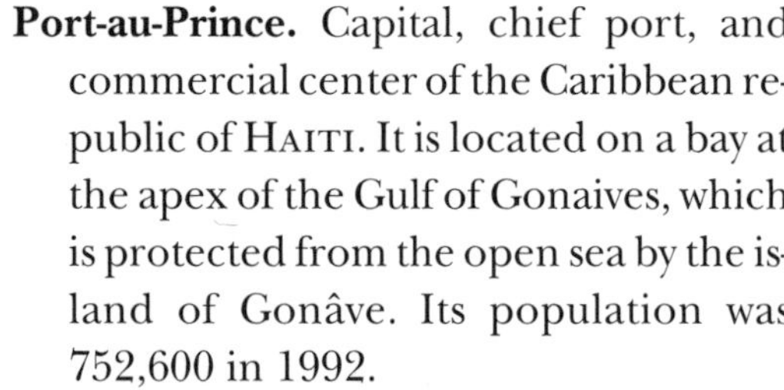

Port-au-Prince. Capital, chief port, and commercial center of the Caribbean republic of Haiti. It is located on a bay at the apex of the Gulf of Gonaives, which is protected from the open sea by the island of Gonâve. Its population was 752,600 in 1992.

Portland Page 579

Portland. Oregon's largest city (1998 population, 503,891). Located on the Willamette River near confluence with the Columbia River, at 77 feet (23 meters) elevation.

Prairie Provinces. Collective term for the Canadian provinces of Manitoba, Saskatchewan, and Alberta in the northern Great Plains region of North America. These provinces constitute the great wheat-producing region of Canada and have large petroleum and natural gas reserves.

Prince Edward Island. The smallest province in Canada; capital is Charlottetown. Bounded on the north by the Gulf of St. Lawrence and on the south by the Northumberland Strait. Located at approximately 46 degrees north latitude, longitude 63 degrees west. Known for its fine farmland, potatoes, red soils, and beautiful beaches. It covers 2,184 square miles (5,663 sq. km.), slightly larger than the state of Delaware, and had a population of 137,796 in 1999. Most are descendants of English, Irish, or Scottish background, many dating to the pre-Loyalist and Loyalist period of the American Revolution.

Puerto Vallarta Page 579

Puebla. State in east central Mexico. Its capital is also called Puebla. The state is bounded on the east by Veracruz and by the Federal District on the west. Its 13,090-square-mile (33,902 sq. km.) territory occupies the southeastern corner of the Anahuac Plateau. It varies in elevation from 5,000 to 8,000 feet (1,500-2,400 meters). Numerous fertile valleys are formed by the Sierra Madre Oriental. Coffee, sugarcane, fibers, and corn are the principal crops. Its population was 3,347,685 in 1980. The city of Puebla was founded in 1532. Because of its strategic location on the route between Mexico City and Veracruz, Puebla it has been considered a military key to Mexico. Its population was 771,000 in 1980.

Puerto Rico. Smallest and most easterly of the Greater Antilles islands in the Caribbean Sea. Its capital, San Juan, is one of the best-preserved Spanish colonial cities in the Caribbean. The island is 110 miles (177 km.) long and 35 miles (56 km.) wide. It is dominated by Cordillera Central, a central mountain range that rises to more than 4,000 feet (1,220 meters). North of this range is rain forest; south of it, the land is arid and covered with cactus. Three-quarters of the island is mountainous with fertile coastal plains. Puerto Rico includes two offshore islands—Vieques and Culebra. The population of 3.7 million is predominantly Hispanic, Spanish-speaking, and Roman Catholic. Puerto Rico is a commonwealth territory of the United States; its residents are U.S. citizens, eligible for federal aid and military draft but not required to pay federal income tax. Several public referenda have been held regarding statehood, with support growing to become the fifty-first state. Tourism is the main economic activity.

Puerto Vallarta. Popular Mexican resort located on the Pacific coast. The city rings Bahia Banderas, the largest natural bay in Mexico and the third largest in the world. It was a small port and waystation throughout most of the colonial period. After the American film *Night of the Iguana* was made there in the 1960's, tourism accelerated. Now full of condos and high-rise buildings, the town still retains its quaint Mexican charm.

Puget Sound. Arm of the Pacific Ocean, extending about 80 miles (130 km.) inland to Olympia, Washington. Seattle and Tacoma, Washington, also are located on the sound. Named for Peter Puget, explorer of the Pacific Northwest in the 1790's.

Qaanaaq (Thule). Administrative capital of northern Greenland and the world's northernmost inhabited area. It is the main town (population five hundred) of the municipality of Avanersuaq (total population eight hundred). Located at 77°30′ north latitude, longitude 69°12′ west. Greenlanders were moved here from their original location 60 miles (100 km.) south, now the site of the Thule Air Base. Qaanaaq was the base and the destination for several explorers, including Robert Peary, Elisha Kane, and Knud Johan Victor Rasmussen.

Qaqortoq (Julianehåb). One of the largest towns in South Greenland, with a population of thirty-one hundred. Located at 60°40′ north latitude, longitude 46°0′ west, it has a slightly warmer climate than more northern areas, and sheep farming is an important aspect of the economy. The largest of the Viking settlements, the Eastern Settlement called "Österbygden"—which was established by the twelfth century and had disappeared by the fifteenth century—was found here. The remains of many Norse farmsteads, including Brattahlid, the home of Erik the Red, have been identified. Greenlandic for "the White."

Qasigiannguit (Christianshåb). Oldest town on Disko Bay, founded as the first Danish colony in northern West Greenland. Located at 68°50′ north latitude, longitude 51°10′ west. Its population is sixteen thousand; its economy is dependent on shrimping. Greenlandic for "Small Variegated Seals," because of the plentiful seal population.

Quebec. A French-speaking province of Canada. Bounded on the east by Labrador, New Brunswick, and the Gulf of St. Lawrence; on the north by Hudson Bay and Ungava Bay; on the west by Ontario; and on the south by New York, Vermont, New Hampshire, and Maine. Formerly called Lower Canada, it joined the Canadian Confederation in 1867 as one of its founding provinces. It has an area of 594,860 square miles (1,542,470 sq. km.), slightly larger than Alaska, with a population of 7.36 million in 1999. Most people are concentrated in the southern portion of the province, where Montreal and Quebec City dominate. Rich natural resources are found in the Canadian Shield, where logging, mining, and hydroelectric facilities abound. The French ethnicity and language are dominant throughout the province.

Quebec City. Capital city of Quebec, Canada. Located on the north shore of the St. Lawrence River at the terminus of the Gulf of St. Lawrence. In 1998 it had a population of 687,200. Founded by the French explorer Samuel de Champlain in 1604, it is the oldest continuous urban settlement in Canada. The city's old section has retained its old European style of narrow winding streets and quaint buildings.

Quebec City Page 449

Queen Charlotte Islands. Archipelago of the western coast of British Columbia near the Alaska Panhandle. Discovered by Spaniard Juan Pérez in 1774. The Haida tribe lives on these islands.

Querétaro. Mexican state north of Mexico City, in the geographic heart of

Mexico; capital city has the same name. This mountainous state was the center for the conspiracy that eventually led to the overthrow of the Spanish colony and the establishment of the Republic of Mexico. Querétaro city was the temporary capital of Mexico when the U.S. army took over Mexico City in 1848. Here, the Treaty of Guadalupe Hidalgo was signed, relinquishing much of Mexico's land to the United States. Emperor Maximilian was executed here in 1866, and the present Mexican Constitution was drafted here in 1916.

Quintana Roo. State on the east coast of Mexico's YUCATÁN PENINSULA; its capital is Chetumal, located on the border with Belize. The east coast of the state is lined with Maya ruins marking the heyday of the Putun Maya traders. It was an undeveloped and ignored for many years, until it was named for an army general, Andres Quintana Roo, who had never seen it. When the value of this tropical paradise as a tourist area was recognized, roads were built and resorts such as CANCÚN now flourish.

Red River. River beginning at the confluence of the Bois de Sioux and Otter Tail Rivers at the twin cities of Wahpeton, NORTH DAKOTA, and Breckenridge, MINNESOTA. The river flows north for 545 miles (877 km.), and for 440 miles (710 km.) forms the boundary between North Dakota and Minnesota, before entering MANITOBA, Canada, and emptying into Lake WINNIPEG. The Red River Valley region is one of North America's best farming regions.

Regina. Provincial capital of SASKATCHEWAN, Canada. Originally settled along the Canadian Transcontinental Railway line, on flat prairie land with a small creek running through the area. In 1998 the population of Regina was almost 200,000. The Royal Canadian Mounted Police is headquartered here.

Research Triangle Park. Largest planned research center in the United States, formed by Duke University, the University of North Carolina, and North Carolina State University. Located in the triangle between Durham, Chapel Hill, and Raleigh, sites of the three universities. Over thirty-four thousand employees in sixty companies conduct research in biotechnology, environmental science, telecommunications, medicine and health, and other areas. Home of the North Carolina Supercomputer Center; has one of the highest concentrations of doctoral degrees in the United States.

Reversing Falls. See Bay of FUNDY.

Reynosa. Modern, industrial city on the United States-Mexico border. Reynosa lacks historic sites because a flood in 1800 destroyed the town and forced its residents to move to its current site on top of a small *meseta* (rise). It is located directly across the border from the small town of Hidalgo, TEXAS.

Rhode Island. Last of the thirteen original U.S. states; ratified Constitution on May 29, 1790. Located in New England. Total area of 1,545 square miles (4,002 sq. km.) with 1998 population of 988,480. Origin of name unknown. Smallest state in total area. Settled by religious exiles from MASSACHUSETTS, including Roger Williams, who established Providence in 1636. Granted royal charter in 1663. Official name is "State of Rhode Island and Providence Plantations." Capital and largest city is Providence (1998 population, 150,890).

Rio Bravo del Norte. Mexican name for the border river known to Americans as the RIO GRANDE.

Rio Grande. River that begins in the San Juan Mountains of COLORADO and flows through central New Mexico to the Mexican border at El Paso, where it forms the border between Texas and Mexico to the east. Known as Rio Bravo del Norte in Mexico. Total length is about 1,885 miles (3,034 km.), making it one of the longest rivers in North America. It is generally too shallow for navigation and is used primarily for drinking water and agriculture.

Rocky Mountains. One of greatest chains of mountains in North America, stretching from northeastern Canada into central New Mexico. The highest point is Mount Elbert at 14,433 feet (4,399 meters), in Colorado.

Rushmore, Mount. Peak in the Black Hills of South Dakota. Memorial busts of U.S. presidents George Washington, Thomas Jefferson, Abraham Lincoln, and Theodore Roosevelt are carved into granite face of the mountain. Established in 1925 and carved from 1927 to 1941 by Gutzon Borglum.

Saba. One of the Netherlands Antilles Windward Islands in the Caribbean Sea; capital is The Bottom. The island, 5 square miles (13 sq. km.) in area, is a volcano that has been extinct for five thousand years; its peak, Mount Scenery, soars to 2,854 feet (870 meters). The population is about one thousand. There are no beaches because steep cliffs rise sharply from the sea. Well's Bay on the northwestern coast has a black sand beach for a few months during the summer, but it disappears back into the sea the rest of the year. The island's only flat point—named Flat Point—is the site of Saba's airstrip. Columbus saw Saba in 1493, but it remained uninhabited except for a few Carib Indians until the Dutch colonized it in 1640. Saba changed hands twelve times as colonial powers vied for the island.

Mount Rushmore. (PhotoDisc)

Rocky Mountains Page 384

Sacramento. Capital of California. Its 1998 population was 404,168. Located at the confluence of the American and Sacramento Rivers in the Sacramento Valley, at 25 feet (8 meters) elevation. The first European resident of the area was John A. Sutter, a Swiss immigrant who received the land grant from Mexican government in 1839. In 1848 gold was discovered at Sutter's lumber mill. Sacramento became the state capital in 1854; in 1860, it became the western terminus of the Pony Express.

St. Augustine. Oldest permanent European settlement in the United States. Located in Florida on the Matanzas and San Sebastian Rivers. Home of Castillo de San Marcos, begun in 1672, and Cathedral of St. Augustine, erected in 1790's. Established in 1565 by Spanish explorer Pedro Menéndez de Avilés. In 1821 the Spanish ceded St. Augustine to the United States. Population in 1998 was 12,573.

St. Croix. Largest of the U.S.-owned Virgin Islands. Located 40 miles (65 km.) south of St. Thomas, with an area of 84 square miles (218 sq. km.). The island has a lush rain forest in the northwest and dry conditions on the eastern end. Beaches line the coast, attracting many tourists. The capital, Christiansted, is a restored Danish port on a coral-bound bay on the northeastern shore.

St. Eustatius (Statia). One of the Netherland Antilles islands of the Caribbean Sea; capital and only city is Oranjestad. Located 178 miles (287 km.) east of Puerto Rico and 35 miles (56 km.) south of Sint Maarten. Anchored at the north and south ends by extinct volcanoes separated by an arid central plain. Its higher elevations are covered with rich vegetation. Colonized in 1636 by the Dutch, it was once the most powerful trading center in the Caribbean. This island was the first to officially acknowledge the United States of America as an independent nation.

St. John. Smallest, least developed of the U.S.-owned Virgin Islands. Located 3 miles (5 km.) east of St. Thomas across the Pillsbury Sound. Administrative capital is Cruz Bay. In 1956 Laurence Rockefeller donated two-thirds of St. John's 20 square miles (53 sq. km.) to the United States as a national park. Steep, volcanic hills are a tropical paradise of lush forests and jungles.

St. John. Largest city in New Brunswick, Canada. Located at the mouth of the St. John River on the eastern shores of the Bay of Fundy. The first incorporated city in Canada (1784), after thousands of British Loyalists arrived from the United States in 1783, including Benedict Arnold. A major shipping and oil-refining center, the city claims to have the highest concentration of Irish in Canada. Its population was 127,300 in 1998.

St. John's. Capital of Newfoundland, located at the eastern edge of Canada, and one of the oldest settlements in North America. Its exceptional natural harbor brought the earliest European fishermen to this site. It is the easternmost terminus of the Trans-Canada Highway, which spans the country. Its population was 173,600 in 1998.

St. Kitts. Lush, fertile island in the Caribbean Sea, which, along with the island of Nevis, forms an independent nation; capital is Basseterre. It has an area of 65 square miles (168 sq. km.). It is known as the mother colony of the West Indies, because it was from here that English and French settlers spread out to settle other islands.

St. Lawrence, Gulf of. Portion of the Atlantic north of Prince Edward Island and east of New Brunswick.

St. Lawrence River. River that runs 745 miles (1,200 km.) from Lake Ontario in the west, bordering the United States and Canada between the state of New York and the province of Ontario, and drains into the Gulf of St. Lawrence and the Atlantic Ocean near Quebec City. It has been an important trade route to the interior, and completion of the St. Lawrence Seaway in 1959 opened shipping traffic from the Atlantic Ocean to the Great Lakes, benefiting both the United States and Canada.

St. Louis. Second largest city in Missouri. Its 1998 population was 339,316. Located on the Mississippi River just south of confluence with Missouri River, at 455 feet (139 meters) elevation. Settled by the French in 1764.

St. Lucia. Island in the Caribbean WINDWARD ISLANDS; capital is Castries. Located between MARTINIQUE and ST. VINCENT, 100 miles (160 km.) west of BARBADOS, with an area of 238 square miles (616 sq. km.). The old French capital, Soufriere, was the first settlement on the island; however, it was replaced by Castries, which has a better harbor. A volcano of the same name located nearby is actually a sulfur-spewing volcanic vent that steams continuously. Marigot Bay, on the west coast, once sheltered pirates but is now a scenic port for cruise ships. Off the coast of Soufriere, the Pitons, two pyramid-shaped volcanic mountains, are covered in rain forests that soar from the CARIBBEAN SEA to heights of 2,439 feet (743 meters) and 2,620 feet (799 meters).

St. Martin. Northern, French half of a small Caribbean island; the southern half is SINT MAARTEN, a Dutch territory. This is the smallest island in the world to fly two flags. Capital is Marigot. The coastline has many coves and white sand beaches. The main landmass has many lagoons and salt ponds and one of the largest natural lakes in the Antilles; the Dutch and French share this lake. Its two main islands are Ilet Pinel (Penal Island) and Cape Verte off the eastern coast.

St. Thomas. The capital island of the U.S.-owned VIRGIN ISLANDS in the CARIBBEAN SEA. A mountainous island with a prosperous tourist industry, it has an area of 32 square miles (83 sq. km.). The city of Charlotte Amalie is a bustling port with one of the best waterfronts in the Caribbean. Its excellent harbor is sheltered by hills and protected by islands. Pirate ships and trading vessels have been replaced by cruise ships and yachts.

St. Louis, Missouri, viewed from the east side of the Mississippi River. (PhotoDisc)

St. Vincent and the Grenadines. String of thirty-three islands that make up a single nation; part of the WINDWARD ISLANDS chain in the southern CARIBBEAN SEA. Located 13 degrees north of the equator, the islands extend in a 45-mile (73-kilometer) arc southwest to GRENADA. La Soufrière is an active volcano that last erupted in 1979 on St. Vincent. Population of 118,400 lives in abject poverty. St. Vincent is a fertile island that exports bananas and arrowroot.

St. Thomas Page 582

San Francisco Pages 446, 508

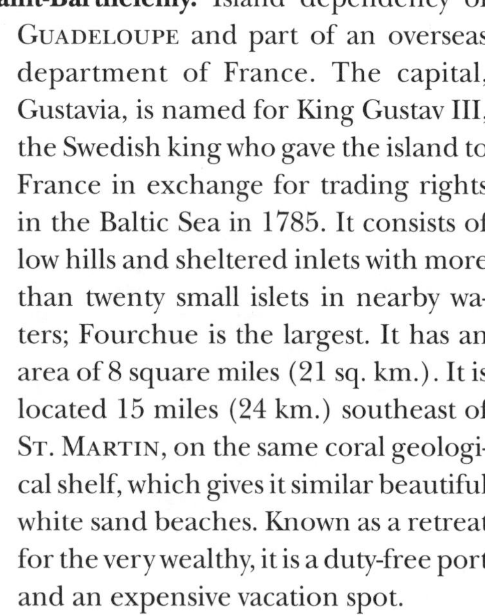

Saint-Barthélemy. Island dependency of Guadeloupe and part of an overseas department of France. The capital, Gustavia, is named for King Gustav III, the Swedish king who gave the island to France in exchange for trading rights in the Baltic Sea in 1785. It consists of low hills and sheltered inlets with more than twenty small islets in nearby waters; Fourchue is the largest. It has an area of 8 square miles (21 sq. km.). It is located 15 miles (24 km.) southeast of St. Martin, on the same coral geological shelf, which gives it similar beautiful white sand beaches. Known as a retreat for the very wealthy, it is a duty-free port and an expensive vacation spot.

Salt Lake City Page 580

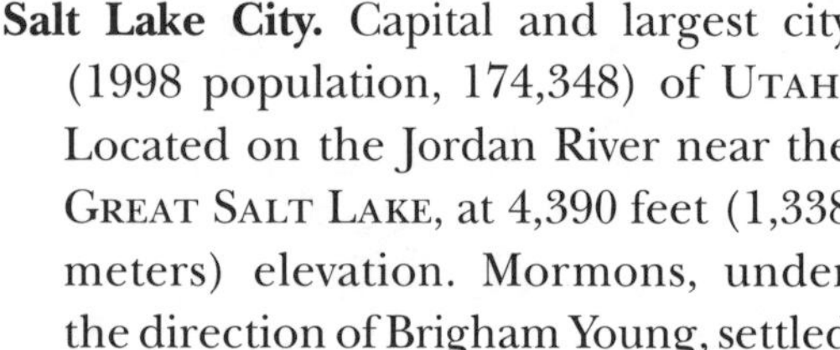

Salt Lake City. Capital and largest city (1998 population, 174,348) of Utah. Located on the Jordan River near the Great Salt Lake, at 4,390 feet (1,338 meters) elevation. Mormons, under the direction of Brigham Young, settled here in 1847.

San Antonio. Second largest city in Texas. Its 1998 population was 1.1 million. Located on the San Antonio River at 650 feet (198 meters) elevation. It was captured by Texans from Mexico in 1835. In 1836 Mexican soldiers stormed the Alamo and killed 187 Texans.

San Cristóbal de las Casas. Colonial capital and market center of the southern Mexican state of Chiapas. In 1994 the indigenous people of the area led a revolt—the Zapatista rebellion—against the non-Indian Mexican towns and the Mexican government over health care, education, and land distribution issues, resulting in the establishment of a strong military presence.

San Diego Page 580

San Diego. Second largest city in California. Its 1998 population was 1.2 million. Located on San Diego Bay, at 20 feet (6 meters) elevation. Spaniards established California's first presidio and first mission there in 1769.

San Francisco. Located in California on a peninsula between the Pacific Ocean and San Francisco Bay, at 65 feet (20 meters) elevation. Spanish built a presidio there in 1776. Earthquakes in 1906 and 1989 caused great destruction.

San Juan. Capital and largest city of Puerto Rico, located on the northern coast of the island on the Atlantic Ocean. It is the oldest city under U.S. jurisdiction. The Spanish explorer Juan Ponce de León founded the original settlement, Caparra, which became San Juan in 1508. De León is buried in the San Juan cathedral. In the early sixteenth century San Juan was the point of departure for Spanish expeditions to unknown parts of the New World. San Juan, along with all of Puerto Rico, passed to the United States with Spain's defeat in the Spanish-American War of 1898. San Juan is the largest industrial and processing center of the island. Its population was estimated at 433,705 in 1996.

San Luis Potosí. Vast Mexican state; capital city of the same name. Founded in 1592 when gold and silver were discovered in the area, the city is Mexico's gateway to the north and a major transportation hub at the center of Mexico. Highways crisscross here, linking Mexico City and Guadalajara with Ciudad Juárez and Nuevo Laredo on the United States-Mexico border.

San Miguel de Allende. Mexican city founded in 1542 by a Franciscan friar. During colonial times, it was a busy crossroads for the great mining towns of the *bajio* region, Guanajuato and Zacatecas. It was declared a Mexican National Monument in 1926 to protect its architectural and cultural integrity.

Santa Fe. Capital of New Mexico. Its 1998 population was 67,879. Located on the

Santa Fe River, at 6,950 feet (2,118 meters) elevation. Established as the capital of New Mexico in 1610 by the Spanish (making it the oldest capital city in the United States); in 1851, as a U.S. territorial capital; and in 1912, as a state capital.

Santo Domingo. Capital of the Dominican Republic and the oldest permanent city established by Europeans in the Western Hemisphere. It is located on the southeast coast of the island of Hispaniola at the mouth of the Ozama River. Bartolomeo Columbus, brother of Christopher Columbus, founded the city in 1496. Santo Domingo is the industrial, commercial, and financial center of the Dominican Republic and claims the oldest university in the Western Hemisphere. The colonial era cathedral contains the reputed remains of Christopher Columbus. Its population was 2,100,000 in 1993.

Saskatchewan. Central province of the Canada's Prairie Provinces. Bounded by Alberta on the west, Manitoba on the east, the Northwest Territories on the north, and the states of Montana and North Dakota in the south. The 251,700-square-mile (652,660 square-kilometer) area is slightly larger than the states of North Dakota, South Dakota, and Nebraska combined. Many residents are of German and Ukrainian background. Wheat farming dominates the southern half of the province, with boreal forest in the north. In 1999, 1.03 million people lived in the province. The provincial capital, Regina, and Saskatoon are the largest cities.

Saskatoon. Largest city in the province of Saskatchewan, Canada. Located on the banks of the South Saskatchewan River, it is the processing and distribution center for a large agricultural region. In 1998 the population was 229,300 people (1998). Known as the "City of Bridges."

Savannah. Oldest city in Georgia. Located near mouth of Savannah River at 20 feet (6 meters) elevation. Founded by James Oglethorpe in 1733. Was the original capital of Georgia Colony in the eighteenth century.

Sea of Cortés. See California, Gulf of.

Seattle. Largest city in Washington State. Its 1998 population was 536,978. Located between Puget Sound and Lake Washington, at 10 feet (3 meters) elevation. Founded in 1852.

Seattle Page 581

Sibley Peninsula. Home to Canada's Sibley Provincial Park and the "Sleeping Giant," a naturally occurring rock formation in the north shore of Lake Superior, which appears to have the shape of a person lying down. When seen from the shores of Thunder Bay, the "Sleeping Giant" is an anomaly in an otherwise flat, featureless landscape and park. According to local legend, this landscape was formed by the god Nanabijou to ward off white men who sought silver in the region. Located at 48.5 degrees north latitude, longitude 89 degrees west.

Sierra Madre del Sur. High, rugged mountains in southern Mexico.

Sierra Madre Occidental. Rugged, volcanic mountain range in Mexico. It rises 2,000-3,000 feet (600 to 900 meters) above the high arid plains and borders the Mexican Plateau on the west. The Spanish discovered some of the world's richest silver deposits here in the mid-sixteenth century.

Sierra Madre Page 384

Sierra Madre Oriental. Mountain range in Mexico. It rises abruptly from the Gulf coastal plain to border the Mexican Plateau on the east. Elevations exceed 10,000 feet (3,050 meters) in many areas. Historically, it has been a rugged barrier to the interior from the east.

Sierra Nevada. Mountain range that extends northwest to southeast, approximating the eastern border of California with Nevada, for about 400 miles (640 km.). Location of Mount Whitney, the tallest peak in the continental United States.

Sierra Tarahumara. One of the highest and most rugged portions of Mexico's Sierra Occidental. This is the traditional homeland of Mexico's Tarahumara indigenous people. Also known as Copper Canyon because of the coppery color of the walls of the many deep canyons of this region. Gold, silver, amethyst, and turquoise are mined here.

Sinaloa. State in northwestern Mexico on the Gulf of California and the Pacific Ocean. The 22,521 square miles (58,328 sq. km.) of territory consist of a barren, tropical coastal plain that rises inland to the Sierra Madre Occidental and is crossed by five main rivers. Its economy is based on agriculture and mining. Its population was 2,210,766 in 1990.

Sint Maarten. Southern, Dutch half of a small Caribbean island; the northern half is St. Martin, a French territory. Smallest island in the world to fly two flags. The capital, Philipsburg, is set on a narrow spit of land between Great Bay and the Great Salt Pond, the source of salt that originally attracted the Dutch West Indies Company to the island. The population of forty thousand relies on tourism for revenue

Sleeping Giant. See Sibley Peninsula.

Sonora. Mexican state bordered by the United States to the north and the Gulf of California to the west. Mexico's most important fisheries are located here on the Gulf of California, and citrus fruits, grapes, and vegetables are grown on the Yaqui River and Sonora River plains. Cotton, winter wheat, and oil seed are the principal crops grown here. The Sonoran Desert is the most diverse desert in the world, with three hundred species of cactus adapted to retain water and withstand fierce climatic extremes.

Sonoran Desert. Desert covering 120,000 square miles (310,800 sq. km.) in southwestern Arizona and southeastern California, and including much of the Mexican state of Baja California and the western half of the Mexican state of Sonora. Irrigation has produced many fertile agricultural areas such as the Imperial Valley in southeastern California.

South Carolina. Eighth of the thirteen original U.S. states; ratified Constitution on May 23, 1788. Located in the South. Total area of 32,008 square miles (82,901 sq. km.), with a 1998 population of 3.8 million. First explored by Spanish in the early sixteenth century. Granted by Charles II of England to eight of his supporters in 1663. Divided into colonies of North Carolina and South Carolina in 1729. First state to secede from the Union, in 1860. Columbia is capital and largest city (1998 population, 110,840).

South Dakota. Became fortieth state on November 2, 1889. Located in the Upper Midwest of the United States. Total area of 77,121 square miles (199,744 sq. km.) with 1998 population of 738,171. "Dakota" is Sioux for "friend." The French first visited in the early 1740's. Acquired by the United States in 1803 via the Louisiana Purchase. Its first permanent European settlement was in 1859. Dakota Territory was established in 1861 and split into northern and southern in 1867. Pierre (1998 population, 13,267) is the capital; Sioux Falls (1998 population, 116,762) is the largest city.

Statia. See St. Eustatius.

Sukkertoppen. See Maniitsoq.

Superior, Lake. See Great Lakes.

Tabasco. Mexican state on the southern Gulf Coast; capital is Villahermosa. This green, fertile state was once home to three major pre-Columbian cultures: the Olmecs, the "mother culture" of Mexico; the Totonacs of central Veracruz; and the Huastecs. Much of the countryside is covered with thick rain forest, coconut and banana groves, and cacao plantations. A twentieth century oil boom enabled improvement of the state's roads, housing, and employment situation; and archaeological sites, such as Comalcalco, attract many tourists.

Tahoe, Lake. Located on the border of Nevada and California in the Sierra Nevada at an altitude of about 6,230 feet (1,900 meters). A major U.S. recreational and tourism area, covering 187 square miles (484 sq. km.).

Tamaulipas. Mexican state along the northern coast of the Gulf of Mexico; capital is Ciudad Victoria. It encompasses the eastern escarpment of the Sierra Madre Oriental as well as tropical and subtropical coastal plains. Under Spanish influence, Tamaulipas became the cradle of cattle ranching in North America, and the ranchero culture continued at the end of the twentieth century. The *maquiladoras* in the border cities Nuevo Laredo, Reynosa, and Matamoros are important sources of revenue. The name means high mountains in the Huastec dialect.

Tampico. Major seaport in Mexico. Located on the Gulf Coast of Mexico, it handles considerable shipping traffic through its Rio Panuco harbor. After oil was discovered here in 1901, Tampico changed from a port ransacked by pirates into an industrial center for the storage, refining, and shipping of oil.

Tehuantepec, Bay of. Body of water in the Pacific Ocean off the south coast of Mexico's Isthmus of Tehuantepec.

Tehuantepec, Isthmus of. Low, hilly depression west of Chiapas, Mexico. The narrowest, and one of the lowest, parts of Mexico. Despite a transcontinental railroad, a highway, and an oil pipeline, it is a relatively isolated and undeveloped region. The Pacific Ocean and Gulf of Mexico are separated here by only about 137 miles (220 km.).

Tennessee. Became sixteenth state on June 1, 1796. Located in the U.S. South. Total area of 42,146 square miles (109,153 sq. km.), with a 1998 population of 5.4 million. Name is thought to have come from "Tanasi," the name of a Cherokee village. First explored by the Spanish in 1540. René-Robert Cavelier, sieur de La Salle, visited Memphis area in 1682; explored by Daniel Boone in 1769. Became part of the United States in 1783. State of Franklin from 1784-1788. Nashville (1998 population, 510,274) is capital; Memphis (1998 population, 603,507) is largest city.

Lake Tahoe Page 386

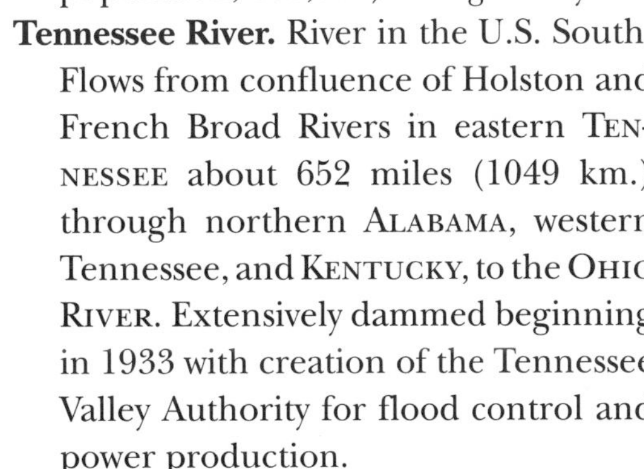

Tennessee River. River in the U.S. South. Flows from confluence of Holston and French Broad Rivers in eastern Tennessee about 652 miles (1049 km.) through northern Alabama, western Tennessee, and Kentucky, to the Ohio River. Extensively dammed beginning in 1933 with creation of the Tennessee Valley Authority for flood control and power production.

Tenochtitlán. Aztec capital city. Built on an island in a lake, it occupied the site that is modern Mexico City. From here, the Aztecs ruled an extensive empire that spread over much of south central Mexico.

Teotihuacan. One of the largest, most impressive archaeological sites in Mesoamerica. Located near Mexico City, it was built between 100 B.C.E. and C.E. 900. Its huge ceremonial temple pyramids extended over 8 square miles (20 sq. km.). Little is known about the people who built these structures. When the Aztecs arrived in 1200, they used the abandoned site as a pilgrimage center. According to Aztec legend, the Sun, Moon, and universe were created here.

Texas. Became twenty-eighth state on December 29, 1845. Located in south central area of the United States. Total area of 268,601 square miles (695,677 sq. km.) with 1998 population of 19.7 million, making it the second largest state in both area and population. Name is a variant of native word for "friends." The Spanish first visited in the sixteenth century and in 1682 built a mission near present-day El Paso. Mexico gained independence from Spain in 1821. In 1836 Texas declared itself a republic free from Mexico. Nine years later, Texas was admitted to the United States, which led to the Mexican War (1846-1848). U.S. victory established the RIO GRANDE as the southern border of Texas and the United States. The capital is Austin (1998 population, 552,434); HOUSTON (1998 population, 1.8 million) is the largest city.

Thule. See QAANAAQ.

Thule Air Base. Giant U.S. air base located at Pituffik on GREENLAND's northwest coast. It was situated here (76°32′ north latitude, longitude 68°51′ west) because of its strategic position between North America and Russia. Built in 1951-1952 during the Cold War, it houses a vast radar installation containing a Ballistic Missile Early Warning System.

Toronto Page 507

Thunder Bay. City in ONTARIO, Canada, on the western end of Lake Superior. It was originally two rival cities—Port Arthur and Fort William. The fur-trading Fort William of the Northwest Company was founded in 1812 at the mouth of the Kaministiquia River. Port Arthur began developing in the 1850's. The two cities merged in 1970 to form Thunder Bay. Its many grain elevators handle much of the grain shipped through the GREAT LAKES to the east and abroad. Thunder Bay has the highest concentration of Finnish people in Canada, some 10 percent of the city's population of 128,600 (1998).

Tijuana. One of Mexico's largest border cities and the world's busiest crossing. Located less than 20 miles (32 km.) from SAN DIEGO, California. It is one of Mexico's youngest cities, established as a line of defense against *filibusteros* following the Treaty of Guadalupe Hidalgo in 1848. Pollution is a major problem as rapid industrialization progresses.

Tlaxcala. Mexican state; capital city has the same name. The beautiful colonial city was founded jointly by Hernán Cortés and Franciscan friars in 1520. Although located only 74 miles (120 km.) from MEXICO CITY, it has a population of only 50,000. Its highland location of more than 3,200 feet (2,000 meters) above sea level gives it a cool, sunny, pleasant climate and enables wheat cultivation. Cacaxtla, an important Olmec archaeological site, is nearby.

Tobago. Caribbean island that, along with the island of TRINIDAD, forms a nation in the southernmost LESSER ANTILLES island chain; capital is Port-of-Spain. A peaceful, rural island in contrast to bustling, cosmopolitan Trinidad.

Toronto. Capital of ONTARIO, Canada. Located on the northern shore of Lake Ontario, this is the largest city in Canada, with a metropolitan population of 4.6 million in 1998. Its CN Tower was the tallest freestanding structure in the world at the end of the twentieth century. It has a large ethnic population of

Chinese, Italians, and other groups, and is the heart of Canadian cultural and economic development.

Torreon. City in Coahuila state, in north central Mexico. Established in 1887 as a rail center by Mexican, U.S., British, and French interests, it now is a modern, economically prosperous city in the Chihuahuan Desert.

Tortola. Largest and most populated of the British Virgin Islands in the Caribbean Sea. It is approximately 10 square miles (26 sq. km.) in area.

Trans-Canada Highway. World's longest national road, extending, from east to west, across all ten Canadian provinces over 4,860 miles (7,821 km.). It runs between Victoria, British Columbia, and St. John's, Newfoundland, and is linked by car ferries with Prince Edward Island, Nova Scotia, and Newfoundland. It was dedicated in 1962 but was not completed until 1965.

Trinidad. Caribbean island that, along with the island of Tobago, forms a nation in the southernmost Lesser Antilles island chain; capital is Port-of-Spain. Located 9 miles (14.5 km.) off the coast of Venezuela, outside the path of most devastating Caribbean hurricanes. Its mountains are thought to be the northernmost Andes Mountains, making it a part of the South American continent. Crude oil production has led to a stable, thriving economy and a literate middle class. One-quarter of the diverse population of 1.3 million is Hindu. Steel band music originated here. Its annual pre-Lenten Carnival celebration is the largest and liveliest in the Caribbean region.

Tucson. Second largest city in Arizona (1998 population, 460,466). Located on the Santa Cruz River, at 2,390 feet (728 meters) elevation. Spanish Jesuit Eusebio Kino explored the area in the early 1690's. The Spanish established a presidio in 1776. Tucson was a territorial capital from 1867 to 1877.

Tucson, Arizona. (PhotoDisc)

Trinidad carnival Page 450

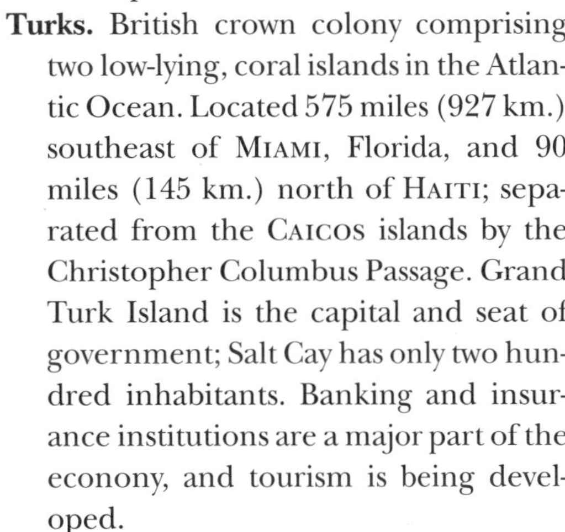

Turks. British crown colony comprising two low-lying, coral islands in the Atlantic Ocean. Located 575 miles (927 km.) southeast of Miami, Florida, and 90 miles (145 km.) north of Haiti; separated from the Caicos islands by the Christopher Columbus Passage. Grand Turk Island is the capital and seat of government; Salt Cay has only two hundred inhabitants. Banking and insurance institutions are a major part of the econony, and tourism is being developed.

Tuxtla Gutierrez. Capital of the Mexican state of Chiapas. A modern, working city, it replaced San Cristóbal de las Casas as capital of Chiapas in 1892. It is at the center of a thriving coffee-growing zone and has a population of 250,000.

Salt Lake City Page 580

Utah. Became forty-fifth U.S. state on January 4, 1896. Located in the west central area of the United States. Total area of 84,904 square miles (219,902 sq. km.) with 1998 population of 2.1 million. Name comes from the Navajo word for "higher up." The first European to enter the region was Spaniard Juan Maria Antonio de Rivera in 1765. In 1846 Mormons, persecuted in OHIO, MISSOURI, and ILLINOIS for religious beliefs, moved into what was then Mexico. In 1847 Brigham Young established the region's first permanent European settlement. After the Mexican War (1846-1848), the region was transferred to the United States. Brigham Young lobbied for creation of new state called Deseret, which included all or part of eight present-day states. In 1850 Congress created new territories, one of which was Utah. Brigham Young was appointed the first territorial governor, but was suspended after reports of disregard of federal authority by Mormon leaders. Utah's petitions for statehood were consistently refused until 1890, when Mormon leadership mandated church members to abstain from polygamy. The capital and largest city is SALT LAKE CITY (1998 population, 174,348)

Vancouver Page 581

Victoria Page 582

Vancouver. Largest city in BRITISH COLUMbia and the third largest city in Canada. Located near the mouth of the FRASER RIVER in the southwestern part of British Columbia. The city has 472,000 residents; the metropolitan area, which includes numerous adjacent cities, boosts the population to more than 2 million (1998). Originally settled in the 1870's as a sawmill town, Vancouver has grown into a major shipping port and the industrial, financial, and commercial center of the province. A large Asian population is found here, unlike in most of Canada, where European ethnicities such as the Swedes predominate.

Vancouver Island. Largest island on the west coast of the North American continent. Located off the coast of BRITISH COLUMBIA. Discovered by James Cook in 1778 and named after George Vancouver, who surveyed the island in 1792.

Veracruz. Mexican state on the lush tropical plains along the Gulf of Mexico; capital is Xalapa. In 1519 Spanish conquistador Hernán Cortés disembarked here, burnt his boats, and set off to conquer the Aztecs. For the next three centuries, the vibrant port of Veracruz shipped huge quantities of gold and silver back to Europe.

Vermont. Became fourteenth U.S. state on March 4, 1791. Located in New England. Total area of 9,615 square miles (24,490 sq. km.), with a 1998 population of 588,978. Name comes from French "green mountain." Explored by Samuel de Champlain in 1610 and permanently settled by British in 1724. NEW HAMPSHIRE, NEW YORK, and MASSACHUSETTS all attempted land claims, leading to the formation of Green Mountain Boys (of which Ethan Allen was a member). Montpelier (1998 population, 7,734) is capital; Burlington (1998 population, 38,453) is largest city.

Victoria. Capital city of BRITISH COLUMBIA. Located at the southern tip of VANCOUVER ISLAND on Canada's west coast, with a population of 318,100 in 1998. Known as the retirement capital of Canada because of its very mild climate, the city is the western terminus of the TRANS-CANADA HIGHWAY, which spans the country.

Villahermosa. Capital of the Mexican state of TABASCO along the southern Gulf of Mexico coast. Located on the banks of the Grijalva River. Now a friendly, bustling city, it was founded in the late sixteenth century by coastal inhabitants who were forced to move inland by repeated pirate attacks. La Venta, 73 miles (117 km.) to the west of Villahermosa, is the site of the most important ancient Olmec settlement.

Virgin Gorda. Second largest of the British Virgin Islands in the Caribbean Sea. It has an area of 8 square miles (21 sq. km.).

Virgin Islands, British. Approximately fifty islands, inlets, and cays in the Caribbean Sea. Tortola, Virgin Gorda, Jost Van Dyke, Great Camanoe, Norman, Peter, Salt, Cooper, Ginger, Dead Chest, and Anegada are the largest of these islands. Very hilly and volcanic, except for Anegada. Close to the U.S.-owned Virgin Islands, but quieter and more relaxed. Tortola, at 10 square miles (26 sq. km.), is the largest and most populated of the islands; Virgin Gorda is second in size. English is the official language.

Virgin Islands, U.S. U.S. territory in the Caribbean Sea, comprising the islands of St. Thomas, St. Croix, and St. John. Located east of Puerto Rico, 1,000 miles (1,600 km.) from the southern tip of the U.S. mainland. They were named by Christopher Columbus for their pristine beauty. Collectively, they were called the Danish West Indies until the United States purchased them from Denmark for strategic reasons in 1917. The islands' more than 100,000 inhabitants are U.S. citizens. Poor agricultural land and insufficient water supply limit food production to local markets. Tourism is the main industry, with some industrial development. Charlotte Amalie, on St. Thomas, is the major urban and commercial center of the islands.

Virginia. Tenth of the thirteen original U.S. states; ratified Constitution on June 26, 1788. Located along mid-Atlantic Coast. Total area of 42,777 square miles (110,793 sq. km.) with 1998 population of 6.8 million. First permanent North American English settlement was Jamestown, Virginia, in 1607. Named for the Virgin Queen, Elizabeth I of England. Richmond (1998 population, 194,173) became capital in 1779 and was the capital of the Confederate States of America 1861-1865. Largest city is Virginia Beach (1998 population, 432,380).

Jamestown Page 583

Washington, D.C. City and capital of the United States of America. The city of Washington, which is coextensive with the District of Columbia, is located at the navigational head of the Potomac River between Maryland to the northeast and Virginia in the southwest. Congress chose the District of Columbia in 1790 as the site for a permanent seat of government for the new nation. Its area is 69 square miles (179 sq. km.). Its population was 606,900 in 1990.

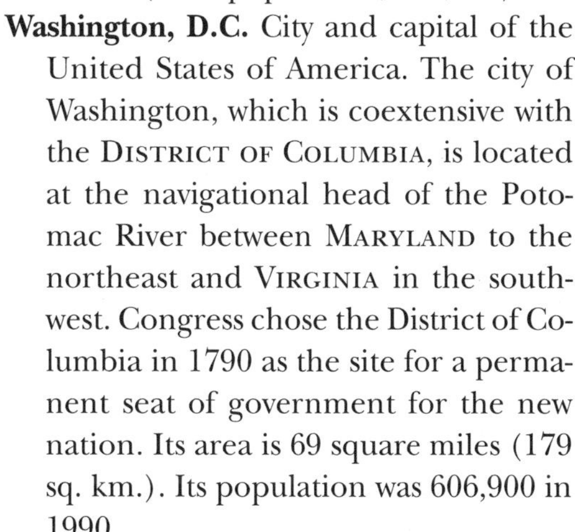

Washington State. Became forty-second state on November 11, 1889. Located in the Pacific Northwest of the United States. Total area of 71,302 square miles (184,672 sq. km.) with 1998 population of 5.7 million. Named after George Washington. In 1792 British captain George Vancouver surveyed the coast and inland waters, and U.S. captain Robert Gray discovered the mouth of the Columbia River. Therefore, both countries had claims to the territory. Acquired by the United States in 1803 via the Louisiana Purchase. In 1848 Oregon Territory was created; Washington Territory was created from that in 1853. Olympia (1998 population, 39,188) is the capital; Seattle (1998 population, 536,978) is the largest city.

St. Thomas Page 582

West Indies. Archipelago of more than seven thousand mostly uninhabited islands, cays, coral reefs, and rocks that form the northern and eastern boundaries of the CARIBBEAN SEA. The islands fall into one of three groupings: coral islands such as the BAHAMAS; GREATER ANTILLES islands, such as CUBA, PUERTO RICO, HISPANIOLA, and JAMAICA, which are older, worn-down peaks of sunken mountains; and the LESSER ANTILLES islands—an arc of smaller volcanically formed islands. Eastern trade winds moderate the tropical heat, and the rich volcanic or alluvial soils promote agriculture. Sugar and bananas are the major crops. Tourism has also become a major revenue source.

West Virginia Page 583

West Virginia. Became thirty-fifth state on June 20, 1863. Located in U.S. mid-Atlantic area. Total area of 24,231 square miles (62,758 sq. km.), with a 1998 population of 1.8 million. Until 1863, was part of VIRGINIA, but split over succession from the United States. Capital and largest city is Charleston (1998 population, 55,056).

Western Hemisphere. Portion of the earth that contains North and South America; generally demarcated as within longitude 20° west and 160° east. Historically known as the NEW WORLD.

Whitehorse. Capital and largest city of the YUKON TERRITORY, Canada. Located in the south central part of the territory, on the banks of the Yukon River. Named the capital of the territory in 1952. Transportation, communications, mining, and government functions are the main industries. Its population was 15,199 in 1991.

Whitney, Mount. Highest mountain in the contiguous United States at 14,494 feet (4,418 meters). Located in the SIERRA NEVADA, it is named for Josiah Dwight Whitney, the geologist who led the expedition that discovered it in 1864.

Windward Islands. Four volcanic islands—GRENADA, ST. LUCIA, DOMINICA, and ST. VINCENT—in the CARIBBEAN SEA. Still-active volcanoes periodically erupt. The islands were colonized by both the British and the French; most inhabitants are descendants of African slaves.

Winnipeg. Capital city of MANITOBA, Canada. Located at the confluence of the Red and Assiniboine Rivers, it had a population of 676,400 in 1998. Originally a fur-trading fort, it grew into the "Gateway to the West" as thousands of immigrants moving west traveled through it. Its Symington Railway Yard is one of the biggest in the world.

Winnipeg, Lake. The thirteenth largest lake in the world, located in the southern part of MANITOBA, Canada. It is 264 miles (425 km.) long and up to 68 miles (109 km.) wide, with an area of 9,416 square miles (24,387 sq. km.). The name comes from the Cree Indian words for "muddy water." The lake is fairly shallow, with an average depth of about 50 feet (15 meters). It is important for shipping and commercial fishing, and its southern shore is a major resort area for the provincial capital of WINNIPEG, 40 miles (64 km.) south.

Wisconsin. Became thirtieth U.S. state on May 29, 1848. Located in north central (Upper Midwest) region. Total area is 65,499 square miles (169,839 sq. km.), with a 1998 population of 5.2 million. Name comes from Ojibwa word that may mean "gathering of the waters" or "place of the beaver." First explored by French in 1630's. French controlled area (first permanent settlement in 1766) until French and Indian War, after which the British assumed control until 1783. Part of NORTHWEST TERRITORY 1787-1800. Capital is Madison (1998 population, 209,306) and largest city is Milwaukee (1998 population, 578,364).

Wyoming. Became forty-forth state on July 10, 1890. Located in northern Rocky Mountains/Great Plains of the United States. Total area of 97,818 square miles (253,349 sq. km.) with 1998 population of 480,907 (making it the smallest state in population). The name is a native word for "at big plains." Acquired by the United States in 1803 via the Louisiana Purchase. The first European settlement was in 1834 at Fort Laramie. The capital and largest city is Cheyenne (1998 population, 53,640).

Yaqui River. River in the Sierra Madre Occidental of Mexico. It is used to irrigate arid farmlands on its journey to the Gulf of California.

Yellowknife. Territorial capital and largest city in Canada's Northwest Territories. Located on the northern shore of Great Slave Lake in the south central part of Northwest Territories. Founded in 1935, one year after gold was discovered in the area, and derived its name from the Yellowknife band of Athabascan Indians who live in the region. Its population was 15,179 in 1991.

Yellowstone National Park. First national park, established in 1872. Located in the Rocky Mountains, it covers 3,469 square miles (8,983 sq. km.) over Wyoming, Montana, and Idaho. The park is known for wildlife, geysers, waterfalls, and canyons.

York Factory. National historic site on the southwestern shore of Hudson Bay in north central Canada, in the northeastern corner of Manitoba. Originally founded as the Hudson's Bay Company post (Fort Nelson) in 1682, it was later renamed York Factory. It was the chief port, supply depot, and headquarters for the fur-trading centers of northern Canada. The trading post closed in 1957, ending 275 years of nearly continuous operation. It is accessible only by air or canoe.

Devil's Tower, in northeastern Wyoming, was declared the first U.S. national monument in 1906. (Corbis)

Yosemite National Park. Established in 1890 in the Sierra Nevada, covering 1,189 square miles (3,079 sq. km.) of California. The park is famous for beautiful scenery, such as waterfalls and cataracts.

Yosemite Page 584

Young Island. One of the lush, mountainous Grenadine Islands in the Caribbean Sea and the closest to St. Vincent. It is a private resort with only twenty cottages.

Yucatán. Mexican state on the Yucatán Peninsula; capital is Mérida. The state has no rivers or lakes above ground; it depends on subterranean rivers and

Ruins of the late classic Maya town of Tulum on the coast of the Yucatán Peninsula. (PhotoDisc)

freshwater wells called *cenotes* for its water supply. Coastal estuaries are sanctuaries for exotic resident birds and many wintering migratory birds. The state's main industries are tourism, fishing, and commerce. Chichén Itzá, one of the finest and best-preserved Maya architectural sites in the northern Yucatán Peninsula, was a commercial, religious, and military center until the thirteenth century. The ruins comprise three distinct zones spread across a plain 75 miles (120 km.) east of Mérida.

Yucatán Peninsula. The flattest part of Mexico, occupying an area of approximately 43,630 square miles (113,000 sq. km.). Includes the states of Campeche, Yucatán, and Quintana Roo and famous resorts such as Cancún and Cozumel. When rain falls there, it seeps into the earth, gradually dissolving the limestone and creating underground caverns. When the roofs of caverns collapse, sinkholes, called *cenotes*, form; the Maya used them as wells. Some of the finest archaeological sites in the Americas are found there. Maya ruins at Chichén Itzá and Uxmal draw many tourists each year.

Yukon Territory. Region in the northwestern corner of Canada; the capital is Whitehorse, through which the Alaska Highway passes. Bounded on the east by the Northwest Territories, on the north by the Arctic Ocean, on the west by the state of Alaska, and on the south by the province of British Columbia. The area has many high plateaus and mountains, including the highest peak in Canada. Mining is the main industry and dates to the Klondike gold rushes of the 1890's. The total land area is 186,660 square miles (483,450 sq. km.)—about one-third the size of Alaska; the population was 30,688 in 1999.

Zacatecas. Mexican state; capital city of the same name. The city is Mexico's second highest, at 8,200 feet (2,500 meters), and sits on a high plateau surrounded by arid hills. Already an old town when the Spaniards arrived in 1546, Zacatecas soon supplied silver to the Spanish crown and became one of Mexico's richest colonial treasures.

Carol Ann Gillespie; Catherine A. Hooey; James D. Lowry, Jr.; Dana P. McDermott; Mika Roinila

Index to Volume 2

See volume 8 for a comprehensive index to all eight volumes in set.

Acapulco, 587, 511
Acosta, José de, 431
African Americans, 465, 467; and cities, 495
African culture, in Caribbean, 471
Agriculture; Caribbean, 525-527; North America, 503-504, 521-525
Aguascalientes, 587
Air transportation, North America, 549
Alabama, 587
Alaska, 587; oil, 408-409
Alaska Highway, 548, 587
Alberta, 587; oil, 541; population, 458
Albuquerque, 587
Alligators, 423
American Falls. *See* Niagara Falls
Amerindians, 432. *See also* Native Americans
Amish, 465, 467, 544-545
Amphibians; Caribbean, 427; North America, 422
Amtrak, 547
Anchorage, 512
Anegada, 588
Anglo-America, 438
Anguilla, 588
Antigua, 588
Appalachian Mountains, 362, 364, 588; coal, 409
Aquaculture, 522
Arawaks, 436, 478, 480; destruction of, 471
Arcadia, 609
Arctic, 352, 354-355
Arctic Territories, 588
Arizona, 588; population, 458
Arkansas, 588
Army Corps of Engineers, U.S., 538-539
ARPANET, 565-566
Aruba, 488, 589; communications, 567
Asian Americans, 469
Association of Caribbean States, 490
Atlanta, 589
Atlantic City, 574
Atlantic Ocean, and Caribbean, 355, 400
Atlantic Provinces (Canada), 462
Atolls, Caribbean, 588
Automobiles; North America, 548; production, 531
Ayllon, Vasquez de, 474

Badlands, 365
Baffin Island, 589
Bahamas, 589, 389; discovery of, 479
Baikal, Lake, 369
Baja California, 349, 589
Balboa, Vasco Nuñez de, 474, 480
Baltimore, 492, 589, 512
Bananas, Caribbean, 525-526, 558-559
Banff National Park, 589, 513
Barbados, 488, 589; discovery of, 480
Barbuda, 590
Barrier islands, 365
Bauxite, 534; Caribbean, 412
Belize, 356
Bell, Alexander Graham, 562
Bequia, 590
Bering Strait, 340, 420, 432, 590
Bermuda, 488; discovery of, 480
Birds; Arctic, 420; Caribbean, 426; North America, 421-423
Black Hills, 362
Bonaire, 590
Bonneville, Benjamin, 477
Bonneville, Lake, 370, 601
Boone, Daniel, 476
Borders, North America, 340, 486
Boston, 590
Boundaries. *See* Borders
Brendan, St., 473
Bridges, North America, 539-540
British Columbia, 346, 590; population, 458
British Honduras. *See* Belize
British Leeward Islands. *See* Leeward Islands
British West Indies, 488
Buffalo, 591

Cabo San Lucas, 591, 513
Cabot, John, 340, 343-344
Cabot, Sebastian, 344
Cacao, Carribean, 526
CACM. *See* Central American Common Market
Caicos, 591
Calgary, 591
California, 591; forests, 531; oil, 411; population, 458; water plan, 371
California, Gulf of, 591, 515
Camels, North America, 434
Campeche (state), 591
Campeche, Bay of, 592
Canada, 343, 346-347; borders, 340; coastal waterways, 545; communications, 561, 563-565; economy, 531, 554; fishing, 407-408; forest products, 406; French settlers, 462; immigration, 346-347; multiculturalism, 346; political history, 482-483, 485; population, 438-440, 457; postal system, 562; trade, 486; urbanization, 458, 496-497; water resources, 367, 369, 406
Canadian Falls. *See* Niagara Falls
Canadian Pacific Railroad, 531
Canadian Shield, 345, 366, 592; iron ore, 345; minerals, 410
Canals; North America, 545; and transportation, 440; United States, 492, 529-530, 539
Cancún, 592

Cape Breton Island, 592
Cape Canaveral, 515, 592
Cape Cod, 516
Cape Farewell, 592
Cape Morris Jesup, 593
Cape Spear, 593
Caribbean, 355, 357; agriculture, 525-527; climate, 399-401; communications, 566-568; culture regions, 470-472; endangered species, 427; and European Union, 559; exploration of, 478-481; fauna, 424-427; flora, 424-427; hurricanes, 400; industries, 533-536; mountains, 374-376, 399-400; peopling of, 436-437; physiography of, 373-376; political geography, 487-490; population, 459-460; resources, 412-413; tourism, 533-534, 550-551; trade, 558-560; transportation, 550-552; urbanization, 498-499; water resources, 376, 412-413. *See also individual countries and physical features*
Caribbean Basin Initiative, 560
Caribbean Community and Common Market, 489, 560
Caribbean Free Trade Area, 489
Caribbean Regional Development Bank, 489
Caribs, 436, 478; destruction of, 471
CARICOM. *See* Caribbean Community and Common Market
Cartier, Jacques, 345, 474
Cascade Mountains, 361
Cascade Range, 339, 593, 516; forests, 414
Castro, Fidel, 489
Cattle, North America, 522
Cayman Islands, 593
CBI. *See* Caribbean Basin Initiative
Central American Common Market, 489
Champlain, Samuel de, 344-345, 476
Chapala, Lake, 369
Chaparral, North America, 417
Charleston, 593
Charlotte, 593
Charlottetown, 593
Chesapeake Bay, 594
Chiapas, 594
Chicago, 492, 594, 507
Chichén Itzá, 351, 594, 379, 510
Chihuahua, 594
Chihuahuan Desert, 351, 594
Chinese; in Canada, 464; in Caribbean, 436-437
Christianshåb. *See* Qasigiannguit
Churchill, 594
Cincinnati, 594
Cities. *See* Urbanization
Civil War, U.S., and railways, 547
Clark, William, 476; route, 453
Clarke, Arthur C., 563
Cleveland, 594
Climate; Caribbean, 399-401; North America, 393-399
Clinton, Bill, 490; and NAFTA, 557
Clovis culture, 431
Coahuila, 595
Coal, North America, 409-410
Coffee; Caribbean, 526; Jamaica, 526
Colima, 595
Colorado, 595
Colorado River, 371-372, 406, 595, 517; Hoover Dam, 542, 388
Columbia River, 595
Columbus, Christopher, 340, 629; expeditions, 478-480; geographical knowledge of, 473-474, 478
Columbus, Ohio, 595
Communications; Caribbean, 566-568; North America, 561-566
Connecticut, 596
Continental crust, 362
Continental Divide, 363, 368
Continents, formation of, 366
Copper; Canada, 366; Carribean, 412; Mexico, 532
Copper Canyon. *See* Sierra Tarahumara
Coral islands. *See* Atolls
Cordillera Central, 596
Corn, 504
Corn Belt, 504, 522
Coronado, Francisco, 475, 606
Cortés, Hernán, 482, 596, 610, 632, 634
Cotton, 522; Mexico, 351, 554, 589, 595, 630; United States, 408, 467, 522, 530
Cozumel, 596
Crater Lake, 596
Creoles; Caribbean, 472; Louisiana, 467
Cuba, 596; architecture, 471; independence of, 488; minerals, 412; mining, 534; population, 459; roads, 551; slavery, 437; and United States, 489-490, 559
Cuban Americans, 466
Cuernavaca, 596
Curaçao, 596
Cyclones; tropical, 396. *See also* Hurricanes

Dahlon, Claude, 476
Dallas, 597
Dams, North America, 541
Dawson, 597
Dawson Creek, 597
De Soto, Hernando, 475, 588, 600, 612
Death Valley, California, 362-363, 597
Deforestation, Carribean, 424-425, 603
Delaware, 597
Delaware River, 577
Dene, 464
Denmark, and Virgin Islands, 437
Denver, 597, 518
Desertification, Haiti, 425

Deserts, North America, 394, 398, 417-418
Detroit, 531, 597
Devil's Tower, 637
Diastrophism, 362
Disease, Caribbean, 401
Dismal Swamp, 365
District of Columbia, 635
Dominica, 597
Dominican Republic, 472, 598; economy, 535; minerals, 412; population, 460; roads, 551; trade, 559
Drainage basins, North America, 367-369
Durango, 598
Dust Bowl, 523

Eads, James B., 537, 540
Earthquakes; Caribbean, 374; Mexico, 348
Edmonton, 598
Ellesmere Island, 598
Endangered species; Caribbean, 427; North America, 421
Energy. *See also* Nuclear energy
Engineering projects, North America, 537-543
English Harbour, 598
Equator, and climate, 397
Erie, Lake, 346, 616, 620-621
Erie Canal, 440, 529, 539
Erik the Red, 354, 439, 461, 473, 623
Eriksson, Leif, 439, 462, 473
Eskimos. *See* Inuits
Euro, and U.S. dollar, 555
European Union; and Caribbean, 559; and North America, 555, 557
Everglades National Park, 598
Exploration; Caribbean, 478-481; North America, 473-478

Farm Aid concerts, 503
Fauna; Caribbean, 424-427; North America, 419-424
Federal Communications Commission, 563
Fishing, 407-408
Flooding; control, 371, 541; and rice cultivation, 521-522; seasonal, 370, 537-539; and storms, 400. *See also* Dams
Flora; Caribbean, 424-427; North America, 414-419
Florida, 599, 518; discovery of, 474; Fountain of Youth, 474
Ford, Henry, 548
Forests; Canada, 406; North America, 414-416; United States, 406
Foxes, 421-422; arctic, 353, 420
Franklin, Benjamin, 562
Fraser River, 599
Fredericton, 599
Frémont, John C., 477
French and Indian War, 482
French Antilles, 489, 599
French West Indies. *See* French Antilles
Fundy, Bay of, 599

Gadsden Purchase, 340
Ganja, 526; Caribbean, 559
Gaspe, 599
Geographic Information System, 539
Georgia, 600
Glaciation, 371. *See also* Snow
Glaciers. *See* Glaciation
Glen Canyon Dam, 371
Godthåb. *See* Nuuk
Godthåbsfjord, 600
Gold; Canada, 366; Caribbean, 412, 480, 534; North America, 410, 464, 495, 532
Golden Gate Bridge, 540
Government, forms of. *See* Political geography
Grand Canyon, 600, 517
Grand Cayman, 600
Grand Tetons, 384
Grasslands, 416-417, 421
Great Basin, 339, 600; exploration of, 477; flora, 418
Great Bear Lake, 369, 600
Great Lakes, 369, 411, 601, 388; commerce, 529, 545, 548; exploration of, 476; ; fisheries, 522; Welland Ship Canal, 509
Great Plains, 339-340, 601; exploration of, 476
Great Salt Lake, 369, 601
Great Slave Lake, 369, 601
Great Smoky Mountains National Park, 601
Greater Antilles, 355, 488, 601; physiography, 374-375
Greenland, 354-355, 601; cultures of, 461-462; exploration of, 475; ice cap, 354, 398, 601; population, 438, 457
Grenada, 488, 560, 602
Grenadine Islands. *See* Saint Vincent and the Grenadines
Groundwater, 370
Guadalajara, 602
Guadeloupe, 489, 559, 602
Guanajuato, 602
Guerrero, 602
Gulf of Mexico. *See* Mexico, Gulf of
Guyana, 489

Haiti, 603; African cultural influences, 471; economy, 535; independence of, 488; minerals, 412; population, 460; roads, 551-552; slavery, 436; trade, 559; Voodoo, 471
Halifax, 603
Hamilton, 603
Hardwoods; Canada, 407, 421; United States, 407, 421
Havana, 460, 498-499, 568, 603
Hawaiian Islands, 603; volcanoes, 571
Heartland-hinterland concept, 345
Herbivores, North America, 420-421
Hermasillo, 603
Hidalgo, 603

High Plains Aquifer, 370
Hinduism, in Caribbean, 472, 559
Hispaniola, 604; discovery of, 479; original inhabitants, 436
Hogs, 522
Holland Tunnel, 540
Homo erectus, 434
Homo sapiens, 434
Hoover Dam, 371-372, 542, 604
Horses, and transportation, 544, 548, 562
Horseshoe Falls. *See* Niagara Falls
Hot spots, 339
Houston, 604, 519
Hudson, Henry, 475, 604
Hudson Bay, 346, 604
Hudson River, 604
Hummingbirds, 421, 426
Huntsville, 604
Huron, Lake, 476
Hurricane Camille, 396
Hurricanes, Caribbean, 356, 376, 400, 525, 633
Hydroelectric projects, North America, 541
Hydrology, North America, 367-373

Ice Age, 432; animal life, 420; early humans, 431; and sea level, 432
Ice caps, Greenland, 354, 398, 601
Ice sheets, Greenland, 371
Icebergs, Arctic, 604
Idaho, 604
Illinois, 530, 604; coal, 410-411
Ilulissat Icefjord (Jakobshavn Glacier), 604
Immigration; Canada, 346-347, 462; United States, 340-342, 466, 468-469, 484-485, 492, 494-495, 553
Imperial Valley, 605
Indiana, 605
Indianapolis, 605
Indians, in Caribbean, 472
Industries; Caribbean, 533-536; North America, 528-533
Intelsat, 563, 567
Internet; Caribbean, 568; e-mail, 566; invention of, 565-566
Inuits, 352, 354; Canada, 343, 462, 464; Greenland, 438, 440, 461
Iowa, 605
Iqaluit, 605
Iron ore, North America, 410
Isla Mujeres, 605
Isla Tiburon, 605

Jakobshavn Glacier. *See* Ilulissat Icefjord
Jalisco, 605
Jamaica, 605; bauxite, 412; Cockpit Country, 374; discovery of, 480; ganja trade, 559; independence of, 488; markets, 527; population, 460; slavery, 436
Jamestown, Virginia, 476, 583
Johnstown flood, 541
Joliet, Louis, 476
Joshua tree, 418
Jost Van Dyke, 606
Juárez, 606
Juárez, Benito, 483
Julianehåb. *See* Qaqortoq

Kansas, 606; and Dust Bowl, 523
Kansas City, Kansas, 606
Kansas City, Missouri, 606
Karst, Caribbean, 374
Kentucky, 606
Kingston, 607

La Malinche, 607
La Salle, Robert, 476
Labrador, 607; and Vikings, 473
Lakes; Arctic, 353; North America, 366-370, 592
Land grant colleges, 523
L'Anse aux Meadows, 343, 607
Las Vegas, 607
Laurentian Shield, 366
Leeward Islands, 471, 607
Legumes, 521
Lesser Antilles, 355, 607; exploration of, 479-480; physiography, 374-375
Lewis, Meriweather, 476; route, 453
Little Cayman, 607
Livestock, 522, 544; overgrazing, 424
Logan, Mount, 607
Los Alamos National Laboratory, 607
Los Angeles, 607
Louisbourg, 607
Louisiana, 467, 608; Acadians, 467; oil, 531
Louisiana Purchase, 340, 476
Lunenburg, 608

Mackenzie River, 369, 608
McKinley, Mount, 363, 608
Madoc, 473
Magazines, 561
Mahogany, Caribbean, 424-425
Maine, 608
Mammals, Caribbean, 426
Mammoth Cave National Park, 608
Maniitsoq (Sukkertoppen), 608
Manitoba, 608
Manufacturing; Caribbean, 535-536; North America, 410; and resources, 410
Maquiladoras; Dominican Republic, 536; Mexico, 351, 532, 557, 631
Marconi, Guglielmo, 562
Maritime Provinces (Canada), 343, 345, 485, 609; fishing, 408; oil, 541
Marquette, Jacques, 476
Martinique, 489, 559, 570, 609
Maryland, 465, 609
Massachusetts, 340, 609
Matamoros, 609
Mauna Loa, 571
Maximilian, Archduke, 483
Maya, 351
Maya ruins, 638, 379, 510

Mazatlán, 610
Mead, Lake, 372
Mediterranean climate, 395
Memphis, 610
Mennonites, 544
Mérida, 610
Mesa Central, 610
Mesa del Norte, 610
Mexican-American War, 340, 483
Mexican Plateau, 349, 610
Mexican Revolution, 547
Mexico, 348, 352; Border Industrialization Program, 532; borders, 348; communications, 561, 563-566; culture, 470; economy, 529, 532, 553-554; fauna, 423; Federal District, 599; forests, 416; migration within, 458; oil, 408; political history, 482-483, 485; population, 438, 440, 457; postal system, 562; railways, 457; rivers, 369; trade, 486; urbanization, 458, 497; water resources, 369
Mexico (state), 610
Mexico, Gulf of, 611
Mexico, Valley of, 611
Mexico City, 349, 458, 497, 610, 448; earthquakes, 348; floating gardens, 571; growth, 438
Miami, 611, 572
Michigan, 611
Michigan, Lake, 369
Michoacan, 611
Milwaukee, 611
Minneapolis, 611, 572
Minnesota, 612
Mississippi, 612
Mississippi River, 368, 612, 508, 573; bridging of, 540; drainage basin, 367; engineering of, 537-538; exploration of, 475-476
Missouri, 612
Missouri River, 406; exploration of, 477
Mojave Desert, 418
Monroe Doctrine, 340
Montana, 612
Monterrey, 613
Montreal, 613
Montserrat, 613; volcanic eruption, 375
Morelia, 613
Morelos, 613
Morse, Samuel F. B., 562
Mountains. *See individual mountains and ranges*
Multinational corporations, and Mexico, 486, 557

NAFTA. *See* North American Free Trade Association
Narsaq, 614
Nashville, 614
Nassau, 614
National parks, volcanic, 362
Native Americans, 466, 468-469; origins of, 431-435. *See also* Amerindians
Natural gas, North America, 409
Nayarit, 614
Nearctic realm, 419
Nebraska, 614
Neotropical realm, 419
Netherlands Antilles, 488, 614
Nevada, 614; population, 458
Nevis, 615
New Brunswick, 344, 463, 615
New England, commerce, 529
New Hampshire, 615
New Jersey, 615
New Mexico, 615
New Orleans, 615
New Spain, 616
New World, 616
New York, 616
New York City, 616, 575; Brooklyn Bridge, 540; Central Park, 454
Newfoundland, 343, 364, 439, 462, 616; oil, 541
Newspapers; Caribbean, 568; North America, 561
Niagara Falls, 346, 539, 616, 576
Nicolet, Jean, 476
North America; agriculture, 503-504, 521-525; climate, 393-399; coal, 409-410; colonization of, 440; communications, 561-566; culture regions, 461-470; deserts, 394, 398, 417-418; drainage basins, 367; endangered mammals, 421; engineering projects, 537-543; and European Union, 555, 557; exploration of, 473-478; fauna, 419-424; flora, 414-419; hydroelectric projects, 541; hydrology, 367-373; industries, 528-533; natural gas, 409; oil, 408; peopling of, 431-435; political geography, 482-487; population, 438-440, 457-459; railways, 457; resources, 405-411; soil, 408; trade, 553-558; transportation, 440, 544-550; urbanization, 491-498; water resources, 405
North American Free Trade Agreement, 486, 532, 554, 556-557; and Cuba, 490; and Mexico, 533
North Carolina, 617
North Dakota, 617
Northumberland Strait, 617
Northwest Passage, search for, 474-476
Northwest Territories, 464, 617
Northwest Territory, 617
Nova Scotia, 343, 463, 617
Nuclear energy, 543, 618
Nuevo Laredo, 617
Nuevo León, 618
Nunavut, 462, 546, 618
Nuuk (Godthåb), 618

Oak Ridge, 618
Oaxaca, 618
Ogallala Aquifer, 370, 405-406
Ohio, 618
Ohio River, 618, 578
Oil; Caribbean, 534; drilling technology, 543; Mexico, 408,

553; North America, 408; Trinidad, 412
Okeechobee, Lake, 518
Okefenokee Swamp, 365
Oklahoma, 619; coal, 410; and Dust Bowl, 523; oil, 411, 531
Oklahoma City, 619
Olmecs, 350
Olympic Games; Atlanta, 589; Calgary, 591
Ontario, 345, 463, 619
Oodaaq Island, 619
Oranjestad, 589
Orchids, Caribbean, 424-425
Oregon, 619; Cannon Beach, 576; forests, 531
Oregon Trail, 477, 619
Orizaba, Mount, 349, 619
Ottawa, 345, 620
Ovando, Nicolás, 480
Ozark Mountains, 365

Pacific Ocean, discovery of, 480
Palenque, 620, 577
Pan-American Highway, 539
Paricutin Volcano, 620
Patowmack Canal, 539
Pattie, Sylvester, 477
Pelée, Mount, 375, 609, 620
Pelee Island, 346, 620
Pennsylvania, 620
Peopling; Caribbean, 436-437; North America, 431-435
Pershing, John J., 483
Peter Island, 621
Petroleum. *See* Oil
Philadelphia, 621, 577
Phoenix, 621
Physiography; Caribbean, 373-376; North America, 361-367
Pike, Zebulon, 477
Pipelines, 549, 540
Pittsburgh, 621, 578
Plant diseases, and forests, 416
Pleistocene epoch, 431-432, 601; mammal life, 431
Point Pelee, 621
Political geography; Caribbean, 487-490; North America, 482-487
Ponce de León, Juan, 474, 480, 599, 628
Popocatepetl, 621, 578
Population distribution; Caribbean, 459-460; North America, 438-440, 457-459
Port-au-Prince, 622
Portland, Oregon, 579, 622
Ports; Caribbean, 552; North America, 539, 545; river, 440
Portsmouth Naval Shipyard, 539
Postal systems, North America, 562
Potato famine, Irish, 492
Potatoes; Canada, 345; Caribbean, 526
Powell, Lake, 388
Prairie Provinces (Canada), 346, 464, 622
Precipitation; Caribbean, 374-376, 399-401, 412-413; Greenland, 398; North America, 367, 393-398, 405-406, 416, 522
Prince Edward Island, 345, 463, 622
Puebla, 622
Pueblos, 468
Puerto Rico, 357, 374-375, 471, 484, 487, 489, 622; agriculture, 525-526; climate, 400; discovery of, 474, 479; manufacturing, 536; newspapers, 568; political status of, 486; population, 460; radio, 567; slavery, 437; tourism, 533; trade, 559; urbanization, 498
Puerto Vallarta, 622, 579
Puget Sound, 623

Qaanaaq (Thule), 623
Qaqortoq (Julianehåb), 623
Qasigiannguit (Christianshåb), 623
Quebec, 345, 439, 463, 553, 623; exploration of, 475-476; separatist movements, 485
Quebec City, 623, 449
Queen Charlotte Islands, 623
Querétaro, 623
Quetzalcoatl, 379
Quintana Roo, 624

Radio, 562-563; Canada, 463, 564; Caribbean, 566-567; invention of, 562; Mexico, 564; United States, 563-564
Railways; Canada, 457; Caribbean, 552; North America, 457, 546-547; refrigerated boxcars, 546; and urbanization, 492, 494-495
Rain forests, Caribbean, 424
Rain-shadow effect; Caribbean, 400; North America, 394
Red River, 624
Redwood trees, 414
Regina, 624
Remington, Frederic, 476
Reptiles; Arctic, 354; Caribbean, 427; North America, 422
Research Triangle Park, 624
Reservations, Indian, 466-469
Reservoirs, North America, 541
Resources; Caribbean, 412-413; North America, 405-411
Reynosa, 624
Rhode Island, 624
Rice, 467, 521-522
Rideau Canal, 539
Ring of Fire, 339
Rio Bravo del Norte. *See* Rio Grande
Rio Grande, 369, 624
Rivers, North America, 350, 365-369, 372, 374, 406. *See also individual rivers*
Roads, 548-549
Rocky Mountains, 363, 366, 398, 625; Canadian, 343; drainage, 368; fauna, 422; forests, 407, 414; minerals, 410; U.S., 339

Roebling, John A., 540
Rushmore, Mount, 625

Saba, 625
Sacajawea, 477
Sacramento, 625
St. Augustine, Florida, 340, 625
Saint-Barthélemy, 628
St. Clair River Tunnel, 540
St. Croix, 626
St. Eustatius (Statia), 626
St. Francis Dam, 541
St. Helens, Mount, 362, 593
St. John, Virgin Islands, 626
St. John, New Brunswick, 344, 626
St. John's, Newfoundland, 626
St. Kitts, 626
St. Lawrence, Gulf of, 626
St. Lawrence River, 369, 435, 439-440, 474, 626; exploration of, 345, 475, 545
St. Lawrence Seaway, 539; commerce, 545
St. Louis, Missouri, 626
St. Lucia, 627
St. Martin, 627
St. Thomas, 582, 627
St. Vincent and the Grenadines, 627
Salt Lake City, 628, 580
San Antonio, 628
San Cristóbal de las Casas, 628
San Diego, 628, 580
San Francisco, 628; Golden Gate Bridge, 508
San Juan, 628
San Luis Potosí, 628
San Miguel de Allende, 628
Sandwich Islands. *See* Hawaii
Santa Fe, 628
Santo Domingo, 629
Saskatchewan, 629
Saskatoon, 629
Satellites, and communications, 563-564, 568
Savanna, North America, 416
Savannah, Georgia, 629
Seattle, 629, 581
Sediments, and rivers, 538
Sequoia trees, 414
Seven Cities, legend of, 473
Shale oil, North America, 409, 411
Shantytowns, Caribbean, 499
Sharks, 605
Shasta, Mount, 516
Sibley Peninsula, 629
Sierra Madre del Sur, 349, 629
Sierra Madre Occidental, 349, 629
Sierra Madre Oriental, 349, 629
Sierra Nevada, 339, 363, 630; forests, 414; formation of, 362
Sierra Tarahumara, 630
Sinaloa, 630
Sint Maarten, 630
Slave trade, and Caribbean, 436
Snake River, 384, 386
Snow, 393, 395, 406. *See also* Glaciation
Soils; arctic, 352, 408, 416
Sonora, 630
Sonoran Desert, 340, 351, 417-418, 630
South Carolina, 630
South Dakota, 630
South Fork Dam, 541
Soybeans, United States, 408, 504, 521
Spain; colonial empire, 356, 440, 480; and exploration, 340, 478-480, 591
Spanish-American War, 483, 486, 488, 628
Statia. *See* Saint Eustatius
Steinbeck, John, 524
Steppes, North America, 393-394
Storms. *See also* Cyclones; Hurricanes; Tornadoes; Typhoons
Subways, 540
Sugar; Caribbean, 357, 436, 525-526, 534, 558-559; Louisiana, 521
Sukkertoppen. *See* Maniitsoq
Superior, Lake, 369, 629, 632
Supreme Court, U.S., 484
Tabasco, 631
Tahoe, Lake, 370, 631, 386
Tamaulipas, 631
Tampico, 631
Tehuantepec, Bay of, 631
Tehuantepec, Isthmus of, 349, 631
Telegraph, invention of, 562
Telenet, 565
Telephones; cellular, 563; invention of, 562; long-distance, 562
Television; Canada, 565; Caribbean, 566-567; invention of, 564; Mexico, 565; United States, 564
Temperate zones, rain forests, 363, 414
Tennessee, 631
Tennessee River, 631
Tennessee Valley Authority, 496, 541
Tenochtitlán, 349, 482, 491, 497, 610, 631
Teotihuacan, 631
Texas, 467, 632; agriculture, 521; annexation of, 340; cattle, 522; forests, 416; industries, 532; oil, 411, 531; population, 458
Thule. *See* Qaanaaq
Thule Air Base, 632
Thunder Bay, 632
Tijuana, 632
Time zones, 547
Tlaxcala, 632
Tobacco; Caribbean, 401, 436, 459, 471, 525-526, 559; Cuba, 559, 596; North America, 408, 435, 440
Tobago, 632
Toltecs, 449
Tornadoes, North America, 393
Toronto, 345, 347, 497, 530, 632; population, 439, 463
Torreon, 633
Tortola, 633
Tourism; Caribbean, 533-534, 550-551; Mexico, 553

Trade; Caribbean, 552, 558-560; North America, 486, 553-558
Trade winds, 399
Trans-Alaska pipeline, 409, 538
Trans-Canada Highway, 539, 548, 633
Transportation; Caribbean, 550-552; North America, 544-550. *See also* Air transportation; Railways
Trees. *See* Forests
Trinidad, 633; agriculture, 526, 506; oil, 412, 534
Trinidad and Tobago; independence of, 488
Tropical rain forests. *See* Rain forests
Trucking, North America, 549
Tucson, 633
Tula, 449
Tundra, North America, 397, 418
Tunnels, North America, 540-541
Turks, 633
Turtles, sea, 427, 593, 614
Tuxtla Gutierrez, 633
TVA. *See* Tennessee Valley Authority

United States, 339-342; agriculture, 504; automobiles, 458; borders, 340, 348; climate, 339-340; and Cuba, 489-490, 559; economy, 342, 528; fishing, 407-408; forest products, 406; illegal immigration, 484-485; immigration, 340-342, 465-466, 468-469, 492, 494-495, 553; manufacturing, 554; political history, 483-484; population, 438, 440, 457-458; and Puerto Rico, 486; regions, 341; slavery, 465; topography of, 339; Tornadoes, 393; trade, 559; transportation, 458; urbanization, 342, 438-439, 457-458, 491-496; water resources, 367, 371, 373, 405-406
Uranium, Canada, 366
Urbanization; Caribbean, 498-499; North America, 491-498; United States, 342
U.S. *See* United States
Utah, 634

Vancouver, 634
Vancouver Island, 634
Veracruz, Mexico, 350, 634
Vermont, 634
Verrazano, Giovanni da, 474, 604
Verrazano Narrows Bridge, 539
Victoria, British Columbia, 346, 464, 634, 582
Vikings; in Greenland, 354; in North America, 340, 343, 435, 439, 473, 600, 607, 623
Villa, Pancho, 483
Villahermosa, 634
Vinland, 473
Virgin Gorda, 635
Virgin Islands, British, 635
Virgin Islands, U.S., 437, 635
Virginia, 635
Volcanoes, 362; and diastrophism, 361; Caribbean, 374-376; and earth formation, 361-362; Hawaii, 339; Mexico, 348, 408, 611; Montserrat, 375; North America, 361-362
Voodoo, 471

Walcott, Derek, 472
Washington (state), 635; forests, 531
Washington, D.C., 547, 635; population, 438
Water resources; Caribbean, 376. *See also* Hydrology; Lakes; Rivers
Waterfowl, North America, 421
Weather. *See* Climate
Welland Ship Canal, 509
West Indies, 635
West Indies Federation, 489
West Indies Shipping Corporation, 560
West Virginia, 636
Western Hemisphere, 636
Western Highlands, 363
Wetlands; Canada, 370; North America, 370
Whales, 349; Arctic, 353-354, 420
Wheat, 504
Whitehorse, 636
Whitney, Mount, 636
Windward Islands, 471, 636
Winnipeg, 636
Winnipeg, Lake, 369, 636
Wisconsin, 636
Wool; North America, 522; reindeer, 461
World Trade Organization, protests against, 557
World War II; and migration, 496; technological advances, 532
World Wide Web, 565
Wrangell Mountains, 384
WTO. *See* World Trade Organization
Wyoming, 637

Yaqui River, 637
Yellowknife, 637
Yellowstone National Park, 637
Yellowstone River, 373
York Factory, 637
Yosemite National Park, 637, 584; waterfalls, 584
Young Island, 637
Yucatán, 349-350, 637; archaeological sites, 638, 379, 510
Yucatán Peninsula, 638
Yukon, 464
Yukon Territory, 638

Zacatecas, 638

F L A G S O F T H E W O R L D

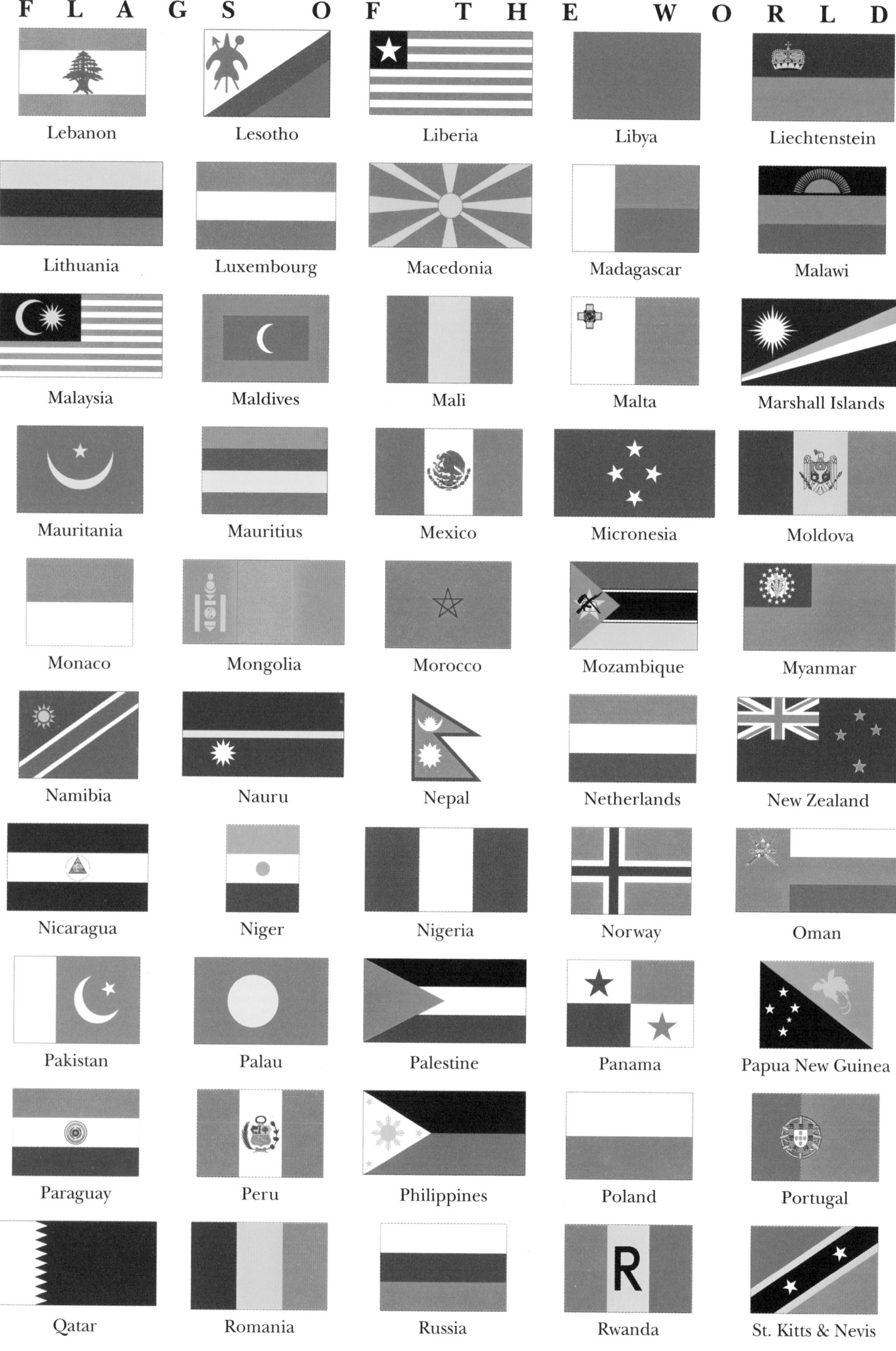

Lebanon Lesotho Liberia Libya Liechtenstein
Lithuania Luxembourg Macedonia Madagascar Malawi
Malaysia Maldives Mali Malta Marshall Islands
Mauritania Mauritius Mexico Micronesia Moldova
Monaco Mongolia Morocco Mozambique Myanmar
Namibia Nauru Nepal Netherlands New Zealand
Nicaragua Niger Nigeria Norway Oman
Pakistan Palau Palestine Panama Papua New Guinea
Paraguay Peru Philippines Poland Portugal
Qatar Romania Russia Rwanda St. Kitts & Nevis